Laboratory Manual for Principles of General Chemistry

Ninth Edition

J.A. Beran

Custom Edition prepared for the Department of Chemistry

Northern Virginia Community College

Annandale Campus and Extended Learning Institute

The author of this manual has outlined extensive safety precautions in each experiment. Ultimately, it is your responsibility to follow safe laboratory guidelines and procedures. The author and publisher disclaim any liability for any loss or damage claimed to have resulted from or been related to the experiments.

To order books or for customer service, please call 1(800)-CALL-WILEY (225-5945).

Printed in the United States of America.

ISBN 978-1-118-16802-8

Printed and bound by ePAC Technologies, Inc.

10 9 8 7 6

Laboratory Manual for Principles of General Chemistry

Ninth Edition

J. A. Beran

Regents Professor, Texas A&M University System
Texas A & M University—Kingsville

WILEY

John Wiley & Sons, Inc.

The author of this manual has outlined extensive safety precautions in each experiment. Ultimately, it is your responsibility to practice safe laboratory guidelines. The author and publisher disclaim any liability for any loss or damage claimed to have resulted from, or been related to, the experiments.

PUBLISHER   Kaye Pace
ASSOCIATE PUBLISHER   Petra Recter
ACQUISITIONS EDITOR   Nick Ferrari
PROJECT EDITOR   Jennifer Yee
PRODUCTION MANAGER   Dorothy Sinclair
PRODUCTION EDITOR   Erin Bascom
MARKETING MANAGER   Kristine Ruff
CREATIVE DIRECTOR   Harry Nolan
SENIOR DESIGNER   Kevin Murphy
PRODUCTION MANAGEMENT SERVICES   MPS Limited
SENIOR ILLUSTRATION EDITOR   Anna Melhorn
MANAGER, PHOTO DEPARTMENT   Hilary Newman
EDITORIAL ASSISTANT   Cathy Donovan
MEDIA EDITOR   Thomas Kulesa
COVER PHOTO   ©Stuart Gregory/Getty Images, Inc.

This book was set in Times New Roman by MPS Limited, and printed and bound by Courier Westford. The cover was printed by Courier Westford.

This book is printed on acid free paper. ∞

Library of Congress Cataloging-in-Publication Data

Beran, Jo A.
    Laboratory manual for principles of general chemistry / J.A. Beran. — 9th ed.
        p.   cm.
    ISBN 978-0-470-64789-9 (pbk.)
        1. Chemistry—Laboratory manuals.   I. Title.
QD45.B475   2010
542—dc22

                                                            2010026597

Printed in the United States of America

10 9 8 7 6 5 4 3 2 1

Chemistry laboratories have changed with advances in technology and safety issues.

Preface

Welcome to the ninth edition! Writing the ninth edition has been the most challenging of the nine editions of this manual. The eighth edition was one of the most successful laboratory manuals that Wiley has ever produced for general chemistry. Reviewers' comments were supportive of the challenges and format offered in the eighth edition with only a handful of suggestions—the experiments are interesting, challenging, and have good pedagogy regarding laboratory techniques, safety, and experimental procedures. The reporting and analyzing of data and the questions (pre- and post-lab) sought to focus on the intuitiveness of the experiment. The challenge for the ninth edition was to improve on what already appeared to be the general chemistry laboratory manual that "students and faculty want and expect."

Consequently, the "good" from the eighth has been retained, but added depth, relevance, and appreciation of the laboratory experience has been intertwined. Trends toward safer, more modern laboratory equipment, computer usage, and on-line information are included. The open-endedness of each experiment is encouraged in "The Next Step" where, on completion of the experiment, the student has the tools and experience to employ for studying additional chemical systems or topics of his or her interest. It is hoped that laboratory instructors and students will add their own Next Step for pursuing personal areas of interest and investigation.

The Front Cover: The front cover for this ninth edition was chosen to convey the message to students that this laboratory experience is not as an end in itself. Rather, as the sun rises to begin a new day, so does the dawn of careers in science, beginning with hands-on involvement into scientific investigations in the laboratory. We wish for students to use scientific logic and quantitative analysis to account for the observed chemical phenomena. Ultimately, we hope these experiences will provide them a strong, basic foundation on which they can build their professional careers, whether they become chemists, biologists, medical-field scientists, or professional chefs.

While all comments of users and reviewers from the previous eight editions have been heavily weighed with each new edition, the task of presenting the "perfect" manual, like chemistry and science in general, is impossible. However, at this point in time, we feel it is the "best" that it can be.

BREADTH (AND LEVEL) OF THE NINTH EDITION

This manual covers two semesters (or three quarters) of a general chemistry laboratory program. A student may expect to spend three hours per experiment in the laboratory; limited, advanced preparation and/or extensive analysis of the data may lengthen this time. The experiments were chosen and written so that they may accompany any general chemistry text.

FEATURES OF THE NINTH EDITION

Safety and Disposal. "Safety first" is again emphasized throughout the manual, with recent advisories and guidelines being added. **Laboratory Safety and Guidelines** outlines personal and laboratory safety rules and issues. Icons in the Experimental Procedures cite **Cautions** for handling various chemicals, the proper **Disposal** of chemicals, and the proper **Cleanup** of laboratory equipment. *Prelaboratory Assignment* questions often ask students to review the safety issues for the experiment.

Laboratory Techniques. Numbered icons cited at the beginning of each experiment and within the Experimental Procedure are referenced to basic laboratory techniques that enable the student to complete the experiment more safely and efficiently. The **Laboratory Techniques** section provides a full explanation of 17 basic general chemistry laboratory techniques (along with the corresponding icons) that are used throughout the manual. Each of the techniques has been closely edited, with one from the eighth edition omitted because it is not cited in the Experimental Procedures of the manual.

Organization. For the eighth edition, the experiments were categorized according to subject matter. This format was widely accepted by users and reviewers and retained in the ninth edition. For example, all redox experiments are grouped in Part E such that the sequential numbering of the experiments within Part E indicates a greater degree of complexity. *Experiment 27*, Oxidation–Reduction Reactions, is the simplest of the experiments involving oxidation–reduction reactions, *not* the 25th most difficult experiment in the manual, and *Experiment 33*, Electrolytic Cells: Avogadro's Number, is perhaps the most difficult of the oxidation–reduction experiemnts.

Report Sheets. Report Sheets are more user-friendly! Data entries on the Report Sheet are distinguished from calculated entries—the calculated entries are shaded on the Report Sheet. Students also are encouraged to engage appropriate software for analyzing and plotting data.

Additionally, at the discretion of the instructor, the web site www.wiley.com/college/chem/brean provides downloadable Excel Report Sheet templates for each experiment where a numerical analysis is required.

Online References. A significant number of web sites are cited in various experiments and dry labs. An extensive list of online references is also provided in the **Laboratory Data** section of the manual.

NEW TO THE NINTH EDITION

Prelaboratory Assignment and Laboratory Questions. Perhaps the most evident revisions appear in the questions in the Prelaboratory Assignments and the Laboratory Questions. More than one-half of the questions are new to the ninth edition, and all of the questions were reviewed for clarity.

Revised Experiments. All of experiments from the eighth edition have been retained but have been addressed for clarity in the Experimental Procedures for obtaining good data while using proper chemical techniques and on the Report Sheet for recording and analyzing data. These refinements have become increasingly important for today's students who continue to develop, in general, a multitude of state-of-the-art electronic skills.

The Next Step. The Next Step is a feature added to the eighth edition and has been met with anticipated inclusion into open-ended laboratory programs. Based on the tools and techniques gained with completion of the experiment, The Next Step takes students from its completion to ideas for an independent, self-designed experience or experiment. The Next Step was developed to answer the student's question, "What more can I *now* do with what I just learned in the laboratory?" Scientific inquiry of the chemical system begins with The Next Step when the student leaves the laboratory, it does not end with "Well, that experiment is over!"

Laboratory Equipment. Simple laboratory glassware and equipment, shown in the early sections of the manual, are necessary for completing most experiments. Where appropriate, the apparatus or technique is shown in the experiment with a line drawing or photograph. Analytical balances, spectrophotometers (*Experiments 34* and *35*), pH meters (*Experiment 18*), and multimeters (*Experiments 32* and *33*) are suggested; however, if this instrumentation is unavailable, these experiments can be modified without penalizing students. In general, hot plates have largely replaced Bunsen burners in the manual; however if not available, the Bunsen flame can still be safely used for heating.

CONTENTS OF THE NINTH EDITION

The manual has five major sections:

- **Laboratory Safety and Guidelines.** Information on self-protection, what to do in case of an accident, general laboratory rules, and work ethics in the laboratory are presented.

- **Laboratory Data.** Guidelines for recording and reporting data are described. Sources of supplementary data (handbooks and World Wide Web sites) are listed. Suggestions for setting up a laboratory notebook are presented.
- **Laboratory Techniques.** Seventeen basic laboratory techniques present the proper procedures for handling chemicals and apparatus. Techniques unique to qualitative analysis (*Experiments 37–39*) are presented in *Dry Lab 4*.
- **Experiments and Dry Labs.** Thirty-nine experiments and four "dry labs" are subdivided into 12 basic chemical principles.
- **Appendices.** Seven appendices include conversion factors, the treatment of data, the graphing of data, names of common chemicals, vapor pressure of water, concentrations of acids and bases, and water solubility of inorganic salts.

CONTENTS OF EACH EXPERIMENT

Each experiment has six sections:

- *Objectives.* One or more statements establish the purposes and goals of the experiment. The "flavor" of the experiment is introduced with an opening photograph.
- *Techniques.* Icons identify various laboratory techniques that are used in the Experimental Procedure. The icons refer students to the **Laboratory Techniques** section where the techniques are described and illustrated.
- *Introduction.* The chemical principles, including appropriate equations and calculations that are applicable to the experiment, and general interest information are presented in the opening paragraphs. New and revised illustrations have been added to this section to further enhance the understanding of the chemical principles that are used in the experiment.
- *Experimental Procedure.* The Procedure Overview, a short introductory paragraph, provides a perspective of the Experimental Procedure. Detailed, stepwise directions are presented in the Experimental Procedure. Occasionally, calculations for amounts of chemicals to be used in the experiment must precede any experimentation.
- *Prelaboratory Assignment.* Questions and problems about the experiment prepare students for the laboratory experience. The questions and problems can be answered easily after studying the Introduction and Experimental Procedure. Approximately 60 percent of the Prelaboratory questions and problems are new to the ninth edition.
- *Report Sheet.* The Report Sheet organizes the observations and the collection and analysis of data. Data entries on the Report Sheet are distinguished from calculated (shaded) entries. Laboratory Questions, for which students must have a thorough understanding of the experiment, appear at the end of the Report Sheet. Approximately 50 percent of the Laboratory Questions are new to the ninth edition.

INSTRUCTOR'S RESOURCE MANUAL

The *Instructor's Resource Manual* (available to instructors from Wiley) continues to be most explicit in presenting the details of each experiment. Sections for each experiment include

- an Overview of the experiment
- an instructor's Lecture Outline
- Teaching Hints
- representative or expected data and results
- Chemicals Required
- Special Equipment
- Suggested Unknowns
- answers to the Prelaboratory Assignment questions and Laboratory Questions
- a Laboratory Quiz.

Offered as a supplement to the *Instructor's Resource Manual* is a Report Sheet template for those experiments requiring the numerical analysis of data. The format of the templates is based on Microsoft Excel software and is available from Wiley on adoption.

The Appendixes of the *Instructor's Resource Manual* detail the preparation of all of the solutions, including indicators, a list of the pure substances, and a list of the special equipment used in the manual *and* the corresponding experiment number for each listing. Users of the laboratory manual have made mention of the value of the *Instructor's Resource Manual* to the laboratory package.

REVIEWERS

The valuable suggestions provided by the following reviewers for this ninth edition are greatly appreciated:

Steven E. Czerwinski
Harford Community College

Jeanne Domoleczny
Benedictine University

Phillip DeLassus
University of Texas—Pan American

Dimitrios Giarikos
Nova Southeastern University

Todor Gounev
University of Missouri—Kansas City

Stephen Z. Goldberg
Adelphi University

Michael Schuder
Carroll University

ACKNOWLEDGMENTS

The author thanks Dr. John R. Amend, Montana State University, for permission to use his basic idea in using emission spectra (without the aid of a spectroscope) to study atomic structure (*Dry Lab 3*); Dr. Gordon Eggleton, Southeastern Oklahoma State University, for encouraging the inclusion of the paper chromatography experiment (*Experiment 4*); the general chemistry faculty at Penn State University, York Campus for the idea behind the thermodynamics experiment (*Experiment 26*); and to Dr. Stephen Goldberg, Adelphi University, for his insightful chemical and editorial suggestions and opinions throughout the writing of the ninth edition.

What a staff at Wiley! Thanks to Jennifer Yee, Project Editor, for her keen insight, helpful suggestions, and unending commitment to see the manual through its birth; Erin Bascom, Production Editor, for coordinating the production of the manual; Hilary Newman, Photo Editor at Wiley, for assistance in obtaining the photographs for this edition; Kevin Murphy, Senior Designer; Anna Melhorn, Illustration Coordinator; Kristine Ruff, Marketing Manager; Cathy Donovan, Editorial Program Assistant; and Lynn Lustberg, Project Manager.

Thanks also to the Chemistry 1111 and 1112 students, and laboratory assistants and staff at Texas A&M—Kingsville for their keen insight and valuable suggestions; also to my colleagues and assistants for their valuable comments.

A special note of appreciation is for Judi, who has unselfishly permitted me to follow my professional dreams and ambitions since long before the first edition of this manual in 1978. She has been the "rock" in my life. And also to Kyle and Greg, who by now have each launched their own families and careers—a Dad could not be more proud of them and their personal and professional accomplishments. My father and mother gave their children the drive, initiative, work ethic, and their blessings to challenge the world beyond that of our small Kansas farm. I shall be forever grateful to them for giving us those tools for success.

James E. Brady, St. Johns University, Jamaica, NY, who was a coauthor of the manual in the early editions, remains the motivator to review and update the manual and to stay at the forefront of general chemistry education. Gary Carlson, my *first* chemistry editor at Wiley, gave me the opportunity to kick off my career in a way I never thought possible or even anticipated. Thanks Jim and Gary.

The author invites corrections and suggestions from colleagues and students.

J. A. Beran
Regents Professor, Texas A&M University System
Department of Chemistry
Texas A&M University—Kingsville
Kingsville, TX 78363

Photo Credits

Page v: Granger Collection; page 1 (**top**): Stockbyte/Getty Images, Inc.; page 1 (**bottom**): Adam Gault/Getty Images, Inc.; page 2: Doug Martin/Photo Researchers, Inc; page 3: Jack Hollingsworth/Photodisc/Getty Images, Inc.; page 5: Masterfile; page 7 (**top**): Masterfile; page 7 (**bottom**): Courtesy Fisher Scientific; page 8 (**top left**): Courtesy VWR International, LLC; page 8 (**top center**): Art Vandalay/Getty Images, Inc.; page 8 (**top right**): Courtesy Fisher Scientific; page 8 (**bottom left**): Courtesy VWR International, LLC; page 8 (**bottom center**): Kristen Brochmann/Fundamental Photographs; page 8 (**bottom right**): Courtesy VWR International, LLC; page 9: Yoav Levy/Phototake; page 10: Yoav Levy/Phototake; page 11: Eva Serrabassa/iStockphoto; page 13 (**top**): Ken Karp; page 13 (**center**): Courtesy Fisher Scientfiic; page 13 (**bottom left**): Courtesy Fisher Scientific; page 14 (**top**): Martyn F. Chillmaid/Photo Researchers; page 14 (**bottom left**): Courtesy Fisher Scientific; page 14 (**bottom right**): Courtesy Fisher Scientific; page 15: Peter Lerman; page 16 (**top**): Courtesy VWR International, LLC; page 16 (**bottom**): Courtesy Fisher Scientific; page 17 (**top left**): Courtesy Scientech, Inc.; page 17 (**top center**): Courtesy VWR International, LLC; page 17 (**top right**): Courtesy Sartorius Co.; page 17 (**bottom right**): Courtesy Corning Glass Works; page 17 (**bottom far right**): Courtesy Fisher Scientific; page 18 (**bottom left**): Ken Karp; page 19 (**top left**): Courtesy Professor Jo A. Beran; page 19 (**top right**): Courtesy Professor Jo A. Beran; page 19 (**bottom**): Courtesy Professor Jo A. Beran; page 20 (**top left**): Courtesy Professor Jo A. Beran; page 20 (**top right**): Courtesy Professor Jo A. Beran; page 20 (**bottom left**): Ken Karp; page 20 (**bottom right**): Ken Karp; page 21: Courtesy Professor Jo A. Beran; page 22 (**top left**): Courtesy Professor Jo A. Beran; page 22 (**top right**): Courtesy Professor Jo A. Beran; page 22 (**bottom**): Courtesy VWR International, LLC; page 24 (**top left**): Courtesy VWR International, LLC; page 24 (**top right**): Courtesy Professor Jo A. Beran; page 24 (**bottom center**): Courtesy Professor Jo A. Beran; page 24 (**bottom right**): Courtesy Professor Jo A. Beran; page 25 (**top left**): Ken Karp; page 25 (**top center**): Courtesy Professor Jo A. Beran; page 25 (**top right**): Courtesy Professor Jo A. Beran; page 24 (**bottom left**): Courtesy Fisher Scientific; page 26 (**left**): Courtesy Professor Jo A. Beran; page 26 (**right**): Courtesy Professor Jo A. Beran; page 27 (**left**): Courtesy Fisher Scientific; page 27 (**center**): Courtesy Fisher Scientific; page 27 (**right**): Courtesy Fisher Scientific; page 28 (**top left**): Ken Karp; page 28 (**top center**): Ken Karp; page 28 (**top right**): Ken Karp; page 29 (**top left**): Courtesy Professor Jo A. Beran; page 29 (**top right**): Courtesy Professor Jo A. Beran; page 29 (**center**): Courtesy Fisher Scientific; page 30 (**left**): Courtesy VWR International, LLC; page 30 (**center**): Courtesy Professor Jo A. Beran; page 30 (**right**): Courtesy Professor Jo A. Beran; page 31 (**top left**): Ken Karp; page 31 (**top center**): Courtesy Fisher Scientific; page 31 (**top right**): Courtesy Professor Jo A. Beran; page 31 (**bottom left**): Courtesy Professor Jo A. Beran; page 31 (**bottom center**): Courtesy Professor Jo A. Beran; page 31 (**bottom right**): Courtesy Professor Jo A. Beran; page 32: Ken Karp; page 33: Courtesy Micro Essential Labs; page 37: Courtesy Fisher Scientific; page 38: Courtesy Fisher Scientific; page 39: Courtesy Professor Jo A. Beran; page 40: Terry Gleason/Visuals Unlimited; page 42: iStockphoto; page 43 (**top**): NASA/GSFC; page 43 (**center**): iStockphoto; page 43 (**bottom**): Dan Eckert/iStockphoto; page 44 (**top**): ALEAImage/iStockphoto; page 44 (**center**): Yoav Levy/Phototake; page 44 (**bottom**): Courtesy Professor Jo A. Beran; page 45: Richard Megna/Fundamental Photographs; page 46 (**left**): Courtesy Fisher Scientific; page 46 (**right**): Courtesy VWR International, LLC; page 47: Courtesy Professor Jo A. Beran; page 48 (**left**): Courtesy Professor Jo A. Beran; page 48 (**right**): Courtesy Professor Jo A. Beran; page 49: David Claassen/iStockphoto; page 50: Richard Megna/Fundamental Photographs; page 53: Michael Watson; page 54 (**top**): OPC, Inc.; page 54 (**bottom**): Andy Washnik; page 56: Ken Karp; page 61: iStockphoto; page 63: Courtesy Professor Jo A. Beran; page 69: Richard Megna/Fundamental Photographs; page 72 (**top**): Courtesy Norton Seal View; page 72 (**center**): Courtesy Fisher Scientific; page 79 (**top**): Michael Watson; page 79 (**bottom**): Courtesy Professor Jo A. Beran; page 80: Courtesy Fisher Scientific; page 81: Oliver Childs/iStockphoto; page 85 (**top**): Charles D. Winters/Photo Researchers, Inc.; page 88: Richard Megna/Fundamental Photographs; page 89: Andy Washnik; page 91: Peter Lerman; page 92: Peter Lerman; page 96: Kathy Bendo; page 94: Robert Capece; page 97: Peter Lerman; page 98: Andy Washnik; page 99 (**top right**): Kathy Bendo and Jim Brady; page 99 (**bottom left**): Kathy Bendo and Jim Brady; page 99 (**bottom right**): Peter Lerman; page 100: Courtesy VWR International, LLC; page 102: Nigel Cattlin/Alamy; page 109: Ken Karp; page 111: Courtesy Professor Jo A. Beran; page 113: Richard Megna/Fundamental Photographs; page 117: Scimat/Photo Researchers, Inc.; page 120: Courtesy Professor Jo A. Beran; page 121: Ken Karp; page 127: Michael Watson; page 130 (**left**): Courtesy VWR International, LLC; page 130 (**right**): Courtesy VWR International, LLC; page 131: Courtesy Fisher Scientific; page 137: Richard Megna/Fundamental Photographs; page 138: Courtesy Fisher Scientific; page 140: Victor de Schwanberg/Photo Researchers, Inc.; page 143 (**top**): Richard Megna/Fundamental Photographs; page 143 (**bottom**): The Granger Collection, New York; page 144 (**top**): Roger Rossmeyer/Corbis; page 144 (**bottom**): Michael Watson; page 148: Courtesy Professor Jo A. Beran; page 155: Jacob Hamblin/iStockphoto; page 157: Bausch & Lomb; page 158: Courtesy Library of Congress; page 167: Courtesy VWR International, LLC; page 169 (**left**): Ken Karp; page 169 (**right**): Courtesy Professor Jo A. Beran; page 175 (**top**): Andy Washnik; page 175 (**bottom**): Bruce Roberts/Photo Researchers, Inc.; page 178: Hugh Lieck; page 183 (**top**): Courtesy Fisher Scientific; page 183 (**bottom**): Hugh Lieck; page 186 (**bottom**): Hugh Lieck; page 187: Courtesy Professor Jo A. Beran; page 186 (**top**): Courtesy Fisher Scientific; page 190: Photodynamic/iStockphoto; page 193 (**top**): Michael Watson; page 193 (**bottom**): Courtesy Professor Jo A. Beran; page 195: Courtesy Professor Jo A. Beran; page 196 (**left**): Courtesy Fisher Scientific; page 196 (**right**): Ken Karp; page 201: Peter Lerman; page 202: Michael Watson; page 203: Ken Karp; page 204: Courtesy Center for Disease Control; page 205: Ken Karp; page 213 (**top**): Ken Karp; page 213 (**bottom**): Kathy Bendo; page 215 (**left**): Courtesy Professor Jo A. Beran; page 215 (**right**): Courtesy Professor Jo A. Beran; page 218: Andy Washnik; page 221: Courtesy Fisher Scientific; page 225: Courtesy Fisher Scientific; page 222: Courtesy Fisher Scientific; page 224: Richard Megna/Fundamental Photographs; page 231: Ken Karp; page 233: Courtesy Professor Jo A. Beran; page 234: Courtesy Professor Jo A. Beran; page 239: PhotoDisc/Getty Images; page 248: Courtesy Savogran; page 243 (**left**): Courtesy Professor Jo A. Beran; page 243 (**right**): Courtesy Fisher Scientific; page 249: Astrid & Hanns-Frieder Michler/Photo Researchers, Inc; page 250: Bortner/National Audobon Society/Photo Researchers, Inc.; page 257: Michael Watson; page 258: Michael Watson; page 258: Hugh Lieck; page 261: Richard Megna/Fundamental Photographs; page 265 (**top**): OPC, Inc.; page 265 (**bottom**): Courtesy Fisher Scientific; page 267 (**center left**): Courtesy OPC, Inc.; page 267 (**center**): Courtesy OPC, Inc.; page 267 (**center right**): Courtesy OPC, Inc.; page 267 (**bottom**): Courtesy VWR International, LLC; page 271: Adam Hart-Davis/Photo Researchers, Inc.; page 275: Ken Karp; page 287: Andy Washnik; page 290 (**left**): Courtesy Professor Jo A. Beran; page 290 (**right**): Courtesy Fisher Scientific; page 299: Andy Washnik; page 302: Courtesy Fisher Scientific; page 303: Courtesy Fisher Scientific; page 309: Yoav Levy/Phototake; page 311: Fundamental Photographs; page 312: Andy Washnik; page 314: Alaska Stock Images; page 317 (**top**): Michael Watson; page 317 (**bottom**): OPC, Inc.; page 325: OPC, Inc.; page 327 (**top left**): Andy Washnik; page 327 (**top right**): Andy Washnik; page 327 (**bottom**): Courtesy Professor Jo A. Beran; page 328 (**left**): Courtesy VWR International, LLC; page 328 (**right**): Courtesy VWR International, LLC; page 329 (**top left**): Courtesy Professor Jo A. Beran; page 329 (**bottom left**): Hugh Lieck; page 329 (**right**): Courtesy VWR International, LLC; page 332: Ken Karp; page 335 (**top**): Ken Karp; page 335 (**bottom**): Michael Siluk/The Image Works; page 336: Courtesy Professor Jo A. Beran; page 338: Courtesy VWR International, LLC; page 343 (**top**): Courtesy Professor Jo A. Beran; page 343 (**bottom**): Courtesy Fisher Scientific; page 351: Michael Watson; page 355 (**left**): Courtesy Fisher Scientific; page 355 (**right**): Michael Watson; page 363: Charles D. Winters/Photo Researchers; page 364: Michael Watson; page 365: Ken Karp; page 371: Ken Karp; page 372: Courtesy VWR International, LLC; page 375: Courtesy Fisher Scientific; page 383: Andrew Lambert Photography/Photo Researchers, Inc.; page 391: OPC, Inc.; page 392 (**top**): Daryl Benson/Masterfile; page 392 (**bottom**): Courtesy Fisher Scientific; page 393 (**center**): Andy Washnik; page 396: Ken Karp; page 397: Courtesy Professor Jo A. Beran; page 403: Courtesy VWR International, LLC; page 407: Peter Lerman; page 409: Peter Lerman; page 417: Yoav Levy/Phototake; page 419: Andy Washnik; page 421 (**left**): Ken Karp; page 421 (**right**): Courtesy Professor Jo A. Beran; page 427 (**top left**): Martyn F. Chillmaid/Photo Researchers, Inc.; page 427 (**top right**): Andrew Lambert Photography/Photo Researchers, Inc.; page 427 (**bottom**): OPC, Inc.; page 435: Courtesy J. A. Beran; page 443: Kathy Bendo; page 446: Courtesy Fisher Scientific; page 447: Michael Watson

Contents

Laboratory Safety and Guidelines

Wearing proper laboratory attire protects against chemical burns and irritations.

The chemistry laboratory is one of the safest environments in an academic or industrial facility. Every chemist, trained to be aware of the potential dangers of chemicals, is additionally careful in handling, storing, and disposing of chemicals. Laboratory safety should be a constant concern and practice for everyone in the laboratory.

Be sure that you and your partners practice laboratory safety and follow basic laboratory rules. It is your responsibility, *not* the instructor's, to *play it safe*. A little extra effort on your part will assure others that the chemistry laboratory continues to be safe. Accidents do and will occur, but most often they are caused by carelessness, thoughtlessness, or neglect.

The inside front cover of this manual has space to list the location of important safety equipment and other valuable reference information that are useful in the laboratory. You will be asked to complete this at your earliest laboratory meeting.

This section of the manual has guidelines for making laboratory work a safe and meaningful venture. Depending on the specific laboratory setting or experiment, other guidelines for a safe laboratory may be enforced. Study the following guidelines carefully before answering the questions on the *Report Sheet* of *Dry Lab 1*.

A. SELF-PROTECTION

1. Approved safety goggles or eye shields *must be worn* at all times to guard against the laboratory accidents of others as well as your own. Contact lenses should be replaced with prescription glasses. Where contact lenses must be worn, eye protection (safety goggles) is *absolutely necessary*. A person wearing prescription glasses must also wear safety goggles or an eye shield. Discuss any interpretations of this with your laboratory instructor.

2. Shoes *must* be worn. Wear only shoes that shed liquids. High-heeled shoes; open-toed shoes; sandals; shoe tops of canvas, leather, or fabric straps or other woven material are *not* permitted.

3. Clothing should be only nonsynthetic (cotton). Shirts and blouses should not be torn, frilled, frayed, or flared. Sleeves should be close-fit. Clothing should cover the skin from "neck to below the knee (preferable to the ankle) and *at least* to the wrist." Long pants that cover the tops of the shoes are preferred.

   Discuss any interpretations of this with your laboratory instructor. See opening photo.

4. Laboratory aprons or coats (nonflammable, nonporous, and with snap fasteners) are highly recommended to protect outer clothing.

5. Gloves are to be worn to protect the hand when transferring corrosive liquids. If you are known to be allergic to latex gloves, consult with your instructor.

6. Jewelry should be removed. Chemicals can cause a severe irritation if concentrated, under a ring, wristwatch, or bracelet; chemicals on

Laboratory gloves protect the skin from chemicals.

fingers or gloves can cause irritation around earrings, necklaces, and so on. It is just a good practice of laboratory safety to remove jewelry.

7. Secure long hair and remove (or secure) neckties and scarves.

8. Cosmetics, antibiotics, or moisturizers are *not* to be applied in the laboratory.

9. *Never* taste, smell, or touch a chemical or solution unless *specifically* directed to do so (see B.4 below). Individual allergic or sensitivity responses to chemicals cannot be anticipated. Poisonous substances are not always labeled.

10. *Technique 3*, page 14, provides an extensive overview of the proper handling of chemicals, from the dispensing of chemicals to the safety advisories for chemicals (NFPA standards). Additionally, online access to the MSDS collection of chemicals[1] provides further specifics for all chemicals that are used in this manual.

All other techniques in the **Laboratory Techniques** section describe procedures for safely conducting an experiment. Be sure to read each technique carefully before the laboratory session for completing a safe and successful experiment.

11. Wash your hands often during the laboratory, but *always* wash your hands with soap and water before leaving the laboratory! Thereafter, wash your hands and face in the washroom. Toxic or otherwise dangerous chemicals may be inadvertently transferred to the skin and from the skin to the mouth.

Additional information on personal safety in the laboratory can be found at many Web sites on the Internet.

B. LABORATORY ACCIDENTS

An eye wash can quickly remove chemicals from the eyes; a safety shower can quickly remove chemicals from the body.

1. Locate the laboratory safety equipment such as eyewash fountains, safety showers, fire extinguishers, and fume hoods. Identify their locations on the inside front cover of this manual.

2. **Report all accidents** or injuries, even if considered minor, *immediately* to your instructor. A written report of any and all accidents that occur in the laboratory may be required. Consult with your laboratory instructor.

3. If an **accident occurs**, *do not panic*! The most important first action after an accident is the care of the individual. *Alert your laboratory instructor immediately!* If a person is injured, provide or seek aid *immediately*. Clothing and books can be replaced and experiments can be performed again later. Second, take the appropriate action regarding the accident: clean up the chemical (see B.8, page 3), use the fire extinguisher (see B.6 below), and so on.

4. Whenever your skin (hands, arms, face, etc.) comes into contact with chemicals, quickly flush the affected area for several minutes with tap water followed by thorough washing with soap and water. Use the eyewash fountain to flush chemicals from the eyes and face. *Get help immediately.* Do *not* rub the affected area, especially the face or eyes, with your hands before washing.

5. Chemical spills over a large part of the body require immediate action. Using the safety shower, flood the affected area for at least 5 minutes. Remove all contaminated clothing if necessary. Use a mild detergent and water only (no salves, creams, lotions, etc.). Get medical attention as directed by your instructor.

6. In case of fire, discharge a fire extinguisher at the base of the flames and move it from one side to the other. Small flames can be smothered with a watchglass (do *not* use a towel because it may catch on fire). Do *not* discharge a fire extinguisher when a person's clothing is on fire—use the safety shower. Once the fire appears to be out of control, *immediately* evacuate the laboratory.

7. For abrasions or cuts, flush the affected area with water. Any further treatment should be given only after consulting with the laboratory instructor.

---

[1]See http://ilpi.com/msds

For burns, the affected area should be rubbed with ice, submerged in an ice-water bath, or placed under running water for several minutes to withdraw heat from the burned area. More serious burns require immediate medical attention. Consult with your laboratory instructor.

8. Treat chemical spills in the laboratory as follows:
   - Alert your neighbors and the laboratory instructor
   - Clean up the spill as directed by the laboratory instructor
   - If the substance is volatile, flammable, or toxic, warn everyone of the accident

9. *Technique 4*, page 15, provides information for the proper disposal of chemicals after being used in the experiment. Improper disposal can result in serious laboratory accidents. Read that section carefully—it may prevent an "undesirable" laboratory accident. If you are uncertain of the proper procedure for the disposing of a chemical, *ask!*

C. LABORATORY RULES

In addition to the guidelines for self-protection (Part A), the following rules must be followed.

1. *Smoking, drinking, eating, and chewing* (including gum and tobacco) are not permitted at any time because chemicals may inadvertently enter the mouth or lungs. Your hands may be contaminated with an "unsafe" chemical. Do not place any objects, including pens or pencils, in your mouth during or after the laboratory period. These objects may have picked up a contaminant from the laboratory bench.

2. Do *not* work in the laboratory alone. The laboratory instructor must be present.

3. Assemble your laboratory apparatus away from the edge of the lab bench ($\geq$ 8 inches or $\geq$ 20 cm) to avoid accidents.

4. Do *not* leave your experiment unattended during the laboratory period: This is often a time when accidents occur.

5. Inquisitiveness and creativeness in the laboratory are encouraged. However, variations or alterations of the Experimental Procedure are forbidden without prior approval of the laboratory instructor. If your chemical intuition suggests further experimentation, first consult with your laboratory instructor.

6. Maintain an orderly, clean laboratory desk and drawer. Immediately clean up all chemical spills, paper scraps, and glassware. Discard wastes as directed by your laboratory instructor.

7. Keep drawers or cabinets closed and the aisles free of any obstructions. Do *not* place book bags, athletic equipment, or other items on the floor near any lab bench.

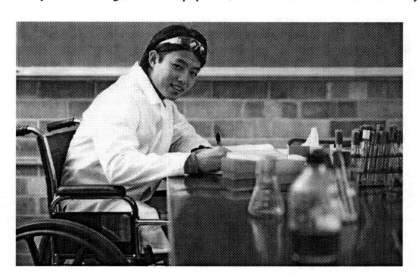

Laboratory facilities must be designed for safety.

8. At the end of the laboratory period, completely clear the lab bench of equipment, clean it with a damp sponge or paper towel (and properly discard), and clean the sinks of all debris. Also clean all glassware used in the experiment (see *Technique 2*, page 13).

9. Be aware of your neighbors' activities: You may be a victim of their mistakes. Advise them of improper techniques or unsafe practices. If necessary, tell the instructor.

10. For all other rules, **listen to your instructor!** Additional laboratory rules and guidelines can be added to this list at the bottom of this page.

D. WORKING IN THE LABORATORY

1. Maintain a wholesome, professional attitude. Horseplay and other careless acts are prohibited.

2. The operation of cell phones and other electronic "entertainment" equipment is strictly forbidden.

3. Do *not* entertain guests in the laboratory. Your total concentration on the experiment is required for a safe, meaningful laboratory experience. You may socialize with others in the lab, but do not have a party! You are expected to maintain a learning, scientific environment.

4. Scientists learn much by discussion with one another. Likewise, you may profit by discussion with your laboratory instructor or classmates—but *not* by copying from them.

5. *Prepare for each experiment.* Review the Objectives and Introduction to determine the "chemistry" of the experiment, the chemical system, the stoichiometry of the reactions, the color changes to anticipate, and the calculations that will be required. A thorough knowledge of the experiment will make the laboratory experience more time efficient and scientifically more meaningful (and result in a better grade!). Complete the ***Prelaboratory Assignment.***

6. Review the Experimental Procedure.

   • Try to understand the purpose of each step.
   • Determine if any extra equipment is needed and be ready to obtain it all at once from the stockroom.
   • Determine what data are to be collected and how they are to be analyzed (calculations, graphs, etc.).
   • Review the **Laboratory Techniques** and the **Cautions,** because they are important for conducting a safe and rewarding experiment.

7. Review the ***Report Sheet.*** Complete any calculations required before data collection can begin during the laboratory period. Determine the data to be collected, the number of suggested trials, and the data analysis required (e.g., calculations, graphs).

8. Review the Laboratory Questions at the conclusion of the ***Report Sheet*** before *and* as you perform the experiment. These questions are intended to enhance your understanding of the chemical principles on which the experiment is based.

9. Above all, *enjoy* the laboratory experience. Be prepared, observe, think, and anticipate during the course of the experiment. Ultimately, you will be rewarded.

NOTES ON LABORATORY SAFETY AND GUIDELINES

Laboratory Data

Laboratory data should be carefully recorded.

The lifeblood of a good scientist depends on the collection of reliable and reproducible data from experimental observations and on the analysis of that data. The data must be presented in a logical and credible format; that is, the data must appear such that other scientists will believe in and rely on the data that you have collected.

Believe in your data, and others will have confidence in it also. A scientist's most priceless possession is integrity. Be a scientist. Scientists are conscientious in their efforts to observe, collect, record, and interpret the experimental data as best possible. Only honest scientific work is acceptable.

You may be asked to present your data on the **Report Sheet** that appears at the end of each experiment, or you may be asked to keep a laboratory notebook (see Part D for guidelines). For either method, a customary procedure for collecting, recording, and presenting data is to be followed. A thorough preview of the experiment will assist in your collection and presentation of data.

A. RECORDING DATA

1. Record all data entries *as they are being collected* on the **Report Sheet** or in your laboratory notebook. Be sure to include appropriate units after numerical entries. Data on scraps of paper (such as mass measurements in the balance room) will be confiscated.

2. Record the data *in permanent ink* as you perform the experiment.

3. If a mistake is made in recording data, cross out the incorrect data entry with a *single* line (do *not* erase, white out, overwrite, or obliterate) and clearly enter the corrected data nearby (see Figure A.1). If a large section of data is deemed incorrect, then write a short notation as to why the data are in error, place a single diagonal line across the data, and note where the correct data are recorded.

4. For clarity, record data entries of values <1 with a zero in the "one" position of the number; for example, record a mass measurement as 0.218 g rather than .218 g (see Figure A.1).

5. Data collected from an instrument or computer printout should be securely attached to the **Report Sheet**.

	Trial 1
Mass of $CaCO_3$ sample, initial	0.218 g
Mass of $CaCO_3$, after heating	0.164 ~~0.184 g~~
Mass of CO_2 in sample	0.054 g

Figure A.1 Procedures for recording and correcting data.

B. REPORTING DATA WITH SIGNIFICANT FIGURES

The quantitative data that are collected must reflect the reliability of the instruments and equipment used to make the measurements. For example, most bathroom scales in the United States weigh to the nearest pound (± 1 lb); therefore, reporting a person's weight should reflect the precision of the measurement—a person's weight should be expressed as, for example, 145 ± 1 pounds and *not* 145.000 . . . pounds! Conversely, if the mass of a substance is measured on a balance that has a precision of ± 0.001 g, the mass of the object should be expressed as, for example, 0.218 g and *not* as 0.2 g.

Scientists use **significant figures** *to clearly express the precision of measurements.* The number of significant figures used to express the measurement is determined by the specific instrument used to make the measurement.

The number of significant figures in a measurement equals the number of figures that are certain in the measurement *plus* one additional figure that expresses uncertainty. The first uncertain figure in a measurement is the last significant figure of the measurement. The above mass measurement (0.218 g) has three significant figures. The first uncertain figure is the 8, which means that the confidence of the measurement is between 0.219 g and 0.217 g, or 0.218 ± 0.001 g.

Rules for expressing the significant figures of a measurement and manipulating data with significant figures can be found in most general chemistry texts.

A simplified overview of the "Rules for Significant Figures" is as follows:

- Significant figures are used to express measurements that indicate the precision of the measuring instrument.
- All definitions (e.g., 12 inches = 1 foot) have an infinite number of significant figures.
- For the addition and subtraction of data with significant figures, the answer is rounded off to the number of decimal places equal to the *fewest* number of decimal places in any one of the measurements.
- For the multiplication and division of data with significant figures, the answer is expressed with the number of significant figures equal to the *fewest* number of significant figures for any one of the measurements.

Expressing measurements in scientific notation often simplifies the recording of measurements with the correct number of significant figures. For example, the mass measurement of 0.218 g, expressed as 2.18×10^{-1} g, clearly indicates three significant figures in the measurement. Zeros at the front end of a measurement are not significant.

Zeros at the end of a measurement of data may or may not be significant. However, again that dilemma is clarified when the measurement is expressed in scientific notation. For example, the volume of a sample written as 200 mL may have one, two, or three significant figures. Expressing the measurement as 2×10^2 mL, 2.0×10^2 mL, or 2.00×10^2 mL clarifies the precision of the measurement as having one, two, or three significant figures, respectively. Zeros at the end of a number *and* to the right of a decimal point are always significant.

In reporting data for your observations in this laboratory manual, follow closely the guidelines for using significant figures to correctly express the precision of your measurements and the reliability of your calculations.

C. ACCESSING SUPPLEMENTARY DATA

You will also profit by frequent references to your textbook or, for tabular data on the properties of chemicals, the *CRC Handbook of Chemistry and Physics,* published by the Chemical Rubber Publishing Company of Cleveland, Ohio, or the *Merck Index,* published by Merck & Co., Inc., of Rahway, New Jersey. Books are generally more reliable and more complete sources of technical information than are classmates.

The World Wide Web has a wealth of information available at your fingertips. Search the Web for additional insights into each experiment. In your search, keep in mind that many Web sites are not peer-reviewed and therefore must be judged for accuracy and truth before being used.

(Suggested only) Web sites that have been reviewed by the author and may enhance your appreciation of the laboratory experience are listed here:

- http://webbook.nist.gov/chemistry (database of technical data)
- http://ilpi.com/msds (MSDS information of chemicals)
- http://physics.nist.gov/cuu (database of technical data)
- http://cas.org (>52 million compounds)
- http://en.wikipedia.org/wiki/Category:Chemistry
- http://webelements.com
- http://chemdex.org
- http://chemistry.about.com
- http://chemtutor.com
- http://chem.ucsd.edu/academic/courses_labs.cfm
- http://pubs.acs.org/cen (Chemical and Engineering News)
- http://pubs.acs.org/jce (Journal of Chemical Education)
- http://chemistry.alanearhart.org
- http://chemlin.net/chemistry
- http://antoine.frostburg.edu/chem/senese/101
- http://chemfinder.camsoft.com (information on compounds)

Scientific data can be obtained from the Internet or analyzed with appropriate software.

D. LABORATORY NOTEBOOK

The laboratory notebook is a personal, permanent record—that is, a journal, of the activities associated with the experiment or laboratory activity. The first 3–4 pages of the notebook should be reserved for a table of contents. The laboratory notebook should have a sewn binding, and the pages must be numbered in sequence.

Each new experiment in the laboratory notebook should begin on the right-hand side of a new page in the laboratory notebook, and it should include the following sections with clear, distinct headings:

- The title of the experiment
- Beginning date of the experiment
- Bibliographic source of the experiment
- Coworkers for the experiment
- The purpose and/or objective(s) of the experiment
- A brief, but clearly written Experimental Procedure that includes the appropriate balanced equations for the chemical reactions and/or any modifications of the procedure
- A list of cautions and safety concerns
- A brief description or sketch of the apparatus
- A section for the data that is recorded (see Parts A and B, *Recording Data* and *Reporting Data with Significant Figures*) as the experiment is in progress, (i.e., the **Report Sheet**). This data section must be planned and organized carefully. The quantitative data is to be organized, neat, and recorded with the appropriate significant figures and units: Any observed, qualitative data must be written legibly, briefly, and with proper grammar. All data must be recorded in *permanent ink*. Allow plenty of room to record observations, comments, notes, and so on.

Laboratory notebook

Appendix B
Appendix C

• A section for data analysis that includes representative calculations, an error analysis (Appendix B), instrument and computer printouts, graphical analyses (Appendix C), and organized tables. Where calculations using data are involved, be orderly with the first set of data. Do *not* clutter the data analysis section with arithmetic details. All computer printouts must be securely attached.

• A section for results and discussion

At the completion of each day's laboratory activities, the laboratory activity should be dated and signed by the chemist, any coworker, *and* the laboratory instructor at the bottom of of each page.

The laboratory instructor will outline any specific instructions that are unique to your laboratory program.

Marking pens help to organize samples.

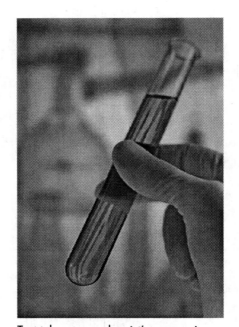

Test tubes are a chemist's companion.

Erlenmeyer flasks are convenient for containing solutions.

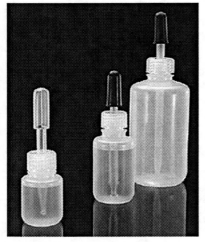

Dropping bottles assist in transferring small volumes of solutions.

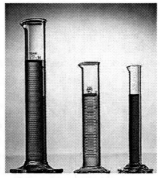

Graduated cylinders measure quantitative volumes of solutions.

A wash bottle containing deionized water must always be handy.

Common Laboratory Desk Equipment Checklist

No.	Quantity	Size	Item	First Term In	First Term Out	Second Term In	Second Term Out	Third Term In	Third Term Out
1	1	10-mL	graduated cylinder	_____	_____	_____	_____	_____	_____
2	1	50-mL	graduated cylinder	_____	_____	_____	_____	_____	_____
3	5	—	beakers	_____	_____	_____	_____	_____	_____
4	2	—	stirring rods	_____	_____	_____	_____	_____	_____
5	1	500-mL	wash bottle	_____	_____	_____	_____	_____	_____
6	1	75-mm, 60°	funnel	_____	_____	_____	_____	_____	_____
7	1	125-mL	Erlenmeyer flask	_____	_____	_____	_____	_____	_____
8	1	250-mL	Erlenmeyer flask	_____	_____	_____	_____	_____	_____
9	2	25 × 200-mm	test tubes	_____	_____	_____	_____	_____	_____
10	6	18 × 150-mm	test tubes	_____	_____	_____	_____	_____	_____
11	8	10 × 75-mm	test tubes	_____	_____	_____	_____	_____	_____
12	1	large	test tube rack	_____	_____	_____	_____	_____	_____
13	1	small	test tube rack	_____	_____	_____	_____	_____	_____
14	1	—	glass plate	_____	_____	_____	_____	_____	_____
15	1	—	wire gauze	_____	_____	_____	_____	_____	_____
16	1	—	crucible tongs	_____	_____	_____	_____	_____	_____
17	1	—	spatula	_____	_____	_____	_____	_____	_____
18	2	—	litmus, red and blue	_____	_____	_____	_____	_____	_____
19	2	90-mm	watch glasses	_____	_____	_____	_____	_____	_____
20	1	75-mm	evaporating dish	_____	_____	_____	_____	_____	_____
21	4	—	dropping pipets	_____	_____	_____	_____	_____	_____
22	1	—	test tube holder	_____	_____	_____	_____	_____	_____
23	1	large	test tube brush	_____	_____	_____	_____	_____	_____
24	1	small	test tube brush	_____	_____	_____	_____	_____	_____
	1	—	marking pen	_____	_____	_____	_____	_____	_____

Special Laboratory Equipment

Number	Item	Number	Item
1	reagent bottles	16	porcelain crucible and cover
2	condenser	17	mortar and pestle
3	500-mL Erlenmeyer flask	18	glass bottle
4	1000-mL beaker	19	pipets
5	Petri dish	20	ring and buret stands
6	Büchner funnel	21	clamp
7	Büchner (filter) flask	22	double buret clamp
8	volumetric flasks	23	Bunsen burner
9	500-mL Florence flask	24	buret brush
10	−10°C–110°C thermometer	25	clay pipe-stem triangle
11	100-mL graduated cylinder	26	rubber stoppers
12	50-mL buret	27	wire loop for flame test
13	glass tubing	28	pneumatic trough
14	U-tube	29	rubber pipet bulb
15	porous ceramic cup	30	iron support ring

Laboratory Techniques

The application of proper laboratory techniques improves data reliability.

Scientific data that are used to analyze the characteristics of a chemical or physical change must be collected with care and patience. The data must be precise; that is, they must be reproducible to within an "acceptable" margin of error. Reproducible data implies that the data collected from an observed chemical or physical change can be again collected at a later date by the same scientist or another scientist in another laboratory.

A scientist who has good laboratory skills and techniques generally collects good, reproducible data (called **quantitative data**). For that reason, careful attention as to the method (or methods) and procedures by which the data are collected is extremely important. This section of the laboratory manual describes a number of techniques that you will need to develop for collecting quantitative data in the chemistry laboratory. You do not need to know the details for all of the techniques at this time (that will come with each successive experiment that you encounter), but you should be aware of their importance, features, and location in the laboratory manual. Become *very* familiar with this section of the laboratory manual! Consult with your laboratory instructor about the completion of the *Laboratory Assignment* at the end of this section.

In the Experimental Procedure of each experiment, icons are placed in the margin at a position where the corresponding laboratory technique is to be applied for the collection of "better" data. The following index of icons identifies the laboratory techniques and page numbers on which they appear:

 Technique 1. Inserting Glass Tubing through a Rubber Stopper *p. 13*

 Technique 2. Cleaning Glassware *p. 13*

 Technique 3. Handling Chemicals *p. 14*

 Technique 4. Disposing of Chemicals *p. 15*

 Technique 5. Preparing Solutions *p. 15*

 Technique 6. Measuring Mass *p. 16*

Technique 7. Handling Small Volumes *p. 16*

 A. Test Tubes for Small Volumes *p. 17*

 B. Well Plates for Small Volumes *p. 17*

Caution: *Perhaps more accidents occur in the general chemistry laboratory as a result of neglect in this simple operation than all other accidents combined. Please review and practice this technique correctly when working with glass tubing. Serious injury can occur to the hand if this technique is performed incorrectly.*

Moisten the glass tubing and the hole in the rubber stopper with glycerol or water (**Note:** glycerol works best). Place your hand on the tubing 2–3 cm (1 in.) from the stopper. Protect your hand with a cloth towel (Figure T.1). Simultaneously *twist* and *push* the tubing slowly and carefully through the hole. Wash off any excess glycerol on the glass or stopper with water and dry.

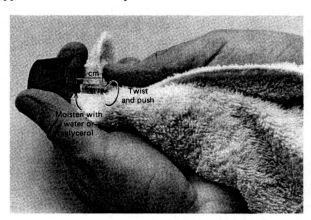

Figure T.1 Inserting glass tubing through a rubber stopper

A chemist is very concerned about contaminants causing errors in experimental data. Cleanliness is extremely important in minimizing errors in the precision and accuracy of data. *Glassware should be clean before you begin an experiment and should be cleaned again immediately after completing the experiment.*

Clean all glassware with a soap or detergent solution using *tap water*. Use a laboratory sponge or a test tube, pipet, or buret brush as appropriate. Once the glassware is thoroughly cleaned, first rinse several times with tap water and then once or twice with *small amounts* of deionized water. Roll each rinse around the entire inner surface of the glass wall for a complete rinse. Discard each rinse through the delivery point of the vessel (i.e., buret tip, pipet tip, beaker spout). For conservation purposes, deionized water should never be used for washing glassware, only for final rinsing.

Invert the clean glassware on a paper towel or rubber mat to dry (Figure T.2a); Do *not* wipe or blow-dry because of possible contamination. Do *not* dry heavy glassware (graduated cylinders, volumetric flasks, or bottles), or for that matter any glassware, over a direct flame.

The glassware is clean if, following the final rinse with deionized water, no water droplets adhere to the clean part of the glassware (Figure T.2b).

A laboratory detergent

Figure T.2a Invert clean glassware on a paper towel or rubber mat to air-dry.

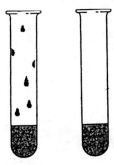

Figure T.2b Water droplets (left) do *not* adhere to the wall of clean glassware (right).

Laboratory Safety and Guidelines also include the handling of chemicals. Chemicals are safe to handle when only a few precautionary guidelines are followed.

- *Read the label* on a reagent bottle at least *twice* before removing any chemicals (Figure T.3a). The wrong chemical may lead to serious accidents or "unexplainable" results in your experiments (see *Dry Lab 2* for an understanding of the rules of chemical nomenclature). *Techniques 9 and 10* illustrate the correct procedures for transferring solids and liquid reagents.
- Avoid using excessive amounts of reagents. *Never* dispense more than the experiment calls for. *Do not return excess chemicals to the reagent bottle!*
- *Never* touch, taste, or smell chemicals unless specifically directed to do so. Skin, nasal, and/or eye irritations may result. If inadvertent contact with a chemical does occur, wash the affected area immediately with copious amounts of water and inform your laboratory instructor (see **Laboratory Safety**, B.4, 5).
- Properly dispose of chemicals. See *Technique 4.*

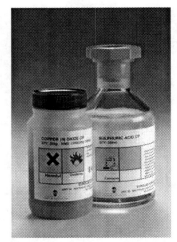

Figure T.3a Chemicals are labeled with systematic names (see *Dry Lab 2*).

Chemicals are often labeled according to National Fire Protection Association (NFPA) standards that describe the four possible hazards of a chemical and a numerical rating from 0 to 4. The four hazards are health hazard (blue), fire hazard (red), reactivity (yellow), and specific hazard (white). A label is shown in Figure T.3b.

If you wish to know more about the properties and hazards of the chemicals you will be working with in the laboratory, safety information about the chemicals is available in a bound collection of Material Safety Data Sheets (MSDS). The MSDS collection is also accessible on various Web sites (see **Laboratory Data**, Part C), (e.g., at www.ilpi.com/msds).

In this manual, the international caution sign (shown at left) is used to identify a potential danger in the handling of a solid chemical or reagent solution or hazardous equipment.

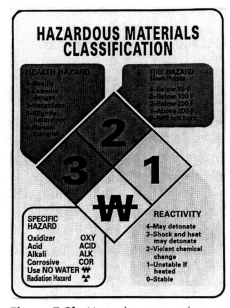

Figure T.3b Hazardous materials classification system

Figure T.4 Waste disposal containers are available in the laboratory.

Most all chemicals used in the experiments of this manual are considered "safe" but must be properly disposed after use for safety and environmental concerns.

- Assume *nothing* (besides soap and water) is to be discarded in the sink.
- Discard waste chemicals as directed in the Experimental Procedure or by the laboratory instructor. *Read the label* on the waste container *at least twice* (Figure T.4) before discarding the chemical. Carelessness that may result in improper mixing of waste chemicals can cause serious laboratory accidents. ***"When in doubt, ask your instructor; it's the safe thing to do!"***
- Note the position of each disposal icon in the Experimental Procedure as the point at which disposal is to occur.

The final disposal of chemicals is the responsibility of the stockroom personnel. Information for the proper disposal of chemicals is also available from the MSDS collection or at various Web sites.

The preparation of an aqueous solution is often required for an Experimental Procedure. The preparation begins with either a solid reagent or a solution more concentrated than the one needed for the experiment. At either starting point, the number of *moles* of compound required for the experiment is calculated: (1) From a solid, the mass and the molar mass of the compound are needed to calculate the number of moles of compound required for the preparation of the solution, (2) from a more concentrated solution, the concentration and volume (or mass) of the diluted solution must be known in order to calculate the number of moles of compound needed for the preparation of the aqueous solution. In both cases, the calculated (and then also measured) moles of compound are diluted to final volume. Knowledge of moles and mole calculations is absolutely necessary.

In the laboratory preparation, *never* insert a pipet, spatula, or dropping pipet into the reagent used for the solution preparation. Always transfer the calculated amount from the reagent bottle as described in *Techniques 9 and 10*.

Solutions are commonly prepared in volumetric flasks (Figure T.5) according to the following procedure:

- Place deionized water (or the less concentrated solution) into the volumetric flask until it is one-third to one-half full.

$$\text{moles solute} = \frac{\text{grams solute}}{\text{molar mass solute}}$$

$$V_{concentrated} = \frac{V_{dilute} \times M_{dilute}}{M_{concentrated}}$$

| (a) | (b) | (c) | (d) |

Figure T.5 Place water (or the less concentrated solution) into the flask before slowly adding the solid or more concentrated solution. Dilute the solution to the "mark" with water; stopper and invert the flask 10–15 times.

- Add the solid (or add the more concentrated reagent) *slowly, while swirling,* to the volumetric flask. (**Caution:** *Never dump it in!*)
- Once the solid compound has dissolved or the more concentrated solution has been diluted, add deionized water (dropwise if necessary) until the calibrated "mark" etched on the volumetric flask is reached (see *Technique 16A* for reading the meniscus). While securely holding the stopper, invert the flask slowly 10–15 times to ensure that the solution is homogeneous.

TECHNIQUE 6. MEASURING MASS

The laboratory balance is perhaps the most used *and abused* piece of equipment in the chemistry laboratory. Therefore, because of its extensive use, you and others must follow several guidelines to maintain the longevity and accuracy of the balance:

- Handle with care; balances are expensive.
- If the balance is not leveled, see your laboratory instructor.
- Use weighing paper, a watchglass, a beaker, or some other container to measure the mass of chemicals; do *not* place chemicals directly on the balance pan.
- Do *not* drop anything on the balance pan.
- If the balance is not operating correctly, see your laboratory instructor. Do *not* attempt to fix it yourself.
- After completing a mass measurement, return the mass settings to the zero position.
- *Clean the balance and balance area of any spilled chemicals.*

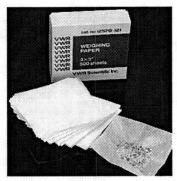

Creased weighing paper is used for measuring the mass of solids.

Tared mass: mass of sample without regard to its container

The mass measurement of a sample can be completed in two ways. In the traditional method, the mass of weighing paper or a clean, dry container (such as a beaker, watchglass, or weighing boat) is first measured and recorded. The sample is then placed on the weighing paper or in the container and this combined mass is measured. The mass of the weighing paper or container is then subtracted from the combined mass to record the mass of the sample.

On modern electronic balances, the mass of the weighing paper or container can be tared out—that is, the balance can be zeroed *after* placing the weighing paper or container on the balance, in effect subtracting its mass immediately (and automatically). The sample is then placed on the weighing paper or in the container, and the balance reading *is* the mass of the sample.

For either method, the resultant mass of the sample is the same and is called the **tared mass** of the sample.

Different electronic balances, having varying degrees of sensitivity, are available for use in the laboratory. It is important to know (by reading the Experimental Procedure) the precision required to make a mass measurement and then to select the appropriate balance. It may save you time during the data analysis. Record mass measurements that reflect the precision of the balance—that is, the correct number of significant figures (see **Laboratory Data**, Part B). These balances are shown in Figures T.6a through T.6c.

Plastic (or aluminum) weighing dishes are used for measuring the masses of solids.

Balance	Sensitivity (g)
Top-loading (Figure T.6a)	±0.01 or ±0.001
Top-loading (Figure T.6b)	±0.0001
Analytical (Figure T.6c)	±0.00001

TECHNIQUE 7. HANDLING SMALL VOLUMES

The use of smaller quantities of chemicals for synthesis and testing in the laboratory offers many safety advantages and presents fewer chemical disposal problems. Many of the Experimental Procedures in this manual were designed with this in mind. Handling small volumes requires special apparatus and technique.

Figure T.6a Top-loading balance, sensitivity of ±0.01 g and/or ±0.001 g.

Figure T.6b Analytical balance, sensitivity of ±0.0001 g.

Figure T.6c Analytical balance, sensitivity of ±0.00001 g.

A. Test Tubes for Small Volumes

Small test tubes are the chemist's choice for handling small volumes. Common laboratory test tubes are generally of three sizes: the 75-mm (or 3-inch) test tube, the 150-mm (or 6-inch) test tube, and the 200-mm (or 8-inch) test tube (Figure T.7a). The approximate volumes of the three test tubes are:

75-mm (3-inch) test tube	~3 mL
150-mm (6-inch) test tube	~25 mL
200-mm (8-inch) test tube	~75 mL

The 75-mm test tube is often recommended for "small volume" experiments.

B. Well Plates for Small Volumes

Alternatively, a "well plate" can be used for several or for a series of reaction vessels (Figure T.7b). The well plate is especially suited for experiments that require observations from repeated or comparative reactions. The well plate most often recommended is the 24-well plate in which each well has an approximate volume of 3.5 mL (compared to a 3 mL for a small test tube).

For either technique, the Beral pipet, (a plastic, disposable pipet), or a dropping pipet (usually made of glass) is often used to transfer small volumes of solutions to and from the test tubes or well plate. The Beral pipet has a capacity of about 2 mL, and some have volume graduation marks on the stem.

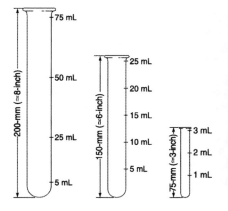

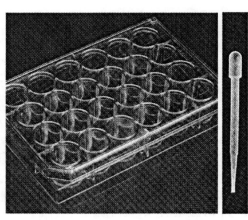

Figure T.7a The three common-size test tubes for containing reagent solutions

Figure T.7b A 24-well plate and Beral pipet are used for containing and transferring small quantities of reagent solutions.

TECHNIQUE 8. COLLECTING WATER-INSOLUBLE GASES

Gases that are relatively insoluble in water are collected by water displacement. The gas pushes the water down and out of the water-filled gas-collecting vessel (Figure T.8a). The gas-collecting vessel (generally a flask or test tube) is first filled with water, covered with a glass plate or plastic wrap (no air bubbles must enter the vessel, Figure T.8b), and then inverted into a deep pan or tray half-filled with water. The glass plate or plastic wrap is removed, and the tubing from the gas generator is inserted into the mouth of the gas-collecting vessel.

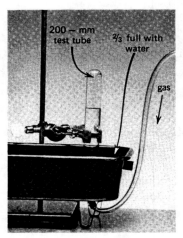

Figure T.8a Collection of water-insoluble gas by the displacement of water

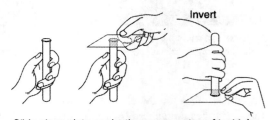

Slide glass plate or plastic wrap over top of test tube.
Do not allow an air bubble
to enter the test tube.

Figure T.8b Inverting a water-filled test tube

TECHNIQUE 9. TRANSFERRING SOLIDS

Read the label on the bottle *twice* to be sure it is the correct chemical. For example, is the chemical iron(II) acetate or iron(III) acetate? Is it the anhydrous, trihydrate, or pentahydrate form of copper(II) sulfate?

Safety, again, is of primary importance. Always be aware of the importance of *Technique 3*. If the reagent bottle has a hollow glass stopper or if it has a screw cap, then place the stopper (or cap) top side down on the bench (Figure T.9a). To dispense a solid from the bottle, hold the label against your hand, tilt, and roll the solid reagent back and forth. Avoid using a spatula or any other object to break up or transfer the reagent to the appropriate container unless your instructor *specifically* instructs you to do so.

- For *larger quantities* of solid reagent, dispense the solid into a beaker (Figure T.9b) until the estimated amount has been transferred. Try not to dispense any more reagent than is necessary for the experiment. Do not return any excess reagent to the reagent bottle—share the excess with another chemist.
- For *smaller quantities* of solid reagent, first dispense the solid into the inverted hollow glass stopper or screw cap. And then transfer the estimated amount of reagent needed for the experiment from the stopper or screw cap to an appropriate vessel. Return the excess reagent in the glass stopper or screw cap to the reagent bottle—in effect, the solid reagent has never left the reagent bottle.

When you have finished dispensing the solid chemical, *recap* and return the reagent bottle to the reagent shelf.

Figure T.9a Transferring a solid chemical from a glass ground reagent bottle. Place the glass stopper top side down.

Figure T.9b Tilt and roll the reagent bottle back and forth until the desired amount of solid chemical has been dispensed.

Read the label. When a liquid or solution is to be transferred from a reagent bottle, remove the glass stopper and hold it between the fingers of the hand used to grasp the reagent bottle (Figures T.10a, b, page 20). Never lay the glass stopper on the laboratory bench; impurities may be picked up and thus contaminate the liquid when the stopper is returned. If the reagent has a screw cap, place the top side down on the lab bench.

To transfer a liquid from one vessel to another, hold a stirring rod against the lip of the vessel containing the liquid and pour the liquid down the stirring rod, which, in turn, should touch the inner wall of the receiving vessel (Figures T.10b, c, page 20). Return the glass stopper or screw cap to the reagent bottle.

Do *not* transfer more liquid than is needed for the experiment. Do *not* return any excess or unused liquid to the original reagent bottle.

TECHNIQUE 10. TRANSFERRING LIQUIDS AND SOLUTIONS

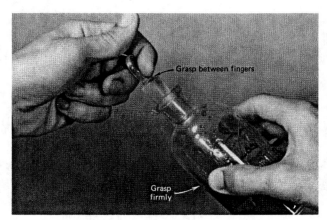

Figure T.10a Remove the glass stopper and hold it between the fingers of the hand that grasps the reagent bottle.

Figure T.10b Transfer the liquid from the reagent bottle with the aid of the stirring rod.

Figure T.10c The stirring rod should touch the lip of the transfer vessel and the inner wall of the receiving vessel.

TECHNIQUE 11. SEPARATING A LIQUID OR SOLUTION FROM A SOLID

A. Decanting a Liquid or Solution from a Solid

A liquid can be decanted (poured off the top) from a solid if the solid clearly separates from the liquid in a reasonably short period of time. Allow the solid to settle to the bottom of the beaker (Figure T.11a) or test tube. Transfer the liquid (called the **supernatant or decantate**) with the aid of a clean stirring rod (Figure T.11b). Do this slowly so as not to disturb the solid. Review *Technique 10* for the transfer of a liquid from one vessel to another.

Figure T.11a Tilt the beaker to allow the precipitate to settle at the side. Use a stirring rod or a similar object to tilt the beaker.

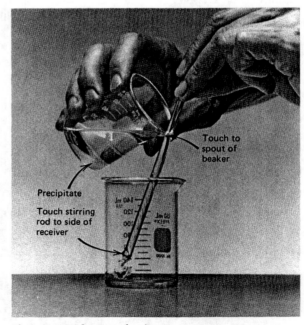

Figure T.11b Transfer the supernatant to a receiving vessel with the aid of a stirring rod.

If a solid is to be separated from the liquid using a filtering process, then the filter paper must be properly prepared. For a **gravity filtration** procedure, first fold the filter paper in half (Figure T.11c), again fold the filter paper to within about 10° of a 90° fold, tear off the corner (a *small* tear) of the outer fold unequally, and open. The tear enables a close seal to be made across the paper's folded portion when placed in a funnel.

Place the folded filter paper snugly into the funnel. Moisten the filter paper with the solvent of the liquid–solid mixture being filtered (most likely this will be deionized water) and press the filter paper against the top wall of the funnel to form a seal. Support the funnel with a clamp or in a funnel rack.

B. Preparing Filter Paper for a Filter Funnel

Transfer the liquid as described in *Technique 10* (Figure T.11d). The tip of the funnel should touch the wall of the receiving beaker to reduce any splashing of the **filtrate.** Fill the bowl of the funnel until it is *less than* two-thirds full with the mixture. Always keep the funnel stem full with the filtrate; the weight of the filtrate in the funnel stem creates a slight suction on the filter in the funnel, and this hastens the filtration process.

C. Gravity Filtration

Filtrate: the solution that passes through the filter in a filtration procedure

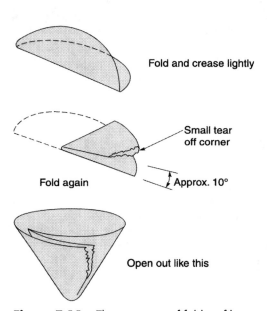

Fold and crease lightly

Fold again

Small tear off corner

Approx. 10°

Open out like this

Figure T.11c The sequence of folding filter paper for a filter funnel in a gravity filtration procedure

Less than two-thirds full

Touch side of funnel

Funnel support (or iron support ring)

Touch wall of receiving flask

Figure T.11d The tip of the funnel should touch the wall of the receiving flask, and the bowl of the funnel should be one-half to two-thirds full.

Flush the precipitate from a beaker using a wash bottle containing the mixture's solvent (usually deionized water). Hold the beaker over the funnel or receiving vessel (Figure T.11e, page 22) at an angle such that the solvent will flow out and down the stirring rod into the funnel.

D. Flushing a Precipitate from the Beaker

Set up the vacuum filtration apparatus as shown in Figure T.11f, page 22. A Büchner funnel (a disk of filter paper fits over the flat, perforated bottom of the funnel) set into a filter flask connected to a water aspirator is the apparatus normally used for vacuum filtration. Seal the disk of filter paper onto the bottom of the funnel by applying a light suction to the filter paper while adding a small amount of solvent.

E. Vacuum Filtration

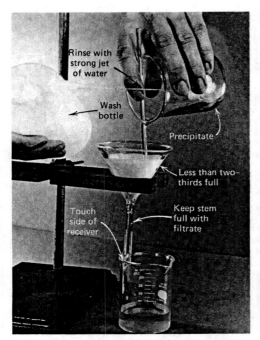

Figure T.11e Flushing the precipitate from a beaker with the aid of a "wash" bottle

Figure T.11f The aspirator should be fully open during the vacuum-filtering operation.

Once the filter paper is sealed, turn the water faucet attached to the aspirator *completely* open to create a full suction. Transfer the mixture to the filter (*Technique 10*) and wash the precipitate with an appropriate liquid. To remove the suction, *first* disconnect the hose from the filter flask and then turn off the water.

F. Centrifugation

Supernatant: the clear liquid covering a precipitate

A centrifuge (Figure T.11g) spins at velocities of 5,000 to 25,000 revolutions per minute! A liquid–solid mixture in a small test tube or centrifuge tube is placed into a sleeve of the rotor of the centrifuge. By centrifugal force, the solid is forced to the bottom of the test tube or centrifuge tube and compacted. The clear liquid, called the **supernatant,** is then easily decanted without any loss of solid (Figure T.11h). This quick separation of liquid from solid requires 20–40 seconds.

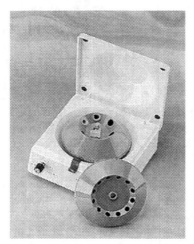

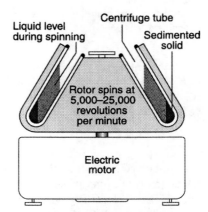

Figure T.11g A laboratory centrifuge forces the precipitate to the bottom of the centrifuge tube.

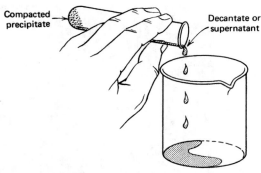

Figure T.11h Decant the supernatant from the compacted precipitate.

Same levels of solution or liquid

Figure T.11i Balance the centrifuge by placing tubes with equal volumes of liquid opposite each other inside the metal sleeves of the rotor.

Observe the following precautions in operating a centrifuge:

- Never fill the centrifuge tubes to a height more than 1 cm from the top.
- Label the centrifuge tubes to avoid confusion of samples.
- *Always* operate the centrifuge with an *even* number of centrifuge tubes containing equal volumes of liquid placed opposite one another in the centrifuge. This *balances* the centrifuge and eliminates excessive vibration and wear. If only one tube needs to be centrifuged, then balance the centrifuge with a tube containing the same volume of solvent (Figure T.11i).
- *Never* attempt to manually stop a centrifuge. When the centrifuge is turned off, let the rotor come to rest on its own.

TECHNIQUE 12. VENTING GASES

Fume hoods (Figure T.12a, page 24) are used for removing "undesirable" gases from a reagent such as concentrated hydrochloric acid or from a chemical reaction. These gases may be toxic, corrosive, irritating, or flammable. If there is a question about the use of a fume hood, hedge on the side of safety and/or consult with your instructor.

When using a fume hood:

- Turn on the hood air flow before beginning the experiment
- Never place your face inside of the fume hood
- Set the equipment and chemicals at least 6 inches back from the hood door
- Do not crowd experimental apparatus when sharing the use of a fume hood

On occasion, the space in the fume hoods is not adequate for an entire class to perform the experiment in a timely manner. With the *approval of your laboratory instructor,* an improvised hood (Figure T.12b, page 24) can be assembled. For the operation of an improvised hood, a water aspirator draws the gaseous product from above the reaction vessel; the gas dissolves in the water. To operate the "hood," completely open the faucet that is connected to the aspirator in order to provide the best suction for the removal of the gases. As a reminder, *never* substitute an improvised hood for a fume hood if space is available in the fume hood.

TECHNIQUE 13. HEATING LIQUIDS AND SOLUTIONS

Liquids and solutions are often heated, for example, to promote the rate of a chemical reaction to or hasten a dissolution or precipitation, in a number of different vessels.

Caution: *Flammable liquids should **never** be heated (directly or indirectly) with a flame. Always use a hot plate—refer to Techniques 13A and 13B where hot plates are used.*

Hot liquids and solutions can be cooled by placing the glass vessel either under flowing tap water or in an ice bath.

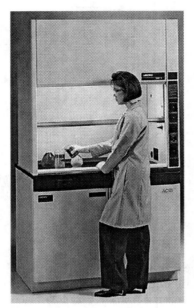

Figure T.12a A modern laboratory fume hood.

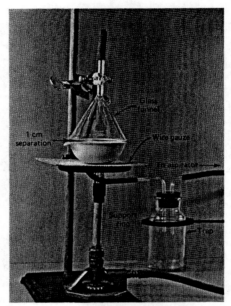

Figure T.12b Position a funnel, connected to a water aspirator, over the escaping gases. A hot plate is often substituted for the Bunsen flame.

A. Beaker or flask

Boiling chips (also called boiling stones): small, porous ceramic pieces—when heated, the air contained within the porous structure is released, gently agitating the liquid and minimizing boiling. Boiling chips also provide nucleation sites on which bubbles can form.

Boiling chips

Nonflammable liquids in beakers or flasks that are more than one-fourth full can be *slowly* heated directly with a hot plate (Figure T.13a). (**Caution:** *Hot plates are hot! Do not touch!*) Caution must be taken *not* to heat the liquid too rapidly as "bumping" (the sudden formation of bubbles from the superheated liquid) may occur. To avoid or to minimize bumping, place a stirring rod followed by constant stirring or **boiling chips** into the liquid. If a stirring hot plate is used, place the stir bar into the liquid and turn on the stirrer (Figure T.13b).

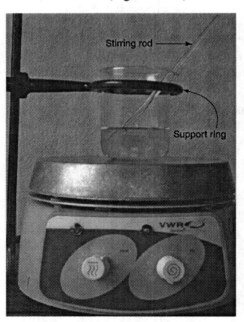

Figure T.13a A hot plate may be used to maintain solutions in a beaker or flask at a constant, elevated temperature for an extended time period.

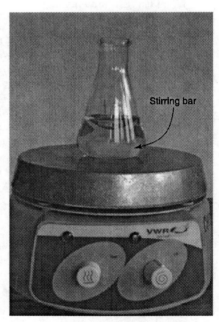

Figure T.13b A stirring hot plate may be used to heat a liquid and minimize "bumping."

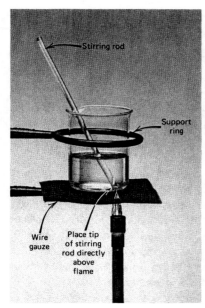

Figure T.13c Place the flame directly beneath the tip of the stirring rod in the beaker. Boiling chips may also be placed in the beaker to avoid "bumping."

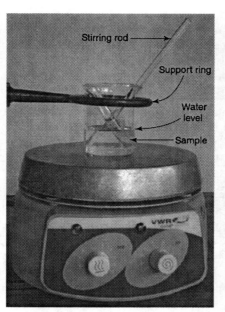

Figure T.13d A hot water bath may be used to maintain solution in test tubes at a constant, elevated temperature for an extended time period.

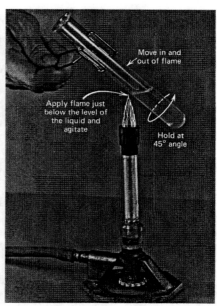

Figure T.13e Move the test tube circularly in and out of the *cool* flame, heating the liquid or solution from top to bottom.

A direct flame may also be used to heat the liquid in a beaker or flask. Support the beaker or flask on a wire gauze that is centered over an iron ring; use a second iron ring placed around the top of the beaker or flask to prevent it from being knocked off. Position the flame directly beneath the tip of the stirring rod (Figure T.13c) or add boiling chips to avoid or to minimize bumping.

Small quantities of liquids in test tubes that need to be maintained at a constant, elevated temperature over a period of time can be placed in a hot water bath (Figure T.13d). The heat source may be a hot plate or direct flame, depending on the chemicals being used. The setup is the same as that for heating a liquid in a beaker (see *Technique 13A*).

B. Test Tubes

Safety first should be followed when using this technique for heating liquids in test tubes.

A **cool flame** is a nonluminous flame supplied with a reduced supply of fuel. In practice, the rule of thumb for creating a cool flame for heating a liquid in a test tube is as follows: *If you can feel the heat of the flame with the hand that is holding the test tube clamp,* ***the flame is too hot!***

For direct heating of a liquid in a test tube, the test tube should be less than one-third full of liquid. Hold the test tube with a test tube holder at an angle of about 45° with the flame. Move the test tube circularly and continuously in and out of the cool flame, heating from top to bottom, mostly near the top of the liquid (Figure T.13e). **Caution:** *Never fix the position of the flame at the base of the test tube, and never point the test tube at anyone; the contents may be ejected violently if the test tube is not heated properly.*

See *Technique 13B* for heating a solution in a test tube to a specified elevated temperature; the hot water bath in *Technique 13B* is a safer, but slower, procedure.

C. Test Tube over a "Cool" Flame

TECHNIQUE 14. EVAPORATING LIQUIDS

To remove a liquid from a vessel by evaporation, the flammability of the liquid must be considered. This is a safety precaution.

Use a fume hood or an improvised hood (*Technique 12*) as recommended to remove irritating or toxic vapors.

A. Use of Direct Heat

A nonflammable liquid can be evaporated with a direct flame (Figure T.14a). Place the liquid in an evaporating dish centered on a wire gauze and iron ring. Use a gentle, "cool" flame to slowly evaporate the liquid.

B. Use of Indirect Heat

Flammable *or* nonflammable liquids can be evaporated using a hot plate as the heat source. Place the liquid in an evaporating dish on top of a beaker according to Figure T.14b. Gentle boiling of the water in the beaker is more efficient than rapid boiling for evaporating the liquid. Avoid breathing the vapors. The use of a fume hood (*Technique 12*) is strongly recommended if large amounts of liquid are to be evaporated into the laboratory. Consult with your laboratory instructor.

For removing the final dampness from a solid that has formed as a result of the evaporation, consider using a drying oven as described in *Technique 15A*.

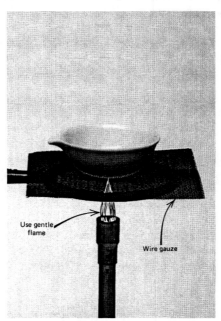

Figure T.14a Evaporation of a nonflammable liquid over a low, direct flame. A hot plate may be substituted for the flame.

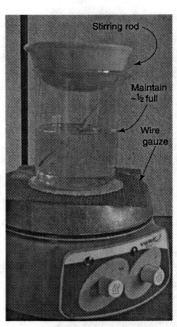

Figure T.14b Evaporation of a flammable liquid over a steam bath using a hot plate for the heat source

TECHNIQUE 15. HEATING SOLIDS

Solids are heated to dry them or to test their thermal stability. A drying oven is often used for low temperature heating, and porcelain crucibles are used for high temperature heating. Beakers and test tubes can be used for moderately high temperature heating.

A. Heating in a Drying Oven

When solid chemicals are left exposed to the atmosphere, they often absorb moisture. If an exact mass of a solid chemical is required for a solution preparation or for a reaction, the absorbed water must be removed before the mass measurement is made on the balance. The chemical is often placed in an open container (usually a Petri dish or beaker) in a drying oven (Figure T.15a) set at a temperature well above room

Figure T.15a A modern laboratory drying oven

Figure T.15b A simple laboratory desicooler (left) or a glass desiccator (right) contains a desiccant (usually anhydrous CaCl₂) to provide a dry atmosphere.

temperature (most often at ~110°C) for several hours to remove the adsorbed water. The container is then removed from the drying oven and placed in a desiccator (*Technique 15B*) for cooling to room temperature. **Caution:** *Hot glass and cold glass look the same—the container from the drying oven is hot and should be handled accordingly.* See your laboratory instructor.

B. Cooling in a Desiccator

When a Petri dish or beaker containing a solid chemical is cooled in the laboratory, moisture tends to condense on the outer surface, adding to the total mass. To minimize this mass error, and for quantitative work, substances and mixtures that may tend to be hygroscopic are placed into a desiccator (Figure T.15b) until they have reached ambient temperature.

A desiccator is a laboratory apparatus that provides a dry atmosphere. A desiccant, typically anhydrous calcium chloride, $CaCl_2$, absorbs the water vapor from within the enclosure of the desiccator. The anhydrous calcium chloride forms $CaCl_2 \cdot 2H_2O$; the hydrated water molecules can be easily removed with heat (modified *Technique 14A*), and the calcium chloride can be recycled for subsequent use in the desiccator.

C. Using a Crucible

For high temperature combustion or decomposition of a chemical, porcelain crucibles are commonly used. To avoid contamination of the solid sample, thoroughly clean the crucible (so it is void of volatile impurities) prior to use. Often-used crucibles tend to form stress fractures or fissures. Check the crucible for flaws; if any are found, return the crucible to the stockroom and check out and examine a second crucible.

1. **Drying or firing the crucible.** Support the crucible and lid on a clay triangle (Figure T.15c, page 28) and heat in a hot flame until the bottom of the crucible glows a dull red. Rotate the crucible with crucible tongs to ensure complete "firing" of the crucible—that is, the combustion and volatilization of any impurities in the crucible. Allow the crucible and lid to cool to room temperature while on the clay triangle or *after* several minutes in a desiccator (*Technique 15B*).[1]

[1]If the crucible still contains detectable impurities, add 1–2 mL of 6 M HNO₃ (**Caution:** *Avoid skin contact, flush immediately with water*), and evaporate *slowly* to dryness in the fume hood.

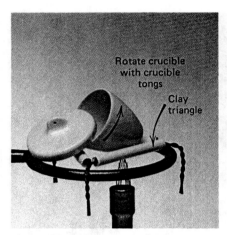

Figure T.15c Drying or firing a crucible and cover

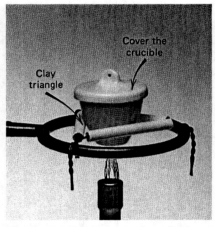

Figure T.15d Ignition of a solid sample in the absence of air

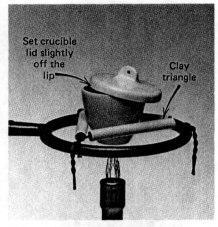

Figure T.15e Ignition of a solid sample in the presence of air for complete combustion

2. **Igniting contents in the absence of air.** To heat a solid sample to a high temperature but *not* allow it to react with the oxygen of the air, set the crucible upright in the clay triangle with the lid covering the crucible (Figure T.15d). Use the crucible tongs to adjust the lid.

3. **Igniting contents for combustion.** To heat a solid sample to a high temperature and allow it to react with the oxygen of the air, slightly tilt the crucible on the clay triangle and adjust the lid so that about two-thirds of the crucible remains covered (Figure T.15e). Use the crucible tongs to adjust the lid.

TECHNIQUE 16. MEASURING VOLUME

The careful measurement and recording of volumes of liquids are necessary to obtain quantitative data for a large number of chemical reactions that occur in solutions. Volumes must be read and recorded as accurately as possible (to the correct number of significant figures) to minimize errors in the data.

A. Reading and Recording

Volumetric glassware: glassware that has a calibration mark(s) that indicates a calibrated volume, as determined by the manufacturer

1. **Reading a meniscus.** For measurements of liquids in graduated cylinders, pipets, burets, and volumetric flasks, the volume of a liquid is read at the *bottom of its meniscus*. Position the eye horizontally at the bottom of the meniscus (Figure T.16a) to read the level of the liquid. A clear or transparent liquid is read more easily, especially in a buret, by positioning a black mark (made on a white card) behind or just below the level portion of the liquid. The black background reflects off the bottom of the meniscus and better defines the level of the liquid (Figure T.16b). Substituting a finger for the black mark on the white card also helps in detecting the bottom of the meniscus but is not as effective.

2. **Recording a volume.** Record the volume of a liquid in **volumetric glassware** using all certain digits (from the labeled calibration marks on the glassware) *plus* one uncertain digit (the last digit, which is the best estimate between the calibration marks). This reading provides the correct number of significant figures for the measurement. See **Laboratory Data**, Part B. In Figure T.16b, the volume of solution in the buret is between the calibration marks of 3.0 and 3.1; the 3 and the 0 are certain; the 5 is the estimate between 3.0 and 3.1. The reading is 3.05 mL. Be aware that all volume readings do *not* end in 0 or 5!

This guideline for reading volumes also applies to reading and recording temperatures on a thermometer.

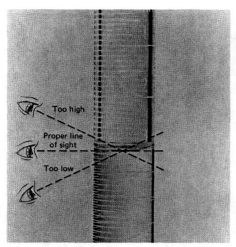

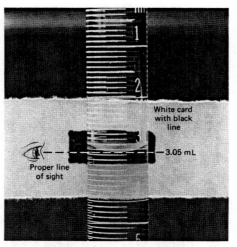

Figure T.16a Read the volume of a liquid with the eye horizontal to the bottom of the meniscus.

Figure T.16b Use a black line drawn on a white card to assist in pinpointing the location of the bottom of the meniscus.

The most common type of pipet in the laboratory is labeled TD at 20°C. A pipet labeled TD at 20°C (to deliver at 20°C) means that the volume of the pipet is calibrated according to the volume it delivers from gravity flow only.

A clean pipet in conjunction with the proper technique for dispensing a liquid from a pipet are important in any quantitative determination.

B. Pipetting a Liquid

1. **Preparation of the pipet.** See *Technique 2* for cleaning glassware. A clean pipet should have no water droplets adhering to its inner wall. Inspect the pipet to ensure it is free of chips or cracks. Transfer the liquid that you intend to pipet from the reagent bottle into a clean, dry beaker; do *not* insert the pipet tip directly into the reagent bottle (*Technique 5*). Dry the outside of the pipet tip with a clean, dust-free towel or tissue (e.g., Kimwipe). Using the suction from a collapsed rubber (pipet) bulb, draw a 2- to 3-mL portion into the pipet as a rinse. Roll the rinse around in the pipet to make certain that the liquid washes the entire surface of the inner wall. Deliver the rinse through the pipet tip into a waste beaker and discard as directed in the experiment. Repeat the rinse 2–3 times.

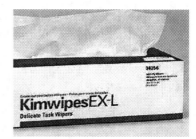

Dust/lint-free tissue.

2. **Filling of the pipet.** Place the pipet tip well below the surface of the liquid in the beaker. Using the collapsed pipet bulb (or a pipet pump—*never* use your mouth!), draw the liquid into the pipet until the level is 2–3 cm above the "mark" on the pipet (Figure T.16c, page 30). Do not "jam" the pipet bulb onto the pipet! Remove the bulb and quickly cover the top of the pipet with your index finger (*not* your thumb!). Remove the tip from the liquid and wipe off the pipet tip with a clean, dust-free towel or tissue. Holding the pipet in a *vertical* position over a waste beaker, control the delivery of the excess liquid until the level is "at the mark" in the pipet (Figure T.16d, page 30). Read the meniscus correctly. Remove any drops suspended from the pipet tip by touching it to the wall of the waste beaker. This is a technique you will need to practice.

3. **Delivery of the liquid.** Deliver the liquid to the receiving vessel (Figure T.16e, page 30) by releasing the index finger from the top of the pipet. Dispense the liquid along the wall of the receiving vessel to avoid splashing. To remove a hanging drop from the pipet tip, touch the side of the receiving flask for its removal. Do *not* blow or shake out the last bit of liquid that remains in the tip; this liquid has been included in the calibration of the pipet . . . remember this is a TD at 20°C pipet!

4. **Cleanup.** Once it is no longer needed in the experiment, rinse the pipet with several portions of deionized water and drain each rinse through the tip.

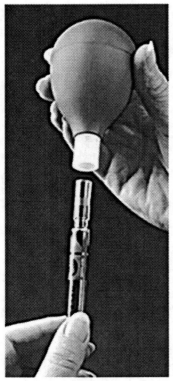

Figure T.16c Draw the liquid into the pipet with the aid of a rubber pipet bulb (*not* the mouth!).

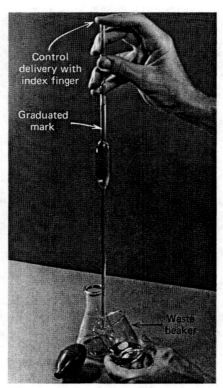

Figure T.16d Control the delivery of the liquid from the pipet with the forefinger (*not* the thumb!).

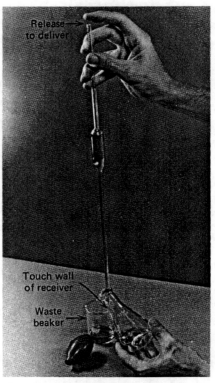

Figure T.16e Deliver the liquid from the vertically positioned pipet with the tip touching the wall of the receiving flask.

C. Titrating a Liquid (Solution)

Titrant: the reagent solution in the buret to be used for the experiment

Record the volume: To record the correct number of significant figures, read the volume in the buret using all certain digits (from the labeled calibration marks on the buret) plus one uncertain digit (the last digit which is the best estimate between the calibration marks).

A clean buret in conjunction with the proper technique for measuring and dispensing a liquid from a buret is important in any quantitative analysis determination.

1. **Preparation of the buret.** See *Technique 2* for cleaning glassware. If a buret brush is needed, be careful to avoid scratching the buret wall with the wire handle. Once the buret is judged to be "clean," close the stopcock. Rinse the buret with several 3- to 5-mL portions of water and then **titrant**. Tilt and roll the barrel of the buret so that each rinse comes into contact with the entire inner wall. Drain each rinse through the buret tip into the waste beaker. Dispose of the rinse as advised in the experiment. Support the buret with a buret clamp (Figure T.16f).

2. **Preparation of the titrant.** Close the stopcock. With the aid of a *clean* funnel, fill the buret with the titrant to just above the zero mark. Open the stopcock briefly to release any air bubbles in the tip *and* allow the meniscus of the titrant to go below the uppermost graduation on the buret. Allow 10–15 seconds for the titrant to drain from the wall, **record the volume** (± 0.02 mL, *Technique 16A.2*) of titrant in the buret. Note that the graduations on a buret *increase* in value from the top down (Figure T.16g).

3. **Operation of the buret.** During the addition of the titrant from the buret, operate the stopcock with your left hand (if right-handed) and swirl the Erlenmeyer flask with your right hand (Figure T.16h). This prevents the stopcock from sliding out of its barrel and allows you to maintain a normal, constant swirling motion of the reaction mixture in the receiving flask as the titrant is added. The opposite procedure, of course, is applicable if you are left-handed (Figure T.16i). Use an Erlenmeyer flask as a receiving flask in order to minimize the loss of solution due to splashing.

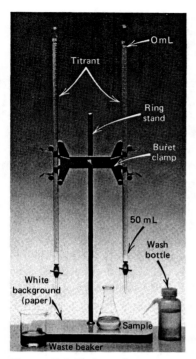

Figure T.16f Setup for a titration analysis

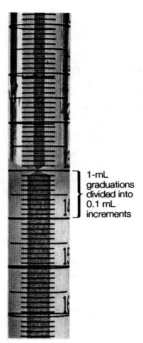

Figure T.16g A 50-mL buret is marked from top to bottom, 0 to 50 mL, with 1-mL gradations divided into 0.1-mL increments.

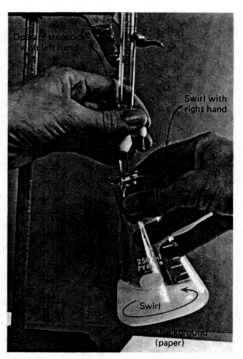

Figure T.16h Titration technique for right-handers

Figure T.16i Titration technique for left-handers.

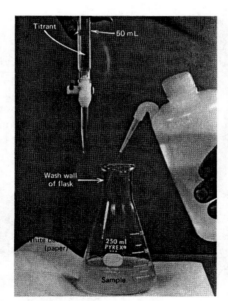

Figure T.16j Place a white background beneath the receiving flask and wash the wall of the receiving flask periodically during the titration.

Figure T.16k A slow color fade of the indicator occurs near the endpoint in the titration.

If a magnetic stirrer is used for mixing the titrant with the analyte, operate at a low speed to minimize any splashing of the reaction mixture and to minimize oxygen of the air from mixing and reacting with either the titrant or analyte. Occasionally, a beaker is used as a receiving flask, especially if a temperature probe (or thermometer) or a pH probe is required during the titration.

4. **Addition of titrant to receiving flask.** Have a white background (a piece of white paper) beneath the receiving flask to better see the endpoint for the titration (the point at which the indicator turns color). If the endpoint is a change from colorless to white, a black background is preferred. Add the titrant to the Erlenmeyer flask as described above; periodically stop its addition and wash the inner wall of the flask with the solvent (generally deionized water) from a wash bottle (Figure T.16j, page 31). Near the endpoint (slower color fade of the indicator, Figure T.16k, page 31), slow the rate of titrant addition until a drop (or less) makes the color change of the indicator persist for 30 seconds. **Stop,** allow 10–15 seconds for the titrant to drain from the buret wall, read, and record the volume in the buret (*Technique 16A.2*).

To add less than a drop of titrant (commonly referred to as a "half-drop") to the receiving flask, suspend a drop from the buret tip, touch it to the side of the receiving flask, and wash the wall of the receiving flask (with deionized water).

5. **Cleanup.** After completing a series of titrations, drain the titrant from the buret, rinse the buret with several portions of deionized water, and drain each rinse through the tip. Discard the excess titrant and the rinses as advised in the experiment. Store the buret as advised by your laboratory instructor.

TECHNIQUE 17. QUICK TESTS

An educated nose is an important and very useful asset to the chemist. Use it with caution, however, because some vapors induce nausea and/or are toxic. *Never* hold your nose directly over a vessel.

A. Testing for Odor

Fan some vapor toward your nose (Figure T.17a). *Always* consult your laboratory instructor before testing the odor of any chemical.

B. Testing for Acidity/Basicity

To test the acidity or basicity of a solution with test paper, insert a *clean* stirring rod into the solution, withdraw it, and touch it to the pH test paper (Figure T.17b). For litmus paper, acidic solutions turn blue litmus red; basic solutions turn red litmus blue. *Never* place the test paper directly into the solution.

Other paper-type indictors, such as pHydrion paper (Figure T.17c), are also used to gauge the acidity or basicity of a solution.

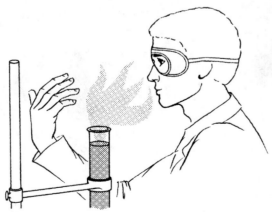

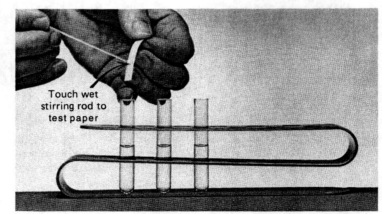

Touch wet stirring rod to test paper

Figure T.17a Fan the vapors gently toward the nose.   **Figure T.17b** Test for acidity or basicity.

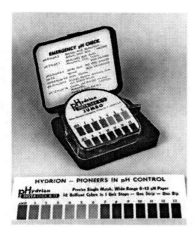

Figure T.17c Test papers impregnated with a mixture of acid–base indicators can be used to measure the approximate pH of a solution.

Disclaimer: The material contained in the **Laboratory Safety and Guidelines** and **Laboratory Techniques** sections of this manual has been compiled from sources believed to be reliable and to represent the best opinions of safety in the laboratory. This manual is intended to provide basic guidelines for safe practices in the undergraduate chemistry laboratory. It cannot be assumed that all necessary warning and precautionary measures are contained in this manual, or that other or additional information or measures may not be required.

Further discussions of these and other laboratory techniques can be found on the World Wide Web. Refer to **Laboratory Data**, Part C.

NOTES ON LABORATORY TECHNIQUES

Laboratory Techniques

Date _____ Lab Sec. _____ Name _____ Desk No. _____

Identify the Technique Icon, at left, for each of the following techniques.

Technique Icon   *Description of technique*

1. _____ To dispense chemicals, read the label at least twice before removing any chemical from the reagent bottle.

2. _____ Water or glycerol should be applied to the glass tubing and the hole in the rubber stopper before inserting the glass tubing.

3. _____ A centrifuge should be balanced with an even number of centrifuge/test tubes, placed across the rotor from one another, with equal volumes of liquid.

4. _____ The volume of a liquid or solution in calibrated volumetric glassware should be read using all-certain digits (from the labeled calibration marks on the glassware) *plus* one uncertain digit (the last digit which is the best estimate *between* the calibration marks)—that is, to the correct number of significant figures.

5. _____ The bowl of the funnel for gravity filtration should be always less than two-thirds full.

6. _____ To dispense a liquid from a pipet, first draw the liquid into the pipet 2–3 cm above the calibration mark with a pipet bulb and then use the index finger to control its flow.

7. _____ The suction created for the vacuum filtration of a precipitate is applied with an aspirator in which the water faucet is fully open.

8. _____ To prepare a solution, always add the solid reagent or more concentrated solution to a volumetric flask that is already approximately one-third full with solvent.

9. _____ While dispensing titrant from a buret, the stopcock should be operated with the left hand (if right-handed) and the Erlenmeyer flask should be swirled with the right hand.

10. _____ To heat a solid to high temperatures in the absence of air, place the solid in a crucible and fully cover the crucible with the crucible lid.

11. _____ Information on the properties and disposal of chemicals can be found in the stockroom or online from the MSDS collection.

12. _____ A buret should be rinsed with several 3- to 5-mL portions of titrant before being filled.

13. _____ Glassware is clean when no water droplets cling to the inner wall of the vessel.

14. _____ For heating a liquid in a test tube, the test tube should be less than one-third full, moved continuously in and out of the "cool" flame at a 45° angle, mostly near the top of the liquid.

15. _____ The volume of a liquid should be read at the bottom of the meniscus.

16. _____ Small quantities of liquids in test tubes are best be heated (safely) in a hot water bath with the heat source being either a hot plate or a direct flame.

17. _____ All chemicals must be properly disposed—either according to the Experimental Procedure or the laboratory instructor.

18. _____ Never place reagents directly onto the weighing pan of a balance—always use weighing paper, a beaker, or some other container.

19. _____ A hot plate (*not* an open flame) is the heat source for heating or evaporating flammable liquids.

20. _____ The tared mass of a sample is its mass without regard to its container.

21. _____ Transfer liquids and solutions from a reagent bottle or beaker with the aid of a stirring rod.

22. _____ A "small" test tube has a volume of ~3 mL.

23. _____ A litmus paper test for the acidity or basicity of a solution requires the use of a stirring rod to remove a portion of the solution to then be touched to the litmus paper.

24. _____ After drying a hygroscopic solid in a drying oven, the solid should be cooled in a desiccator.

25. _____ The color change of the indicator at the endpoint of a titration should persist for 30 seconds.

True or False

Ask your instructor to identify the questions you are to complete.

_____ 1. All clean glassware should be air-dried naturally.

_____ 2. While cleaning glassware, discard all washes and rinses from the delivery point of the glass vessel.

_____ 3. To avoid waste in the use of chemicals, share the unused portion with other chemists before discarding.

_____ 4. Never touch, taste, or smell a chemical unless specifically told to do so.

_____ 5. A chemical with a "blue" hazard label (a number 3 rating) means that the chemical is highly reactive.

_____ 6. If uncertain as to how to dispose of a chemical, dumping it into the sink followed by copious amount of water is a safe disposal procedure.

_____ 7. Use a spatula to transfer solid chemicals from a reagent bottle.

_____ 8. Most all chemicals used in experiments can be discarded into the sink.

_____ 9. The number of significant figures used to record the mass of a chemical should correspond to the sensitivity of the balance used for the measurement.

_____ 10. A 3-inch test tube has a volume of 3 mL; an 8-inch test tube must have a volume of 8 mL.

_____ 11. To transfer a solution, a stirring rod touches the delivery point of the reagent vessel and the wall of the receiving vessel.

_____ 12. The *minimum* number of centrifuge tubes placed in a centrifuge during its operation is two.

_____ 13. A test tube should be less than one-third full when heating with a "cool" flame.

_____ 14. Right-handed students should operate the stopcock of a buret with their left hand and swirl the Erlenmeyer (receiving) flask with the right hand.

_____ 15. The thumb is the digit of choice on controlling the flow of liquid from a pipet.

_____ 16. Blow out the solution remaining in the pipet tip after the solution has drained from the pipet.

_____ 17. A buret must *always* be filled to the top (the zero mark) before every titration procedure.

_____ 18. The volume of solution in a buret should be read and recorded 10–15 seconds after completing the titration.

_____ 19. It is possible to add a half-drop of solution from a buret.

_____ 20. To test the acidity of a solution with pH paper, place the pH paper directly in the solution.

_____ 21. The odor of a chemical should not be tested unless specifically instructed to do so. The vapors of the chemical should be fanned toward the nose.

_____ 22. One must first calculate the number of moles of solute that are required before preparing a solution of known concentration.

Summarize the *Disclaimer* in your own words.

A set of standard SI mass units.

Dry Lab 1

The Laboratory and SI

OBJECTIVES

- To check into the laboratory
- To become familiar with the laboratory and the laboratory manual
- To learn the rules of laboratory safety and the necessity of practicing these rules in the laboratory
- To learn how to properly organize and record laboratory data
- To develop skills in the use of *Le Système International d'Unités* (SI Units)

INTRODUCTION

All chemical principles, tools, and techniques are developed in the laboratory. The experience of observing a chemical phenomenon and then explaining its behavior is one that simply cannot be gained by reading a textbook, listening to a lecturer, searching the Internet, or viewing a video. It is in the laboratory where chemistry comes alive, where chemical principles are learned and applied to the vast natural "chemistry laboratory" that we call our everyday environment. The objectives of a laboratory experience are to design and build apparatus, develop techniques, observe, record and interpret data, and deduce rational theories so that the real world of science is better explained and understood.

In the laboratory, you will use common equipment and safe chemicals to perform experiments. You record your experimental observations and interpret the data on the basis of sound chemical principles. A good scientist is a thinking scientist trying to account for the observed data and rationalize any contradictory data. Cultivate self-reliance and confidence in your data, even if "the data do not look right." This is how many breakthroughs in science occur.

In the first few laboratory sessions you will be introduced to some basic rules, equipment, and techniques and some situations where you use them. These include laboratory safety rules, *Le Système International d'Unités* (SI Units), the Bunsen burner, and the analytical balance. Additional laboratory techniques are illustrated under **Laboratory Techniques** pages 11–33; others are introduced as the need arises.

DRY LAB PROCEDURE

Procedure Overview: Laboratory procedures are introduced. A familiarity with laboratory apparatus, the policies regarding laboratory safety, the procedures for presenting laboratory data, and an encounter with the SI units are emphasized.

A. Laboratory Check-in

At the beginning of the first laboratory period, you are assigned a lab station containing laboratory equipment. Place the laboratory equipment on the laboratory bench and, with the check-in list appearing on page 9, or one provided by your laboratory instructor, check off each piece of chemical apparatus as you return it to the drawer. If you are unsure of a name for the apparatus, refer to the list of chemical "kitchenware" on pages 8–9. Ask your instructor about any items on the check-in list that are not at your lab station.

A good scientist is always neat and well organized; keep your equipment clean and arranged in an orderly manner so that it is ready for immediate use. Have at your lab station dishwashing soap (or detergent) for cleaning glassware and paper towels or a rubber lab mat on which to set the clean glassware for drying.

Obtain your laboratory instructor's approval for the completion of the check-in procedure. Refer to Part A of the *Report Sheet*.

The icon refers to Laboratory Technique 2 on page 13. Read through Laboratory Technique 2 for the proper technique of cleaning laboratory glassware.

B. Laboratory Safety and Guidelines

Your laboratory instructor will discuss laboratory safety and other basic laboratory procedures with you. Remember, however, that your laboratory instructor cannot practice laboratory safety for you or for those who work with you. It is your responsibility to *play it safe!*

On the inside front cover of this manual is space to list the location of some important safety equipment and important information for reference in the laboratory. Fill this out. Obtain your laboratory instructor's approval for its completion.

Read and study the **Laboratory Safety and Guidelines** section on pages 1–4. Complete any other laboratory safety sessions or requirements that are requested by your laboratory instructor. Answer the laboratory safety questions on the *Report Sheet*.

C. Laboratory Data

Each experiment in this manual will require you to observe, record and report data, perform calculations on the data, and then analyze and interpret the data. Scientists are careful in the procedures that are used for handling data so that the reliability and credibility of the experimental data are upheld.

It is important that these procedures are followed at the outset of your laboratory experience. Read and study the **Laboratory Data** section on pages 5–8. Answer the laboratory data questions on the *Report Sheet*.

D. *Le Système International d'Unités* (SI Units)

The SI, a modern version of the metric system, provides a logical and interconnected framework for all basic measurements. The SI, and some of its slight modifications, is used throughout the world by scientists and engineers as the international system for scientific measurements and, in most countries, for everyday measurements. For laboratory measurements, the SI base unit of mass is the **kilogram (kg)** [chemists are most familiar with the **gram (g)**, where 10^3 g = 1 kg]. The SI base unit for length is the **meter (m)** [chemists are most familiar with several subdivisions of the meter]. The SI derived unit for volume is the **cubic meter (m^3)** [chemists are most familiar with the **liter (L)**, where 1 L = 10^{-3} m^3 = 1 dm^3]. Subdivisions and multiples of each unit are

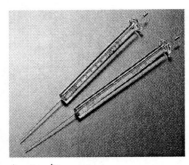

A microliter syringe

Table D1.1 Prefixes in *Le Système International d'Unités*

Prefix	Abbreviation	Meaning (power of ten)	Example Using "grams"
femto-	f	10^{-15}	fg = 10^{-15} g
pico-	p	10^{-12}	pg = 10^{-12} g
nano-	n	10^{-9}	ng = 10^{-9} g
micro-	μ	10^{-6}	μg = 10^{-6} g
milli-	m	10^{-3}	mg = 10^{-3} g
centi-	c	10^{-2}	cg = 10^{-2} g
deci-	d	10^{-1}	dg = 10^{-1} g
kilo-	k	10^3	kg = 10^3 g
mega-	M	10^6	Mg = 10^6 g
giga-	G	10^9	Gg = 10^9 g
tera-	T	10^{12}	Tg = 10^{12} g

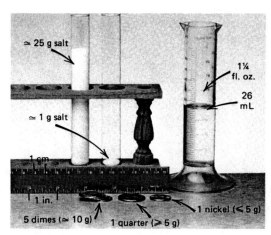

Figure D1.1 Comparisons of SI and English measurements

related to these units by a power of 10. The prefixes used to denote these subdivisions and multiples are shown in Table D1.1. Memorize these prefixes and their meanings.

In Table D1.1, *the prefix indicates the power of 10.* For example, 4.3 *milli*grams means 4.3×10^{-3} grams; *milli* has the same meaning as "$\times 10^{-3}$." Figure D1.1 shows representative SI measurements for mass, length, and volume.

Conversions of measurements within SI are quite simple if the definitions for the prefixes are known and unit conversion factors for problem solving are used. To illustrate the use of unit conversion factors, consider the following example.

Example D1.1 Convert 4.3 nanograms to micrograms.
Solution. From Table D1.1, note that nano- and 10^{-9} are equivalent and that micro- and 10^{-6} are equivalent. Considering mass, it also means that ng $= 10^{-9}$ g *and* μg $= 10^{-6}$ g. This produces two equivalent unit conversion factors for each equality:

$$\frac{10^{-9}\,\text{g}}{\text{ng}}, \quad \frac{\text{ng}}{10^{-9}\text{g}} \quad \text{and} \quad \frac{10^{-6}\,\text{g}}{\mu\text{g}}, \quad \frac{\mu\text{g}}{10^{-6}\text{g}}$$

Beginning our solution to the problem with the measured quantity (i.e., 4.3 ng), we need to convert ng to g and g to μg using the appropriate conversion factors to obtain proper unit cancellation:

$$4.3\ \cancel{\text{ng}} \times \frac{10^{-9}\,\cancel{\text{g}}}{\cancel{\text{ng}}} \times \frac{\mu\text{g}}{10^{-6}\,\cancel{\text{g}}} = 4.3 \times 10^{-3}\ \mu\text{g}$$

ng cancel g cancel

ng $\rightarrow$ g $\rightarrow$ μg $=$ μg

The conversion factors in Example D1.1 have no effect on the magnitude of the mass measurement (the conversion factors $= 1$), only the units by which it is expressed.

The SI is compared with the English system in Table D1.2. SI units of measurement that chemists commonly use in the laboratory are listed in brackets. Appendix A has a more comprehensive table of conversion factors. Conversions between the SI and the English system are quite valuable, especially to Americans because international science and trade communications are in SI or metric units.

Appendix A

Graduated cylinders of different volumes

Table D1.2 Comparison of *Le Système International d'Unités* and English System of Measurements[†]

Physical Quantity	SI Unit	Conversion Factor
Length	meter (m)	1 km = 0.6214 mi 1 m = 39.37 in. 1 in. = 0.0254 m = 2.54 cm
Volume	cubic meter (m^3) [liter (L)][a]	1 L = 10^{-3} m^3 = 1 dm^3 = 10^3 mL 1 mL = 1 cm^3 1 L = 1.057 qt 1 oz (fluid) = 29.57 mL
Mass	kilogram (kg) [gram (g)]	1 lb = 453.6 g 1 kg = 2.205 lb
Pressure	pascal (Pa) [atmosphere (atm)]	1 Pa = 1 N/m^2 1 atm = 101.325 kPa = 760 torr 1 atm = 14.70 $lb/in.^2$ (psi)
Temperature	kelvin (K) [degrees Celsius (°C)]	K = 273 + °C °C = $\dfrac{°F - 32}{1.8}$
Energy	joule (J)	1 cal = 4.184 J 1 Btu = 1054 J

[a]The SI units enclosed in brackets are commonly used in chemical measurements and calculations.
[†]For additional conversion factors, go online to www.onlineconversion.com.

Example D1.2   Using Tables D1.1 and D1.2, determine the volume of 1.00 quart of water in terms of cubic centimeters.
Solution.   As 1 cm = 10^{-2} m, then 1 cm^3 = $(10^{-2}$ m$)^3$ = $(10^{-2})^3$ m^3.
From Table D1.2, we need conversion factors for quarts → liters, liters → m^3, and finally m^3 → cm^3. Starting with 1.00 qt (our measured value in the problem), we have:

$$1.00 \; \cancel{qt} \times \frac{1 \; \cancel{L}}{1.057 \; \cancel{qt}} \times \frac{10^{-3} \; \cancel{m^3}}{1 \; \cancel{L}} \times \frac{cm^3}{(10^{-2})^3 \; \cancel{m^3}} = 946 \; cm^3$$

qt cancel   L cancel m^3 cancel
qt ⟶ L ⟶ m^3 ⟶ cm^3 = cm^3

Note again that the conversion factors in Example D1.2 do not change the magnitude of the measurement, only its form of expression.
Since 1 cm^3 = 1 mL, 1.00 quart is equivalent to 946 mL.

The ***Report Sheet***, Part D, further acquaints you with conversions within the SI and between SI and the English system. Ask your laboratory instructor which of the questions from Part D you are to complete on the ***Report Sheet***.

The Laboratory and SI

Date _____ Lab Sec. _____ Name _____ Desk No. _____

A. Laboratory Check-In

Instructor's approval _____

B. Laboratory Safety and Guidelines

Instructor's approval for completion of inside front cover _____

Read the **Laboratory Safety and Guidelines** section on pages 1–4 and answer the following as *true* or *false*.

_____ 1. Prescription glasses, which are required by law to be "safety glasses," can be worn in place of safety goggles in the laboratory.

_____ 2. Sleeveless blouses and tank tops are *not* appropriate attire for the laboratory.

_____ 3. Only shoes that shed liquids are permitted in the laboratory.

_____ 4. "I just finished my tennis class. I can wear my tennis shorts to lab just this one time, right?"

_____ 5. Your laboratory has an eyewash fountain.

_____ 6. "Oops! I broke a beaker containing deionized water in the sink." An accident as simple as that does not need to be reported to the laboratory instructor.

_____ 7. A beaker containing an acidic solution has broken on the bench top and spilled onto your clothes from the waist down and it burns. Ouch! You should immediately proceed to the safety shower and flood the affected area.

_____ 8. You received a paper cut on your finger and it is bleeding. Immediately go to the medicine cabinet to apply a disinfectant.

_____ 9. It is good laboratory protocol to inform other students when they are not practicing good laboratory safety procedures. If they continue to not follow the safety procedures, you should "rat" on them . . . tell the laboratory instructor.

_____ 10. Cell phones, iPods, and other electronic equipment should be turned off during the laboratory period.

_____ 11. Your friend is a senior chemistry major and thoroughly understands the difficult experiment that you are performing. Therefore, it is advisable (even recommended) that you invite him or her into the laboratory for direct assistance.

_____ 12. You missed lunch but brought a sandwich to the laboratory. Since you cannot eat in the lab, it is okay to leave the sandwich in the hallway and then go in and out to take bites while the laboratory experiment is ongoing.

Write a short response for the following questions.

1. What does the phrase "neck to knee to wrist" mean with regard to laboratory safety?

2. The first action after an accident occurs is:

3. You want to try a variation of the Experimental Procedure because of your chemical curiosity. What is the proper procedure for performing the experiment?

4. A chemical spill has occurred. What should be your first and second action in treating the chemical spill?

5. Describe how you will be dressed when you are about to begin an experiment in the laboratory.

Instructor's approval of your knowledge of laboratory safety. _____

C. Laboratory Data

Read the **Laboratory Data** section on pages 5–8 and answer the following as *true* or *false*.

_____ **1.** "Quick data," such as that of a mass measurement on a balance located at the far side of the laboratory, can be recorded on a paper scrap and then transferred to the *Report Sheet* at your lab station.

_____ **2.** Data that has been mistakenly recorded on the *Report Sheet* can be erased and replaced with the correct data. This is to maintain a neat *Report Sheet*.

_____ **3.** All data should be recorded in permanent ink!

_____ **4.** The laboratory equipment and instrumentation determine the number of significant figures used to record quantitative data.

_____ **5.** Zeros recorded in a measurement are *never* significant figures.

D. *Le Système International d'Unités* (SI Units)

Circle the questions that have been assigned.

1. Complete the following table. Express all answers with the correct number of significant figures (see page 6). Show all work in completing the calculations for the conversions.

	SI Expression	Power of 10 Expression	SI Expression	Power of 10 Expression
Example	1.2 mg	1.2×10^{-3} g		
a.	3.3 gigabytes	_____	**c.** _____	6.72×10^{-3} ampere
b.	_____	7.6×10^{-6} L	**d.** 2.16 kilowatts	_____

2. Convert each of the following using the definitions in Table D1.1 and unit conversion factors. Show the cancellation of units.

a. 4.76 pm $\times$ _____$\dfrac{m}{pm}$ $\times$ _____$\dfrac{\mu m}{m}$ $=$ _____μm

b. 250 mL $\times$ _____ $\times$ _____ $=$ _____cL

3. Determine the volume (in mL) of 1.0 teaspoon. 1 tablespoon = 3 teaspoons; 1 tablespoon = ½ fluid ounce

4. A basketball is inflated to 9.0 psi (pounds per square inch) above atmospheric pressure of 14.7 psi (a total pressure of 23.7 psi). The diameter of the basketball is 10 inches.

a. What is the pressure of the air in the basketball, expressed in atmospheres?

b. What is the volume (in liters) of the basketball? The volume of a sphere $= \frac{4}{3}\pi r^3$.

5. Hurricane Katrina, which hit the Gulf Coast of Louisiana and Mississippi on August 29, 2005, had the second lowest ever recorded barometric pressure at 920 mb. Convert this pressure to units of atmospheres, kilopascals, and inches of Hg (the latter you would see on the evening weather report).

6. Measure the inside diameter and height of any beaker in your laboratory drawer in centimeters.

   Diameter = _____ Height = _____

   a. Using the equation $V = \pi r^2 h$, calculate the volume of the beaker.

   b. Explain why the volume label on the beaker is not the same as your calculated volume.

7. A family used 1,438 kilowatt·hours (kwh) of electricity during the month of October. Express this amount of energy in joules and Btu. See Appendix A.

8. The standard width between rails on North American and most European railroads is 4 ft 8 in. Calculate this distance in meters and centimeters.

9. The heat required to raise the temperature of a large cup of water (for coffee) from room temperature to boiling is approximately 100 kJ. Express this quantity of heat in kilocalories and British thermal units. Show your calculations.

10. An aspirin tablet has a mass of about 325 mg (5 grains). Calculate the total mass of aspirin tablets in a 500-tablet bottle in grams and ounces.

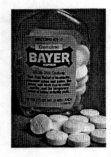

11. A concrete pile from a waterfront pier was pulled from the harbor water at Port Hueneme, California. Its dimensions were 14 in. × 14 in. × 15 ft (1 in. = 2.54 cm).

    a. What is the surface area, expressed in square feet, of a single face of the pile? Exclude the ends of the pile.

    b. Determine the total surface area, expressed in square meters, of the pile, including the ends of the pile.

    c. How many cubic meters of concrete were used to make the pile?

Experiment 1

Identification of a Compound: Physical Properties

Two liquids are immiscible when they are insoluble in one another.

- To identify a substance on the basis of its physical properties
- To learn how to properly assemble a melting point and/or a boiling point apparatus

TECHNIQUES

The following techniques are used in the Experimental Procedure

INTRODUCTION

Gold is yellow, roses are often red, salt is white and crystalline, lead is "heavy," and water is a colorless, clear liquid that freezes at 0°C and boils at 100°C. These are physical properties of substances that are often used for their identification. The more common physical properties include color, odor, density, solubility, melting point, boiling point, and state of the substance (solid, liquid, or gas). Physical properties can be observed or measured without any knowledge of the chemical reactivity of the substance. Additional tests, tests that reveal more information about its chemical or physical properties, may be necessary to confirm the purity of the substance.

The purpose of this experiment is to identify a substance from the data collected on its solubility, density, melting point, and/or boiling point, all of which are physical properties and **intensive properties** of a substance. In Experiment 3, the chemical properties of a substance are used for its identification.

Intensive property: property independent of sample size

Solubility

The **solubility** of a substance is the maximum mass (usually in grams) that dissolves in a fixed mass (usually 100 g) of solvent at a given temperature. A substance has different solubilities in different solvents, reflecting the differences in the molecular compositions and molecular structures of the substance and the solvent. For instance, some substances, such as table salt, are soluble in water but insoluble in gasoline. In this experiment we examine the solubility of a substance in three different solvents: water, ethanol, C_2H_5OH, and acetone, $(CH_3)_2CO$. If further solubility tests are required then cyclohexane, C_6H_{12}, is used as a solvent. Qualitatively each substance is recorded as being soluble (complete dissolution) or insoluble.

Density

The density of a substance is defined as the ratio of the measured mass of the substance to its measured volume. A substance with a large density has a large mass occupying a small volume. We commonly say that lead is "heavy." What we really mean is that lead has a large density; the volume of a lead object need not be large for it to have a large mass.

Melting Point

A solid that is slowly heated changes completely to a liquid phase at a specific temperature called the **melting point**. At the melting point the solid and liquid phases coexist; any lowering of the temperature results in the formation of only solid, and any raising of the temperature results in the existence of only the liquid phase.

Boiling Point

Boiling point: the temperature at which the vapor pressure (the pressure exerted by a vapor when it is in dynamic equilibrium with its liquid) of a liquid equals atmospheric pressure

Atmospheric pressure: the force (or weight) that a column of air exerts over an area of the earth's surface

Intermolecular forces: interactive attractions and repulsions between molecules

When a liquid is heated, there is a temperature at which bubbles form spontaneously and continue to form until all of the liquid has been converted to vapor. This constant temperature is called the **boiling point** of the liquid, a temperature at which the liquid and vapor phases coexist. The boiling point of a liquid depends on the prevailing atmospheric pressure. The boiling point values listed in Table 1.1 are measured at normal **atmospheric pressure** (defined as 1 atmosphere of pressure).

The melting and boiling points of a substance are characteristic of the magnitude of the forces acting between molecules, called **intermolecular forces**. The greater the magnitude of the intermolecular forces (i.e., the stronger the attraction between molecules), the higher the melting and boiling points of the substance. As the magnitude of the intermolecular forces is different for each substance, each has a characteristic melting point and boiling point.

Table 1.1 Physical Properties of Some Common Laboratory Chemicals[a]

Compound	Density (g/cm³)	Melting Point (°C)	Boiling Point (°C)	Solubility			
				Water	Ethanol	Acetone	Cyclohexane
Acetone	0.79	−95	56	s[b]	s	—	s
Acetamide	1.00	82.3	221	s	s		
Acetanilide	1.22	114	304		s	s	s
Anthracene	1.28	216			s	s	s
Benzamide	1.08	132	290	s	s		s
Benzoic acid	1.07	122	249		s	s	s
Benzoin	1.31	137	344		s	s	
2-Butanone	0.81	−86	80	s	s	s	s
Cyclohexane	0.79	6.5	81		s	s	—
Cyclohexene	0.81	−104	83		s	s	s
Ethanol	0.79	−117	79	s	-----	s	s
Ethyl acetate	0.90	−84	77	s	s	s	s
Heptane	0.68	−91	98		s	s	s
n-Hexane	0.66	−95	69		s		
1-Hexene	0.67	−140	63		s		s
Methanol	0.79	−94	65	s	s	s	s
Naphthalene	0.96	80.5	218		s	s	s
1-Propanol	0.80	−127	97	s	s	s	s
2-Propanol	0.79	−90	82	s	s	s	s
Water	1.00	0	100.0	-----	s	s	

[a]Data from *CRC Handbook of Chemistry and Physics* (R. C. West, Ed.), CRC Press, Boca Raton, FL.
[b]s = soluble.

EXPERIMENTAL PROCEDURE

Procedure Overview: A solid or liquid from Table 1.1 is identified on the basis of its density, solubility in various solvents, and melting point (if a solid) or boiling point (if a liquid).

Ask your instructor for an unknown listed in Table 1.1.

1. **Solubility in Water.** To a small test tube add a **pinch** of your solid or 3 drops of your liquid unknown to 1 mL of water. Agitate the contents (Figure 1.1). Does your unknown dissolve? Record your observations.

2. **Solubility in Ethanol and Acetone.** Repeat the test with ethanol and acetone as solvents. (**Caution:** *Avoid breathing vapors; acetone is flammable—keep away from flames!*) Describe the solubility of your unknown as soluble (s) or insoluble (i) in each solvent.

3. **Solubility in Cyclohexane.** If the solubility of the unknown is still uncertain, repeat the solubility tests as described in Parts A.1, 2 using cyclohexane as a solvent.

Complete two trials to determine the density of your liquid unknown.

1. **Determine Mass and Volume.** Determine the mass (± 0.01 g) of your smallest laboratory beaker. Pipet 2 mL of the liquid sample into the dry, clean beaker. Measure the combined mass of the liquid sample and beaker. (**Note:** *Use a rubber pipet bulb in drawing the liquid into the pipet.*) Calculate the density of the liquid.

B. Density of Liquid Unknown

Obtain a 360°C thermometer. Assemble the melting point apparatus in Figure 1.4. Note that cooking oil is the liquid that is heated in the test tube. Complete two measurements for the melting point of your unknown.

1. **Prepare the Sample.** Fill a capillary melting point tube to a depth of 0.5 cm (Figure 1.2) with the solid unknown. Compact the solid to the bottom of the tube by dropping it several times onto the lab bench through a glass tube at least 25 cm in length (Figure 1.3a) or by vibrating the sample with a triangular file (Figure 1.3b). Attach the tube to a 360°C thermometer with a rubber band (or band of rubber tubing). Place the sample alongside the thermometer *bulb* (Figure 1.4).

2. **Determine the Melting Point.** Slowly heat the oil bath (at a rate of about 5°C per minute) until the solid melts. (**Caution:** *The oil bath may be at a temperature greater than 100°C—do not touch!*) Cool the oil bath until the sample solidifies; very slowly (at a rate of about 1°C per minute) heat the bath until the solid again melts. Cycle the cooling and heating of the oil bath until the melting point of the solid has been accurately determined.

C. Melting Point of Solid Unknown

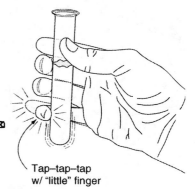

Tap–tap–tap w/ "little" finger

Figure 1.1 Shake the contents of the test tube with the "little" finger.

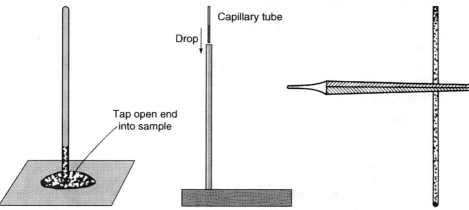

Capillary tube

Drop

Tap open end into sample

Figure 1.2 Invert the capillary melting point tube into the sample and "tap."

Figure 1.3 Compact the sample to the bottom of the capillary melting tube by (a) dropping the capillary tube into a long piece of glass tubing or by (b) vibrating the sample with a triangular file.

Disposal: Dispose of the capillary tube in the "Solid Wastes" container. Return the oil to the "Used Oil" container.

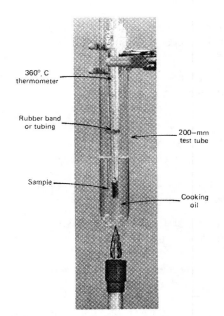

360°, C thermometer

Rubber band or tubing

Sample

200—mm test tube

Cooking oil

Figure 1.4 Melting point apparatus.

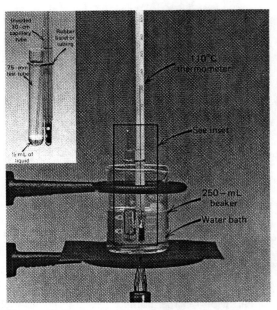

Inserted 10-cm capillary tube

Rubber band or tubing

75-mm test tube

½ mL of liquid

110°C thermometer

See inset

250—mL beaker

Water bath

Figure 1.5 Apparatus for determining the boiling point of a liquid.

D. Boiling Point of Liquid Unknown

Boiling chips.

Obtain a 110°C thermometer. Assemble the boiling point apparatus in Figure 1.5. Complete two measurements for the boiling point of your unknown.

1. **Assemble the Boiling Point Apparatus.** Place 10 drops (~0.5 mL) of the liquid unknown into a "small" (75-mm) test tube.[1] (**Caution:** *The liquid may be flammable—extinguish all flames!*) Position the tube beside the thermometer *bulb* using a rubber band. Invert (open end down) a 10-cm capillary melting point tube in the liquid. Place the apparatus into the water bath.

2. **Measure the Boiling Point.** Place two or three boiling chips in the water bath. Once the apparatus is assembled, ignite the Bunsen flame. Slowly heat the water in the water bath while stirring with the stirring rod. When a rapid and continuous stream of bubbles escapes the capillary tube, discontinue heating the water bath. The stream of bubbles slows as the bath cools. When the bubbles cease to escape and before the liquid reenters the capillary tube, record the temperature. This is the boiling point of the liquid.[2]

3. **Repeat the Measurement.** Determine the boiling point a second time. The same (volume of) liquid may be used; however, the capillary tube must be removed, emptied, and inserted before heating resumes.

4. **Extinguish the Bunsen flame before disassembling the apparatus.**

Disposal: Dispose of the leftover unknown substance in the "Waste Organics" container.

E. Name of Unknown

1. On the basis of the data collected for your sample and from the data in Table 1.1, predict the name of your unknown substance.

---

[1]A 5-cm length of 7-mm glass tubing, closed at one end, can be substituted for the test tube.
[2]If the water in the beaker boils before the liquid unknown reaches its boiling point, remove the heat, record the boiling point of your unknown as >100°C, and consult your laboratory instructor for a more definitive boiling point.

Identification of a Compound: Phyical Properties

Date _____ Lab Sec. _____ Name _____ Desk No. _____

1. From your general experiences, would you select water or gasoline to try dissolving the following?

   a. table sugar (sucrose), used to satisfy your sweet tooth

   b. table salt (sodium chloride), thrown over your shoulder for good luck!

   c. motor oil that has dripped from your automobile onto the garage floor

   d. road tar on the side of your automobile

   e. fertilizer that has spilled from an overturned truck

   f. rubber from the tire marks left on your driveway

   g. blood from a "squished" mosquito

   h. adhesive from a pricing sticker that adheres to a glass vase

2. A student's liquid unknown boils at approximately 65°C and is soluble in water and ethanol. Its measured density is 0.80 g/mL. Which substance in Table 1.1 is the student's unknown?

3. What physical property, measurable in this experiment, distinguishes 1-propanol from 2-propanol?

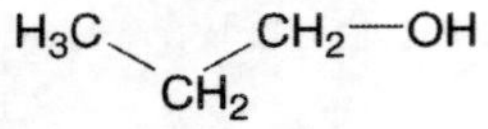

$$H_3C \diagdown_{CH_2} \diagup^{CH_2-OH}$$

1-propanol

$$H_3C \diagdown_{CH} \diagup^{CH_3}$$
$$OH$$

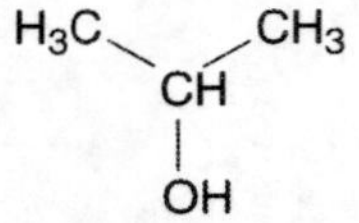

2-propanol

4. With the apparatus in Figure 1.5, when should the boiling point of a liquid be recorded?

5. Identify the essential steps for placing a solid sample in a capillary tube.

Identification of a Compound: Phyical Properties

Date _____ Lab Sec. _____ Name _____ Desk No. _____

A. Solubility

Unknown Number _____	Soluble (√)	Insoluble (√)
1. Solubility in water	_____	_____
2. Solubility in ethanol	_____	_____
3. Solubility in acetone	_____	_____
4. Solubility in cyclohexane, if necessary	_____	_____

B. Density of Liquid Unknown

	Trial 1	Trial 2
1. Mass of beaker and liquid (g)	_____	_____
2. Mass of beaker (g)	_____	_____
3. Mass of liquid (g)	_____	_____
4. Volume of liquid (mL)	_____	_____
5. Density of liquid (g/mL)	_____	_____
6. Average density of liquid (g/mL)	_____	

C. Melting Point of Solid Unknown

1. Observed melting point (°C)	_____	_____
2. Average melting point (°C)	_____	

D. Boiling Point of Liquid Unknown

1. Observed boiling point (°C)	_____	_____
2. Average boiling point (°C)	_____	

E. Name of Unknown

1. Write the name of your liquid/solid unknown _____

Laboratory Questions

Circle the questions that have been assigned.

1. How does atmospheric pressure affect the boiling point of a liquid? Ask your instructor.

2. Suppose that in Part B, the liquid unknown remaining in the pipet is "blown out" after delivery. Will the reported density of the liquid be too high or too low? Explain.

3. If, in Part D.2, the boiling point is recorded *after* the liquid enters the capillary tube (once the heat is removed), will it be reported as being too high or too low? Explain.

4. Besides the physical properties used to identify a substance in this experiment, what other physical properties might be used to characteristically identify a substance?

Dry Lab 2A

Inorganic Nomenclature I. Oxidation Numbers

Sodium chloride salt crystals are a one-to-one combination of sodium cations and chloride anions. The sodium cation has an oxidation number of +1, and the chloride anion has an oxidation number of −1.

OBJECTIVES

- To become familiar with the oxidation numbers of various elements
- To learn to write formulas of compounds based on oxidation numbers

INTRODUCTION

You have probably noticed that members of virtually all professions have a specialized language. Chemists are no exception. For chemists to communicate internationally, some standardized technical language is required. Historically, common names for many compounds evolved and are still universally understood—for example, water, sugar (sucrose), and ammonia—but with new compounds being synthesized and isolated daily, a "familiar" system is no longer viable. Two of the more recent newsworthy common names to appear in the literature are *buckminsterfullerene* (also called *bucky ball*) and *sulflower*.[1]

The Chemical Abstracts Service (CAS) of the American Chemical Society currently has more than 52 million inorganic and organic compounds registered in its database[2] with an average of 2.6 new compounds being registered per second over the past 12 months, 7 days a week, 24 hours a day! Not only does each compound have a unique name, according to a systematic method of nomenclature, but also each compound has a unique molecular structure and set of chemical and physical properties. Therefore, it has become absolutely necessary for the scientific community to properly name compounds according to a universally accepted system of nomenclature.

In the three parts of *Dry Lab 2* (A, B, and C), you will learn a few systematic rules established by the International Union of Pure and Applied Chemistry (IUPAC) for naming and writing formulas for inorganic compounds. You are undoubtedly already familiar with some symbols for the elements and the names for several common compounds. For instance, NaCl is sodium chloride. Continued practice and work in writing formulas and naming compounds will make you even more knowledgeable of the chemist's vocabulary.

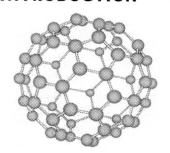

Buckminsterfullerene

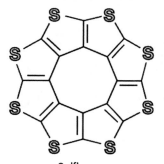

Sulflower

Oxidation Number

Charges are conventionally written "number and charge" (e.g., 3+), but oxidation numbers are written "charge and number" (e.g., −2)

Elements or groups of chemically bonded elements (called **polyatomic** or **molecular groups**) that have **charge** are called **ions**. If the charge is positive, they are called **cations;** if negative, they are **anions.** Oftentimes elements combine to form a compound in which the elements may not have an actual charge but rather an "apparent" charge called its **oxidation number** (or oxidation state). The oxidation number, the charge an atom would have if the electrons in the bond were assigned to the more electronegative element, may be either positive or negative.

---

[1] An extensive listing of common chemical names appears in Appendix D.
[2] http://www.cas.org

While monoatomic and polyatomic ions have an actual charge, the charge of an atom or element within a compound is often uncertain. However, with the application of a few rules, the apparent charge or oxidation number of an atom or element in a compound can be easily determined. Thus, the use of oxidation numbers has a greater range of applicability. For example, knowledge of the oxidation numbers for a range of elements allows us to write the correct chemical formula for a large number of compounds. It is *not* necessary to simply memorize disconnected chemical formulas.

The following "rules" will only use the term *oxidation number* when considering the common charge *or* "apparent" charge for an element. Note in rule 6 that polyatomic ions have an actual charge (not an oxidation number).

1. Any element in the free state (not combined with another element) has an oxidation number of zero, regardless of the complexity of the molecule in which it occurs. Each atom in Ne, O_2, P_4, and S_8 has an oxidation number of 0.

2. Monoatomic ions have an oxidation number equal to the charge of the ion. The ions Ca^{2+}, Fe^{3+}, and Cl^- have oxidation numbers of +2, +3, and -1, respectively.

3. Oxygen in compounds has an assigned oxidation number of -2 (except for a -1 in peroxides; e.g., H_2O_2, and +2 in OF_2). The oxidation number of oxygen is -2 in FeO, Fe_2O_3, $KMnO_4$, and KIO_3.

4. Hydrogen in compounds has an oxidation number of +1 (except for -1 in metal hydrides; e.g., NaH). Its oxidation number is +1 in HCl, $NaHCO_3$, and NH_3.

5. Some elements exhibit only one common oxidation number in certain types of compounds:

   a. Group 1A elements always have an oxidation number of +1 in compounds.

   b. Group 2A elements always have an oxidation number of +2 in compounds.

   c. Boron and aluminum always possess an oxidation number of +3 in compounds.

   d. In **binary compounds** *with metals,* the nonmetallic elements of Group 6A generally exhibit an oxidation number of -2.

   e. In binary compounds *with metals,* the elements of Group 7A have an oxidation number of -1.

6. **Polyatomic ions** have a charge equal to the sum of the oxidation numbers of the elements of the polyatomic group. See Example D2A.2. The polyatomic ions SO_4^{2-}, NO_3^-, and PO_4^{3-} have charges of 2-, 1-, and 3-, respectively.

7. In assigning oxidation numbers to elements in a compound, the element closest to fluorine (the most electronegative element) in the periodic table is always assigned the negative oxidation number. In the compound, P_4O_{10}, oxygen has the negative oxidation number of -2.

8. a. For compounds, the sum of oxidation numbers of all atoms in the compound must equal zero.

   Example D2A.1   For Na_2S, the sum of the oxidation numbers equals zero.

   $$2 \text{ Na atoms, } +1 \text{ for each (rule 5a)} = +2$$

   $$1 \text{ S atom, } -2 \text{ for each (rule 5d)} = -2$$

   Sum of oxidation numbers $(+2) + (-2) = 0$

   b. For polyatomic ions, the sum of the oxidation numbers of the elements must equal the charge of the ion.

   Example D2A.2   For CO_3^{2-} the sum of the oxidation numbers of the elements equals a charge of 2-.

   $$3 \text{ O atoms, } -2 \text{ for each (rule 3)} = -6$$

   $$1 \text{ C atom which must be } +4 = +4$$

   so that $(-6) + (+4) = 2-$, the charge of the CO_3^{2-} ion.

Binary compounds: compounds consisting of only two elements (see Dry Lab 2B)

Polyatomic ions are also called molecular ions (see Dry Lab 2C)

9. Some chemical elements show more than one oxidation number, depending on the compound. The preceding rules may be used to determine their values. Consider the compounds $FeCl_2$ and $FeCl_3$. Since the chlorine atom has an oxidation number of -1 when combined with a metal (rule 5e), the oxidation numbers of iron are $+2$ in $FeCl_2$ and $+3$ in $FeCl_3$.

An extensive listing of oxidation numbers and charges for monoatomic ions and polyatomic ions are presented in *Dry Lab 2C*, Table D2C.1.

The formulas of compounds can be written from a knowledge of the oxidation numbers of the elements that make up the compound. The sum of the oxidation numbers for a compound must equal zero.

Writing Formulas from Charges and Oxidation Numbers

> **Example D2A.3**   Write the formula of the compound formed from Ca^{2+} ions and Cl^- ions.
>
> As the sum of the oxidation numbers must equal zero, two Cl^- are needed for each Ca^{2+}; therefore, the formula of the compound is $CaCl_2$.

Procedure Overview: The oxidation number of an element in a selection of compounds and ions is determined by application of the rules in the Introduction. Additionally, a knowledge of oxidation numbers of elements and the charge on the polyatomic groups will allow you to write the correct formulas for compounds.

DRY LAB PROCEDURE

Your instructor will indicate the questions you are to complete. Answer them on a separate piece of paper. Be sure to indicate the date, your lab section, and your desk number on your *Report Sheet*.

1. Indicate the oxidation number of carbon and sulfur in the following compounds.

   a. CO   **d.** $Na_2C_2O_4$ **g.** SO_2 **j.** Na_2SO_3 **m.** SCl_2

   b. CO_2 **e.** CH_4 **h.** SO_3 **k.** $Na_2S_2O_3$ **n.** Na_2S_2

   c. Na_2CO_3 **f.** H_2CO **i.** Na_2SO_4 **l.** $Na_2S_4O_6$ **o.** $SOCl_2$

2. Indicate the oxidation number of phosphorus, iodine, nitrogen, tellurium, and silicon in the following ions. Remember that the sum of the oxidation numbers for an ion must equal the charge of the ion.

   a. PO_4^{3-} **d.** $P_3O_{10}^{5-}$ **g.** IO^- **j.** NO_2^- **m.** $N_2O_2^{2-}$

   b. PO_3^{3-} **e.** IO_3^- **h.** NH_4^+ **k.** NO^+ **n.** TeO_4^{2-}

   c. HPO_4^{2-} **f.** IO_2^- **i.** NO_3^- **l.** NO_2^+ **o.** SiO_3^{2-}

3. Indicate the oxidation number of the metallic element(s) in the following compounds. None of the compounds listed are peroxides.

   a. Fe_2O_3 **g.** CrO_3 **m.** MnO_2

   b. FeO   **h.** K_2CrO_4 **n.** PbO_2

   c. CoS   **i.** $K_2Cr_2O_7$ **o.** Pb_3O_4

   d. $CoSO_4$ **j.** $KCrO_2$ **p.** ZrI_4

   e. K_3CoCl_6 **k.** K_2MnO_4 **q.** U_3O_8

   f. $CrCl_3$ **l.** Mn_2O_7 **r.** UO_2Cl_2

4. Write formulas for all of the compounds resulting from matching all cations with all anions in each set. Remember that the sum of the oxidation numbers for a compound must equal zero.

Set 1		Set 2		Set 3	
Cations	Anions	Cations	Anions	Cations	Anions
Li^+	Cl^-	Os^{8+}	P^{3-}	Pb^{2+}	SiO_3^{2-}
Ca^{2+}	SO_4^{2-}	Fe^{2+}	N^{3-}	Zr^{4+}	S^{2-}
Na^+	NO_3^-	Al^{3+}	H^-	Co^{3+}	I^-
NH_4^+	O^{2-}	Zn^{2+}	OH^-	Mn^{3+}	ClO^-
V^{5+}	CO_3^{2-}	Cr^{3+}	IO_3^-	Hg^{2+}	CrO_4^{2-}

Dry Lab 2B

Inorganic Nomenclature II.* Binary Compounds

Calcium fluoride, magnesium oxide, and sodium chloride (left to right) are binary compounds of a metal and a nonmetal called **salts**.

OBJECTIVES

- To name and write formulas for the binary compounds of a metal and a nonmetal, of two nonmetals (or metalloid and nonmetal), and of acids
- To name and write formulas for hydrated compounds

INTRODUCTION

The oxidation number of an element helps us to write the formula of a compound and to characterize the chemical nature of the element in the compound. Such information may tell us of the reactivity of the compound. In this dry lab, the correct writing and naming of binary compounds become the first steps in understanding the systematic nomenclature of a large array of chemical compounds.

Binary compounds are the simplest of compounds consisting of a chemical combination of two elements, *not* necessarily two atoms. Compounds such as $NaCl$, SO_3, Cr_2O_3, and HCl are all binary compounds. Binary compounds can be categorized into those of a metal cation and a nonmetal anion, of two nonmetals (or a metalloid and a nonmetal), and of acids.

Metal Cation and Nonmetal Anion—A Binary Salt

Compounds consisting of only two elements are named directly from the elements involved. In naming a binary salt, it is customary to name the more metallic (more electropositive) element first. The root of the second element is then named with the suffix *-ide* added to it. $NaBr$ is sodium brom*ide;* Al_2O_3 is aluminum ox*ide.*

Two polyatomic anions, OH^- and CN^-, have names ending in *-ide* even though their salts are not binary. Thus, KOH is potassium hydrox*ide* and $NaCN$ is sodium cyan*ide.* One polyatomic cation, NH_4^+, is also treated as a single species in the naming of a compound; NH_4Cl is ammonium chlor*ide,* even though NH_4Cl is not a binary compound.

When a metal cation exhibits more than one oxidation number, the nomenclature must reflect that. Multiple oxidation numbers normally exist for the transition metal cations. Two systems are used for expressing different oxidation numbers of metal ions with multiple oxidation states:

1. The "old" system uses a different suffix to reflect the oxidation number of the metal cation; the suffix is usually added to the root of the Latin name for the cation. The *-ous* ending designates the lower of two oxidation numbers for the metal cation, whereas the *-ic* ending indicates the higher one.

*For more information on chemical nomenclature, go online to http://en.wikipedia.org/wiki/ Category:Chemistry or http://chemistry.alanearhart.org.

2. The Stock system uses a Roman numeral after the English name to indicate the oxidation number of the metal cation in the compound.

Examples for the copper, iron, and tin salts are:

Formula	Old System	Stock System
Cu_2O	*cuprous* oxide	copper(I) oxide
CuO	*cupric* oxide	copper(II) oxide
$FeCl_2$	*ferrous* chloride	iron(II) chloride
$FeCl_3$	*ferric* chloride	iron(III) chloride
$SnCl_2$	*stannous* chloride	tin(II) chloride
$SnCl_4$	*stannic* chloride	tin(IV) chloride

In naming compounds of a metal known to have variable oxidation numbers, the Stock system is preferred in chemistry today. Following are the metal cations that are commonly named using both the old and the Stock systems. The metal ions that are still often named using the old system format are in **boldface**.

Fe^{3+}	**ferric**	**iron(III)**	**Cu^{2+}**	**cupric**	**copper(II)**
Fe^{2+}	**ferrous**	**iron(II)**	**Cu^+**	**cuprous**	**copper(I)**
Sn^{4+}	**stannic**	**tin(IV)**	**Hg^{2+}**	**mercuric**	**mercury(II)**
Sn^{2+}	**stannous**	**tin(II)**	**Hg_2^{2+}**	**mercurous**	**mercury(I)**
Cr^{3+}	chromic	chromium(III)	Co^{3+}	cobaltic	cobalt(III)
Cr^{2+}	chromous	chromium(II)	Co^{2+}	cobaltous	cobalt(II)
Pb^{4+}	plumbic	lead(IV)	Mn^{3+}	manganic	manganese(III)
Pb^{2+}	plumbous	lead(II)	Mn^{2+}	manganous	manganese(II)

Old names are still often used in chemical nomenclature.

Often more than two compounds form from the chemical combination of two non-metals or a metalloid and a nonmetal. For example, nitrogen and oxygen combine to form the compounds N_2O, NO, NO_2, N_2O_3, N_2O_4, and N_2O_5. It is obvious that these are all nitrogen ox*ides*, but each must have a unique name.

Two Nonmetals (or a Metalloid and a Nonmetal)

To distinguish between the nitrogen oxides and, in general, to name compounds formed between two nonmetals or a metalloid and a nonmetal, Greek prefixes are used to designate the number of atoms of each element present in the molecule. The common Greek prefixes follow:

Prefix	Meaning	Prefix	Meaning
mono-*	one	hepta-	seven
di-	two	octa-	eight
tri-	three	nona-	nine
tetra-	four	deca-	ten
penta-	five	dodeca-	twelve
hexa-	six		

*mono- is seldom used because "one" is generally implied.

The prefix system is the *preferred* method for naming the binary compounds of two nonmetals and of a metalloid and a nonmetal. The Stock system is occasionally used, but as you can see, this system does not differentiate between the NO_2 and N_2O_4 nitrogen oxides below.

Formula	Prefix System	Stock System
N_2O	*di*nitrogen oxide	nitrogen(I) oxide
NO	nitrogen oxide	nitrogen(II) oxide
NO_2	nitrogen *di*oxide	nitrogen(IV) oxide
N_2O_3	*di*nitrogen *tri*oxide	nitrogen(III) oxide
N_2O_4	*di*nitrogen *tetr*oxide	nitrogen(IV) oxide
N_2O_5	*di*nitrogen *pent*oxide	nitrogen(V) oxide

dinitrogen trioxide

dinitrogen tetroxide

dinitrogen pentoxide

Note that the end vowel of the Greek prefix is occasionally omitted from the spelling for clarity in pronunciation.

Hydrates

Prefixes are also used for the naming of **hydrates,** inorganic salts in which water molecules are a part of the crystalline structure of the solid. The waters of hydration (also called waters of crystallization) are bound to the ions of the salt and, in most cases, can be removed with the application of heat (see *Experiment 5*). For example, barium chloride is often purchased as barium chloride *di*hydrate: $BaCl_2 \cdot 2H_2O$. The formula of iron(III) chloride *hexa*hydrate is $FeCl_3 \cdot 6H_2O$.

Binary Acids

A binary acid is an *aqueous* solution of a compound formed by hydrogen and a more electronegative nonmetal. To name the acid, the prefix *hydro-* and suffix *-ic* are added to the root of the nonmetal name.

Formula	Name
HCl(*aq*)	*hydro*chloric acid
HBr(*aq*)	*hydro*bromic acid
H_2S(*aq*)	*hydro*sulfuric acid

Writing Formulas from Names

In writing formulas for compounds, it is mandatory that the sum of the oxidation numbers (see *Dry Lab 2A*) of the elements equals zero. The name of the compound must dictate how the formula is to be written.

Example D2B.1   Write the formula for calcium nitride.

Calcium is in group 2A and therefore has an oxidation number of $+2 : Ca^{2+}$. The nitrogen atom is always -3 when combined with a metal: N^{3-}. Therefore, for the sum of the oxidation numbers to equal zero, there must be three Ca^{2+} (a total of $+6$) for every two N^{3-} (a total of -6); the formula is Ca_3N_2.

DRY LAB PROCEDURE

Procedure Overview: Given the formula of the compound, the proper names for a large number of compounds are to be written. Given the name of the compound, the formulas for a large number of compounds also are to be written.

Your instructor will assign the exercises you are to complete. Answer them on a separate piece of paper. Be sure to indicate the date, your lab section, and your desk number on your ***Report Sheet***. Use the rules that have been described.

1. Name the following binary salts of the representative elements.

   a. Na_3P d. CaC_2 g. Ca_3P_2 j. K_2S m. NH_4Br p. $AlCl_3$

   b. Na_2O e. CaI_2 h. KCN   k. K_2Te n. $(NH_4)_2S$ q. Al_2O_3

   c. Na_3N f. CaH_2 i. KOH   l. K_2O_2 o. NH_4CN r. AlN

2. Name the following salts according to the old *-ic, -ous* system *and* the Stock system.

   a. CrS   g. $HgCl_2$ m. CoO

   b. Cr_2O_3 h. Hg_2Cl_2 n. $CoBr_3 \cdot 6H_2O$

   c. $CrI_3 \cdot 6H_2O$ i. HgO   o. SnF_4

   d. CuCl   j. Fe_2O_3 p. SnO_2

   e. CuI_2 k. FeS   q. Cu_2O

   f. $CuBr_2 \cdot 4H_2O$ l. $FeI_3 \cdot 6H_2O$ r. $Fe(OH)_3$

3. Name the following binary acids.

   a. HF(*aq*)　　　　　　**d.** HBr(*aq*)

   b. HI(*aq*)　　　　　　**e.** H_2Te(*aq*)

   c. H_2Se(*aq*)　　　　**f.** HCl(*aq*)

4. Name the following binary compounds consisting of two nonmetals or a metalloid and a nonmetal.

a. SO_2	**d.** SF_6	**g.** N_2O_5	**j.** $SiCl_4$	**m.** AsH_3	**p.** XeF_4
b. SO_3	**e.** SCl_4	**h.** N_2S_4	**k.** SiO_2	**n.** AsF_5	**q.** XeF_6
c. S_4N_4	**f.** NO_2	**i.** NF_3	**l.** $AsCl_3$	**o.** HCl	**r.** XeO_3

5. Write formulas for the following compounds consisting of a metal cation and a nonmetal anion.

   a. ferrous sulfide

   b. iron(III) hydroxide

   c. ferric oxide

   d. aluminum iodide

   e. copper(I) chloride

   f. cupric cyanide tetrahydrate

   g. manganese(IV) oxide

   h. nickel(III) oxide

   i. chromium(III) oxide

   j. titanium(IV) chloride

   k. cobalt(II) chloride hexahydrate

   l. cobaltous oxide

   m. mercury(I) chloride

   n. mercuric iodide

6. Write formulas for the following compounds consisting of two nonmetals (or a metalloid and a nonmetal).

   a. hydrochloric acid

   b. hydrosulfuric acid

   c. hydroiodic acid

   d. silicon tetrafluoride

   e. arsenic pentafluoride

   f. xenon hexafluoride

   g. iodine pentafluoride

   h. krypton difluoride

   i. tetrasulfur tetranitride

   j. dichlorine heptaoxide

   k. phosphorus trihydride (phosphine)

   l. tetraphosphorus decoxide

7. Write formulas and name the binary compounds resulting from matching all cations with all anions in each set.

Set 1		Set 2		Set 3	
Cations	Anions	Cations	Anions	Cations	Anions
K^+	Cl^-	Co^{2+}	P^{3-}	Mn^{3+}	O^{2-}
H^+(*aq*)*	S^{2-}	Co^{3+}	Br^-	Sn^{2+}	N^{3-}
Na^+	F^-	Pb^{2+}	O^{2-}	NH_4^+	S^{2-}
Fe^{3+}	CN^-	Pt^{4+}	F^-	Hg_2^{2+}	Se^{2-}
Cu^+	I^-	Ba^{2+}	OH^-	Ce^{4+}	I^-

   *Name as acids

8. Write the formulas for the compounds shown in the photo.

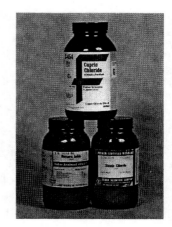

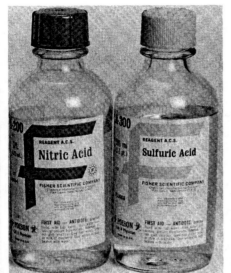

Dry Lab 2C

Inorganic Nomenclature III. Ternary Compounds

Common ternary acids (or oxoacids) in the laboratory are nitric acid and sulfuric acid.

OBJECTIVES

- To name and write formulas for salts and acids containing polyatomic anions
- To name and write formulas for acid salts

INTRODUCTION

In *Dry Lab 2B*, the naming and the writing of formulas for binary compounds, the simplest of compounds, were introduced.

Ternary compounds are generally considered as having a polyatomic anion containing oxygen. Compounds such as $KMnO_4$, $BaSO_4$, $KClO_3$, and HNO_3 are ternary compounds that have the polyatomic anions MnO_4^-, SO_4^{2-}, ClO_3^-, and NO_3^-, respectively. Ternary compounds can be categorized as salts and acids.

Metal Cation and a Polyatomic Anion Containing Oxygen—A Ternary Salt

sulfate ion

nitrate ion

Many polyatomic anions consist of one element (usually a nonmetal) and oxygen; the entire grouping of atoms carries a negative charge. The anion is named by using the root name of the element (not the oxygen) with the suffix *-ate*. As examples, SO_4^{2-} is the sulf*ate* ion and NO_3^- is the nitr*ate* ion.

If *only two* polyatomic anions form from an element and oxygen, the polyatomic anion having the element with the higher oxidation number uses the suffix *-ate;* the polyatomic anion having the element with the lower oxidation number uses the suffix *-ite*. Examples include the following:

Ion	Oxidation Number	Name	Ion	Oxidation Number	Name
SO_4^{2-}	S is +6	sulf*ate*	SO_3^{2-}	S is +4	sulf*ite*
NO_3^-	N is +5	nitr*ate*	NO_2^-	N is +3	nitr*ite*
PO_4^{3-}	P is +5	phosph*ate*	PO_3^{3-}	P is +3	phosph*ite*

The formulas and names of common polyatomic anions are listed in Table D2C.1.

Salts that have a polyatomic anion are named in the same manner as the binary salts: The metal cation (along with the Stock system or *-ic, -ous* distinction) is named first followed by the polyatomic anion. Some examples follow:

Salt	Name
Na_2SO_4	sodium sulfate
Na_2SO_3	sodium sulfite
$Fe(NO_3)_3$	iron(III) or ferric nitrate
$FeSO_4$	iron(II) or ferrous sulfate

phosphate ion

Table D2C.1 Names and Oxidation Numbers and Charges of Common Monoatomic and Polyatomic Ions

A. Metallic and Polyatomic Cations

Oxidation Number of +1; Charges of 1+

NH_4^+	ammonium	Hg_2^{2+}	mercury(I), mercurous
Cu^+	copper(I), cuprous	K^+	potassium
H^+	hydrogen	Ag^+	silver (I)
Li^+	lithium	Na^+	sodium

Oxidation Number of +2; Charges of 2+

Ba^{2+}	barium	Mn^{2+}	manganese(II), manganous
Cd^{2+}	cadmium	Hg^{2+}	mercury(II), mercuric
Ca^{2+}	calcium	Ni^{2+}	nickel(II)
Cr^{2+}	chromium(II), chromous	Sr^{2+}	strontium
Co^{2+}	cobalt(II), cobaltous	Sn^{2+}	tin(II), stannous
Cu^{2+}	copper(II), cupric	UO_2^{2+}	uranyl
Fe^{2+}	iron(II), ferrous	VO^{2+}	vanadyl
Pb^{2+}	lead(II), plumbous	Zn^{2+}	zinc
Mg^{2+}	magnesium		

Oxidation Number of +3; Charges of 3+

Al^{3+}	aluminum	Co^{3+}	cobalt(III), cobaltic
As^{3+}	arsenic(III)	Fe^{3+}	iron(III), ferric
Cr^{3+}	chromium(III), chromic	Mn^{3+}	manganese(III), manganic

Oxidation Number of +4; Charges of 4+

Pb^{4+}	lead(IV), plumbic	Sn^{4+}	tin(IV), stannic

Oxidation Number of +5; Charges of 5+

V^{5+}	vanadium(V)	As^{5+}	arsenic(V)

B. Nonmetallic and Polyatomic Anions

Oxidation Number of −1; Charges of 1−

$CH_3CO_2^-$	acetate *or*	H^-	hydride
$C_2H_3O_2^-$	acetate	ClO^-	hypochlorite
Br^-	bromide	I^-	iodide
ClO_3^-	chlorate	NO_3^-	nitrate
Cl^-	chloride	NO_2^-	nitrite
ClO_2^-	chlorite	ClO_4^-	perchlorate
CN^-	cyanide	IO_4^-	periodate
F^-	fluoride	MnO_4^-	permanganate
OH^-	hydroxide		

Oxidation Number of −2; Charges of 2−

CO_3^{2-}	carbonate	O_2^{2-}	peroxide
CrO_4^{2-}	chromate	SiO_3^{2-}	silicate
$Cr_2O_7^{2-}$	dichromate	SO_4^{2-}	sulfate
MnO_4^{2-}	manganate	S^{2-}	sulfide
O^{2-}	oxide	SO_3^{2-}	sulfite
$C_2O_4^{2-}$	oxalate	$S_2O_3^{2-}$	thiosulfate

Oxidation Number of −3; Charges of 3−

N^{3-}	nitride	BO_3^{3-}	borate
PO_4^{3-}	phosphate	AsO_3^{3-}	arsenite
PO_3^{3-}	phosphite	AsO_4^{3-}	arsenate
P^{3-}	phosphide		

If *more than two* polyatomic anions are formed from a given element and oxygen, the prefixes *per-* and *hypo-* are added to distinguish the additional ions. This appears most often among the polyatomic anions with a halogen as the distinguishing element. The prefixes *per-* and *hypo-* are often used to identify the extremes (the high and low) in oxidation numbers of the element in the anion. Table D2C.2, page 62, summarizes the nomenclature for these and all polyatomic anions.

For example, ClO_4^- is *per*chlor*ate* because the oxidation number of Cl is +7 (the highest oxidation number of the four polyatomic anions of chlorine), whereas ClO^- is *hypo*chlor*ite* because the oxidation number of Cl is +1. Therefore, $NaClO_4$ is sodium perchlorate and $NaClO$ is sodium hypochlorite. The name of $Co(ClO_3)_2$ is cobalt(II) chlorate because the chlorate ion is ClO_3^- (see Table D2C.1) and the oxidation number

Table D2C.2 Nomenclature of Polyatomic Anions and Ternary Acids

Name of Polyatomic Anion	Acid	4A	5A	6A	7A
			Oxidation Number		
per___ate	per___ic acid	—	—	—	+7
___ate	___ic acid	+4	+5	+6	+5
___ite	___ous acid	—	+3	+4	+3
hypo___ite	hypo___ous acid	—	+1	+2	+1

of Cl is +5 (see Table D2C.2). The cobalt is Co^{2+} because two chlorate, ClO_3^-, ions are required for the neutral salt.

Ternary Acids or Oxoacids

The ternary acids (also referred to as **oxoacids**) are compounds of hydrogen and a polyatomic anion. In contrast to the binary acids, the naming of the ternary acids does not include any mention of hydrogen. The ternary acids are named by using the root of the element in the polyatomic anion and adding a suffix; if the polyatomic anion ends in *-ate*, the ternary acid is named an *-ic acid*. If the polyatomic anion ends in *-ite*, the ternary acid is named an *-ous acid*. To understand by example, the following are representative names for ternary acids.

sulfuric acid

perchloric acid

Ion	Name of Ion	Acid	Name of Acid
SO_4^{2-}	sulf*ate* ion	H_2SO_4	sulfur*ic acid*
SO_3^{2-}	sulf*ite* ion	H_2SO_3	sulfur*ous acid*
CO_3^{2-}	carbon*ate* ion	H_2CO_3	carbon*ic acid*
NO_3^-	nitr*ate* ion	HNO_3	nitr*ic acid*
ClO_4^-	perchlor*ate* ion	$HClO_4$	perchlor*ic acid*
IO^-	hypoiod*ite* ion	HIO	hypoiod*ous acid*

Acid Salts

Sodium hydrogen sulphate is commonly called sodium acid sulphate.

Acid salts are salts in which a metal cation replaces *fewer than* all of the hydrogens of an acid having more than one hydrogen (a polyprotic acid). The remaining presence of the hydrogen in the compound is indicated by inserting its name into that of the salt.

Salt	Name
$NaHSO_4$	sodium *hydrogen* sulfate (one Na^+ ion replaces one H^+ ion in H_2SO_4)
$CaHPO_4$	calcium *hydrogen* phosphate (one Ca^{2+} ion replaces two H^+ ions in H_3PO_4)
NaH_2PO_4	sodium *dihydrogen* phosphate (one Na^+ ion replaces one H^+ ion in H_3PO_4)
$NaHCO_3$	sodium *hydrogen* carbonate (one Na^+ ion replaces one H^+ ion in H_2CO_3)
$NaHS$	sodium *hydrogen* sulfide (one Na^+ ion replaces one H^+ ion in H_2S)

An older system of naming acid salts substitutes the prefix *bi* for a *single* hydrogen before naming the polyatomic anion. For example, $NaHCO_3$ is sodium *bi*carbonate, $NaHSO_4$ is sodium *bi*sulfate, and $NaHS$ is sodium *bi*sulfide.

The Next Step

The naming of organic compounds also follows a set of guidelines. IUPAC regularly meets to ensure that new compounds have a systematic name. Review the nomenclature of the simple organic compounds, such as the alcohols, ethers, acids, and amines.

DRY LAB PROCEDURE

Procedure Overview: Given the formula of the compounds, the proper names for a large number of ternary compounds are to be written. Given the name of the compounds, the formulas for a large number of compounds are to be written.

Your instructor will assign the exercises you are to complete. Answer them on a separate piece of paper. Be sure to indicate the date, your lab section, and your desk number on your ***Report Sheet***. Use the rules that have been described.

1. Use Table D2C.2 to name the following polyatomic anions.
   a. BrO_3^-
   b. IO_3^-
   c. PO_2^{3-}
   d. $N_2O_2^{2-}$
   e. AsO_2^-
   f. BrO_2^-
   g. IO_2^-
   h. SO_3^{2-}
   i. SiO_3^{2-}
   j. TeO_4^{2-}
   k. SeO_4^{2-}
   l. NO_2^-

2. Name the following salts of the representative elements.
   a. Na_2SO_4
   b. K_3AsO_4
   c. Li_2CO_3
   d. $Ca_3(PO_4)_2$
   e. $Ca_3(PO_3)_2$
   f. Na_2SiO_3
   g. K_2CrO_4
   h. $K_2Cr_2O_7$
   i. K_2MnO_4
   j. $KMnO_4$
   k. Li_2SO_3
   l. Li_2SO_4
   m. $Li_2S_2O_3$
   n. $Ba(NO_2)_2$
   o. $Ba(NO_3)_2$
   p. KCH_3CO_2

3. Name the following salts of the transition and post-transition elements using the Stock system.
   a. $Fe(OH)_3$
   b. $FePO_4 \cdot 6H_2O$
   c. $FeSO_4 \cdot 7H_2O$
   d. $CuCN$
   e. $CuCO_3$
   f. $CuSO_4 \cdot 5H_2O$
   g. $Sn(NO_3)_2$
   h. $Sn(SO_4)_2$
   i. $MnSO_4$
   j. $Mn(CH_3CO_2)_2$
   k. $Hg_2(NO_3)_2$
   l. $Hg(NO_3)_2 \cdot H_2O$
   m. $CrPO_4$
   n. $CrSO_4 \cdot 6H_2O$
   o. $Co_2(CO_3)_3$
   p. $CoSO_4 \cdot 7H_2O$

4. Name the following ternary acids.
   a. H_2SO_4
   b. H_2SO_3
   c. $H_2S_2O_3$
   d. H_3PO_4
   e. $HMnO_4$
   f. H_2CrO_4
   g. H_3BO_3
   h. HNO_3
   i. HNO_2
   j. H_2CO_3
   k. $H_2C_2O_4$
   l. CH_3COOH
   m. $HClO_4$
   n. $HClO_3$
   o. $HClO_2$
   p. $HClO$

5. Name the following acid salts. Use the "older" system wherever possible.
   a. $NaHCO_3$
   b. $Ca(HCO_3)_2$
   c. KHC_2O_4
   d. NH_4HCO_3
   e. $NaHS$
   f. $KHSO_3$
   g. $NaHSO_4 \cdot H_2O$
   h. Li_2HPO_4
   i. LiH_2PO_4
   j. $MgHAsO_4$
   k. KH_2AsO_4
   l. $KHCrO_4$

6. Write formulas for the following compounds.
   a. potassium permanganate
   b. potassium manganate
   c. calcium carbonate
   d. lead(II) carbonate
   e. ferric carbonate
   f. silver thiosulfate
   g. sodium sulfite
   h. ferrous sulfate heptahydrate
   i. iron(II) oxalate
   j. sodium chromate
   k. potassium dichromate
   l. nickel(II) nitrate hexahydrate
   m. chromous nitrite
   n. vanadyl nitrate
   o. uranyl acetate
   p. barium acetate dihydrate
   q. sodium silicate
   r. calcium hypochlorite
   s. potassium chlorate
   t. ammonium oxalate
   u. sodium borate
   v. cuprous iodate

7. Write formulas for the following acids.
   a. sulfuric acid
   b. thiosulfuric acid
   c. sulfurous acid
   d. periodic acid
   e. iodic acid
   f. hypochlorous acid
   g. nitrous acid
   h. nitric acid
   i. phosphorous acid
   j. phosphoric acid
   k. carbonic acid
   l. bromous acid
   m. chromic acid
   n. permanganic acid
   o. manganic acid
   p. boric acid
   q. oxalic acid
   r. silicic acid

8. Write formulas and name the hodgepodge of compounds resulting from matching all cations with all anions for each set.

Set 1		Set 2		Set 3	
Cations	Anions	Cations	Anions	Cations	Anions
Li^+	Cl^-	Fe^{3+}	PO_4^{3-}	Pb^{2+}	SiO_3^{2-}
Cd^{2+}	SO_4^{2-}	Fe^{2+}	HPO_4^{2-}	NH_4^+	S^{2-}
Na^+	NO_3^-	Al^{3+}	HCO_3^-	$H^+(aq)*$	MnO_4^-
Cu^{2+}	O^{2-}	Zn^{2+}	CN^-	Mn^{3+}	HSO_4^-
V^{5+}	CO_3^{2-}	K^+	$CH_3CO_2^-$ or $C_2H_3O_2^-$	Hg^{2+}	$Cr_2O_7^{2-}$
Mg^{2+}	I^-	VO^{2+}	IO^-	Sr^{2+}	$C_2O_4^{2-}$

*Name as acids

9. Write correct formulas for the following hodgepodge of compounds from *Dry Labs 2A, 2B, and 2C.*

a. vanadium(V) fluoride
b. stannic oxide
c. silicon tetrafluoride
d. mercuric oxide
e. lithium hypochlorite
f. iodine trifluoride
g. ferrous oxalate
h. cuprous oxide
i. copper(I) chloride
j. calcium hydride
k. cadmium iodide
l. barium acetate dihydrate
m. ammonium sulfide

n. vanadium(V) oxide
o. titanium(IV) chloride
p. scandium(III) nitrate
q. nickel(II) acetate hexahydrate
r. mercurous nitrate
s. lead(II) acetate
t. ferric phosphate hexahydrate
u. ferric chromate
v. dinitrogen tetrasulfide
w. chromous acetate
x. calcium nitride
y. ammonium dichromate
z. silver acetate

10. Write the correct formulas for the compounds shown in the photo.

11. Match the chemical name to each of the following common names. See Appendix D.

Common Name	Chemical Name
a. acid of sugar	oxalic acid
b. aqua fortis	nitric acid
c. barium white, fixed white	barium sulfate dihydrate
d. bitter salt, Epsom salts	magnesium sulfate heptahydrate
e. blue vitrol	copper(II) sulfate pentahydrate
f. calomel	mercurous chloride
g. caustic potash	potassium hydroxide
h. Chile saltpeter, sodium nitre	sodium nitrate
i. chrome yellow	lead(IV) chromate
j. Indian red, jeweler's rouge	ferric oxide
k. lime	calcium oxide
l. oil of vitrol	sulfuric acid
m. talc or talcum	magnesium silicate
n. Glauber's salt	sodium sulfate

Experiment 2

Empirical Formulas

Crucibles are fired at high temperatures to volatilize impurities.

OBJECTIVES

- To determine the empirical formulas of two compounds by combination reactions
- To determine the mole ratio of the decomposition products of a compound

TECHNIQUES

The following techniques are used in the Experimental Procedure:

INTRODUCTION

The **empirical formula** of a compound is the simplest whole-number ratio of moles of elements in the compound. The experimental determination of the empirical formula of a compound from its elements requires three steps:

1. Determine the mass of each element in the sample.
2. Calculate the number of moles of each element in the sample.
3. Express the ratio of the moles of each element as small whole numbers.

For example, an analysis of a sample of table salt shows that 2.75 g of sodium and 4.25 g of chlorine are present. The moles of each element are

$$2.75 \text{ g} \times \frac{\text{mol Na}}{22.99 \text{ gNa}} = 0.120 \text{ mol Na}, \qquad 4.25 \text{ g} \times \frac{\text{mol Cl}}{35.45 \text{ g Cl}} = 0.120 \text{ mol Cl}$$

The mole ratio of sodium to chlorine is 0.120 to 0.120. As the empirical formula *must* be expressed in a ratio of small whole numbers, the whole-number ratio is 1 to 1, and the empirical formula of sodium chloride is Na_1Cl_1 or simply NaCl.

The empirical formula also provides a mass ratio of the elements in the compound. The formula NaCl states that 22.99 g (1 mol) of sodium combines with 35.45 g (1 mol) of chlorine to form 58.44 g (1 mol) of sodium chloride.

The mass percentages of sodium and chlorine in sodium chloride are:

$$\frac{22.99}{22.99 + 35.45} \times 100 = 39.34\% \text{ Na} \qquad \frac{35.45}{22.99 + 35.45} \times 100 = 60.66\% \text{ Cl}$$

We can determine the empirical formula of a compound from either a combination reaction or a decomposition reaction. In the **combination reaction,** a known mass of one reactant and the mass of the product are measured. An example of a combination reaction is the reaction of titanium with oxygen: The initial mass of the titanium and the final mass of the titanium oxide product are determined. From the difference

Combination reaction: two elements combine to form a compound

between the masses, the mass of oxygen that reacts and, subsequently, the moles of titanium and oxygen that react to form the product are calculated. This mole ratio of titanium to oxygen yields the empirical formula of the titanium oxide (see *Prelaboratory Assignment* question 2).

Decomposition reaction: a compound decomposes into two or more elements or simpler compounds

In the **decomposition reaction,** the initial mass of the compound used for the analysis and the final mass of at least one of the products are measured. An example would be the decomposition of a mercury oxide to mercury metal and oxygen gas: The initial mass of the mercury oxide and the final mass of the mercury metal are determined. The difference between the measured masses is the mass of oxygen in the mercury oxide. The moles of mercury and oxygen in the original compound are then calculated to provide a whole-number mole ratio of mercury to oxygen (see *Prelaboratory Assignment* question 1).

Your instructor may choose a different compound for decomposition.

In Part B of this experiment, a combination reaction of magnesium and oxygen is used to determine the empirical formula of magnesium oxide. The initial mass of the magnesium and the mass of the product are measured.

In Part C of this experiment, a decomposition reaction of a pure compound into calcium oxide, CaO, and carbon dioxide, CO_2, is analyzed. The masses of the compound and the calcium oxide are measured. Further analysis of the data provides the mole ratio of CaO to CO_2 in the compound.

In Part D of this experiment, a combination reaction of tin and oxygen is used to determine the empirical formula of a tin oxide. Since tin forms more than one oxide, a difference in laboratory technique and persistence may lead to different determinations of the reported empirical formula. The initial measured mass of tin is not reacted directly with the oxygen of the air, but rather with nitric acid to produce the oxide. Because the mass of the final product consists only of tin and oxygen, its empirical formula is calculated.

EXPERIMENTAL PROCEDURE

Procedure Overview: A crucible of constant mass is used to thermally form (Part B) or decompose (Part C) a compound of fixed composition or form a compound of variable composition (Part D). Mass measurements before and after the heating procedure are used to calculate the empirical formula of the compound.

Ask your instructor which part(s) of the experiment you are to complete. If you are to perform more than one part, then you will need to organize some of your data on a separate sheet of paper for the *Report Sheet*.

A. Preparation of a Crucible

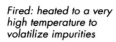

Fired: heated to a very high temperature to volatilize impurities

1. **Prepare a clean crucible.** Obtain a clean crucible and lid. Often-used crucibles tend to form stress fractures or fissures. Check the crucible for flaws; if any are found, obtain a second crucible. Support the crucible and lid on a clay triangle and heat with an intense flame for ~5 minutes. Allow them to cool to room temperature.[1,2]

   Measure the mass of the **fired,** *cool* crucible and lid. Use only clean, dry crucible tongs to handle the crucible and lid for the remainder of the experiment. Do *not* use your fingers. (**Caution:** *Hot and cold crucibles look the same—do not touch!*)

B. Combination Reaction of Magnesium and Oxygen

1. **Prepare the sample.** Polish (with steel wool or sandpaper) 0.15–0.20 g of magnesium ribbon; curl the ribbon to lie in the crucible. Measure and record the mass (± 0.001 g) of the magnesium sample, crucible, and lid.

2. **Heat the sample in air.** Place the crucible containing the Mg ribbon and lid on the clay triangle. Heat *slowly*, occasionally lifting the lid to allow air to reach the Mg ribbon (Figure 2.1).

---

[1]Cool the crucible and lid to room temperature (and perform all other cooling processes in the Experimental Procedure) in a desiccator if one is available. When cool, remove the crucible and lid from the desiccator with crucible tongs and measure the mass of the crucible and lid.
[2]If the crucible remains dirty after heating, *on the advice of your instructor,* move the apparatus to the fume hood, add 1–2 mL of 6 M HNO_3, and gently evaporate to dryness. (**Caution:** *Avoid skin contact, flush immediately with water.*)

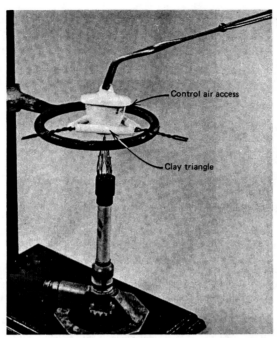

Figure 2.1 Controlling access of air to the magnesium ribbon

If too much air comes in contact with the Mg ribbon, rapid oxidation of the Mg occurs and it burns brightly. (**Caution:** *You do not want this to happen. If it does, do not watch the burn; it may cause temporary blindness!*) Immediately return the lid to the crucible, allow the apparatus to cool, and return to Part A to repeat the experiment.

3. **Heat for complete reaction.** Continue heating the crucible until no visible change is apparent in the magnesium ash at the bottom of the crucible. Remove the lid; continue heating the open crucible and ash for ~30 seconds. Remove the heat and allow the crucible to *cool to room temperature.*[3] *Do not touch!* Measure the mass of the contents in the crucible and with the lid on the same balance that was used earlier and record.

4. **Repeat.** Redo Parts A.1 and B for a second trial.

5. **Calculations.** Determine the mole ratio of magnesium to oxygen, and thus the empirical formula, of the pure compound.

Disposal and cleanup: Wash the cool crucible with a dilute solution of hydrochloric acid and discard in the Waste Acids container. Rinse twice with tap water and twice with deionized water.

The pure compound decomposes to calcium oxide and carbon dioxide. Complete Part A.1 for preparing the crucible for analysis.

1. **Dry the compound.** The pure compound is to be previously dried before analysis. Check with your instructor.

2. **Prepare the sample.** Place about 1 g of the pure compound in the clean crucible prepared in Part A.1 and measure the mass (±0.001 g) of the sample and crucible. The lid need *not* be used for Part C. Record the mass of the compound.

C. Decomposition Reaction of a Pure Compound

---

[3]Place the crucible and lid in a desiccator (if available) for cooling.

3. **Heat the sample.** Heat the crucible, gradually intensifying the heat.[4] Maintain the intense flame for 20–25 minutes. Allow the sample to cool (in a desiccator if available). Determine the mass of the contents and crucible. *Do not touch!*

4. **Analyze the product.** Repeat Part C.2 until ±1% reproducibility of the mass is obtained.

5. **Repeat.** Redo Parts A.1, C.1–3 for a second trial.

6. **Calculations.** Determine the mole ratio of calcium oxide to carbon dioxide in the pure compound.

> *Disposal and cleanup:* Wash the cool crucible with a dilute solution of hydrochloric acid and discard in the Waste Acids container. Rinse twice with tap water and twice with deionized water.

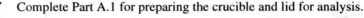

D. Combination Reaction of Tin and Oxygen

Complete Part A.1 for preparing the crucible and lid for analysis.

1. **Prepare the sample.** Place about 0.5 g of granulated tin in the clean crucible prepared in Part A.1; cover with the crucible lid. Record the combined mass (±0.001 g) of the tin sample, crucible, and lid. Only use crucible tongs to handle the crucible and lid.

2. **Transfer the sample to a fume hood.** Add drops of 6 M HNO_3 (**Caution:** *HNO_3 is very corrosive and a severe skin irritant. If it contacts the skin wash immediately with excess water*) to the tin sample until no further reaction is apparent with the tin (**Caution:** *Do not inhale the gaseous, toxic vapors!*). Add 4–5 additional drops of the 6 M HNO_3. Keep the crucible and sample in the fume hood until no further gaseous vapors from the reaction are visible.

Cool flame. If you can feel the heat of the flame with a hand held beside the crucible, the flame is too hot!

3. **Heat to dryness.** Upon approval of your laboratory instructor, return the sample to the laboratory bench.

   a. *Initial dryness.* See Figure T.15e. *Slowly,* and with a **cool flame,** heat the sample until the solid first appears dry (*avoid any popping or spattering of the sample throughout the heating process*).

   b. *Final dryness.* Break up the solid with a stirring rod and resume heating, now with a more intense flame, until the solid appears a pale yellow.

   c. *Cool.* Allow the crucible, lid, and sample to cool (in a desiccator if available) to room temperature. Determine the mass of the tin compound, crucible, and lid.

4. **Constant mass.** Repeat Part D.3 until the combined mass of the tin compound, crucible, and lid has a ±1% reproducibility.

5. **Repeat.** Redo Parts A.1, D.1–3 for a second trial.

6. **Calculations.** Determine the mole ratio of tin to oxygen in the compound and the empirical formula of the tin oxide.

> *Disposal and cleanup:* Wash the cool crucible with a dilute solution of hydrochloric acid and discard in the Waste Acids container. Rinse twice with tap water and twice with deionized water.

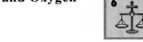

The Next Step

Many compounds are thermally unstable or pass through various phases upon heating, just as water goes through different phases upon heating. A quantitative technique for determining or measuring the thermal stability of a compound or its phases is called **differential thermal analysis (DTA).** The Internet has various sites for the theory and applications of DTA. What are the details of this technique?

---

[4]The pure compound decomposes near 825°C, about the temperature of a well-adjusted Bunsen flame. See *Experiment 1* for producing a hot, intense flame.

Experiment **2** *Prelaboratory Assignment*

Empirical Formulas

Date _____ Lab Sec. _____ Name _____ Desk No. _____

1. Elemental mercury was first discovered when a mercury oxide was decomposed with heat, forming mercury metal and oxygen gas. When a 0.204-g sample of the mercury oxide is heated, 0.189 g of mercury metal remains. *Note:* Do not attempt this experiment in the laboratory because of the release of toxic mercury vapor.
   a. What is the mole ratio of mercury to oxygen in the sample?

   b. What is the empirical formula of the mercury oxide?

2. A 5.90-g sample of titanium chemically combines with oxygen gas to form 9.84 g of a titanium oxide.
   a. What is the empirical formula of titanium oxide?

   b. What is the percent by mass of titanium and the percent by mass of oxygen in the sample?

3. **a.** Experimental Procedure, Part A. List two reasons for using crucible tongs to handle the crucible and lid after their initial firing.

   b. Why is it best to cool the crucible and lid (and sample) in a desiccator rather than on the laboratory bench?

4. Experiment Procedure, Part D.2. State the reason for the use of the fume hood.

5. Experiment Procedure, Part D.3. Characterize a cool flame.

6. A sample of pure iron is covered with an excess of powdered elemental sulfur. The following data were collected:

Mass of crucible and lid (g)   19.746

Mass of iron, crucible, and lid (g)   20.422

The mixture was heated to a temperature where a reaction occurred and the excess sulfur was volatilized. Upon cooling, the following was recorded.

Mass of compound, crucible, and lid (g)   21.195

Complete the following data analysis.

Mass of iron in compound (g)*

Moles of iron in compound (*mol*)*

Mass of sulfur in compound (g)*

Moles of sulfur in compound (*mol*)*

Empirical formula of the iron and sulfur compound

*Show calculations.

Empirical Formulas

Date _____ Lab Sec. _____ Name _____ Desk No. _____

Indicate whether the following data are for Part B, Part C, or Part D. _____

	Trial 1	*Trial 2*
1. Mass of crucible and lid (g)	_____	_____
2. Mass of crucible, lid, and sample (g)	_____	_____
3. Mass of sample (g)	_____	_____
4. Instructor's approval	_____	_____
5. Mass of crucible, lid, and product		
1st mass measurement (g)	_____	_____
2nd mass measurement (g)	_____	_____
3rd mass measurement (g)	_____	_____
6. Final mass of crucible, lid, and of product (g)	_____	_____
7. Mass of product (g)	_____	_____

8. Part B. Combination Reaction of Magnesium and Oxygen

	Trial 1	*Trial 2*
a. Mass ratio of Mg to O	_____	_____
b. Mole ratio of Mg to O	_____	_____

    c. Consensus empirical formula of magnesium oxide _____

    d. Percent by mass (%): _____ % Mg; _____ % O

9. Part C. Decomposition Reaction of a Pure Compound

	Trial 1	*Trial 2*
a. Mass ratio of CaO to CO_2	_____	_____
b. Mole ratio of CaO to CO_2	_____	_____

    c. Consensus mole ratio of CaO to CO_2 _____

    d. Percent by mass (%): _____ % CaO; _____ % CO_2

10. Part D. Combination Reaction of Tin and Oxygen

    a. Mass ratio of Sn to O

    b. Mole ratio of Sn to O

    c. Consensus empirical formula of tin oxide

    d. Percent by mass (%): _____ % Sn; _____ % O

11. Write a balanced equation for the reaction that occured in the part of the experiment that was completed.

Laboratory Questions

Circle the questions that have been assigned.

1. Part A.1. The crucible is not fired, as the procedure suggests, but had retained some impurities from previous use (or it could be oily smudges from fingers). The mass of the "dirty" crucible is recorded. However the impurities are burned off in the experiment. Will the reported mass of the final product be too high, too low, or unchanged as a result of this technique error? Explain.

2. Part B.1. Javier forgot to polish the magnesium metal. Will the reported mole ratio of magnesium to oxygen be too high or too low as a result of his error? Explain.

3. Part B.2. The burning of the magnesium becomes uncontrolled (it burns brightly). Oops! Will the reported mole ratio of magnesium to oxygen be too high or too low as a result of this technique error? Explain.

4. Part B.3. In a hurry to complete the experiment, Josh did not allow all of the magnesium to react. Will his reported magnesium to oxygen ratio be reported too high or too low? Explain.

5. Part C.2. The sample is *not* completely thermally decomposed in the procedure. Will the mole ratio of CaO to CO_2 be too high or too low? Explain.

6. Part C.2. The original sample is *not* pure, but is contaminated with a thermally stable compound. Will the reported mole ratio of CaO to CO_2 be too high, too low, or unaffected? Explain.

7. Part D.2. In an oversight in the experiment Jamie did not add the 4–5 additional drops of 6 *M* HNO_3. As a result, will the reported number of moles of oxygen be too high or too low in the final product? Explain.

8. Part D.3. Spattering does occur and some of the sample is lost onto the laboratory bench. Will the reported mole ratio of tin to oxygen be too high, too low, or unaffected? Explain.

Experiment 3

Chemistry of Copper

The reaction of copper with nitric acid is spontaneous, producing nitrogen dioxide gas and copper(II) ion.

- To observe the chemical properties of copper through a series of chemical reactions
- To use several separation and recovery techniques to isolate the copper compounds from solution
- To determine percent recovery of copper through a cycle of reactions

OBJECTIVES

The following techniques are used in the Experimental Procedure:

TECHNIQUES

Copper is an element that is chemically combined into a variety of compounds in nature, most commonly in the form of a sulfide, as in chalcocite, Cu_2S, and chalcopyrite, $FeCuS_2$. Copper metal is an excellent conductor of heat and electricity and is an **alloying element** in bronze and brass. Copper is a soft metal with a characteristic bright orange-brown color, which we often call *copper color* (Figure 3.1). Copper is relatively inert chemically; it does not readily air oxidize (react with oxygen in air) and is not attacked by simple inorganic acids such as sulfuric and hydrochloric acids. Copper metal that does oxidize in air is called **patina**.

Copper(II) ion forms a number of very colorful compounds; most often, these compounds are blue or blue-green, although other colors are found, depending on the copper(II) compound.

We will observe several chemical and physical properties of copper through a sequence of redox, precipitation, decomposition, and acid–base reactions that produce a number of colorful compounds.

Starting with metallic copper at the top of the cycle, the sequence of products formed is shown in the diagram:

INTRODUCTION

Alloying element: an element of low percent composition in a mixture of metals, the result of which produces an alloy with unique, desirable properties

Figure 3.1 The penny is made of zinc (bottom) with a thin copper coating (top).

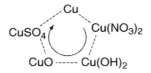

Dissolution of Copper Metal

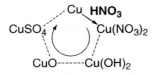

Copper reacts readily with strong oxidizing agents (substances that readily remove electrons from other substances—i.e., $Cu \rightarrow Cu^{2+} + 2e^-$). In this experiment, aqueous nitric acid, HNO_3, oxidizes copper metal to the copper(II) ion (opening photo):

$$Cu(s) + 4\ HNO_3(aq) \rightarrow Cu(NO_3)_2(aq) + 2\ NO_2(g) + 2\ H_2O(l) \qquad (3.1)$$

The products of this reaction are copper(II) nitrate, $Cu(NO_3)_2$ (a water-soluble salt that produces a blue solution), and nitrogen dioxide, NO_2 (a dense, toxic, red-brown gas). The solution remains acidic because an excess of nitric acid is used for the reaction.

The net ionic equation for the reaction is

$$Cu(s) + 4\ H^+(aq) + 2\ NO_3^-(aq) \rightarrow Cu^{2+}(aq) + 2\ NO_2(g) + 2\ H_2O(l) \qquad (3.2)$$

Precipitation of Copper(II) Hydroxide from Solution

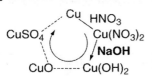

Appendix G

For Part B of the Experimental Procedure, the solution containing the soluble $Cu(NO_3)_2$ is treated with sodium hydroxide, NaOH, a base. Copper(II) hydroxide, $Cu(OH)_2$, a light-blue solid, precipitates from the solution:

$$Cu(NO_3)_2(aq) + 2\ NaOH(aq) \rightarrow Cu(OH)_2(s) + 2\ NaNO_3(aq) \qquad (3.3)$$

Sodium nitrate, $NaNO_3$, is a colorless salt that remains dissolved in solution as $Na^+(aq)$ and $NO_3^-(aq)$—so these two species are spectator ions.

The net ionic equation is

$$Cu^{2+}(aq) + 2\ OH^-(aq) \rightarrow Cu(OH)_2(s) \qquad (3.4)$$

Conversion of Copper(II) Hydroxide to a Second Insoluble Salt

Heat applied to solid copper(II) hydroxide causes black, insoluble copper(II) oxide, CuO, to form and H_2O to vaporize:

$$Cu(OH)_2(s) \overset{\Delta}{\rightarrow} CuO(s) + H_2O(g) \qquad (3.5)$$

Dissolution of Copper(II) Oxide

Copper(II) oxide reacts readily with the addition of aqueous sulfuric acid, H_2SO_4, forming a sky-blue solution as a result of the formation of the water-soluble salt, copper(II) sulfate, $CuSO_4$:

$$CuO(s) + H_2SO_4(aq) \rightarrow CuSO_4(aq) + H_2O(l) \qquad (3.6)$$

The net ionic equation for the reaction is

$$CuO(s) + 2\ H^+(aq) \rightarrow Cu^{2+}(aq) + H_2O(l) \qquad (3.7)$$

Reformation of Copper Metal

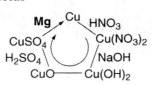

Finally, the addition of magnesium metal, Mg, to the copper(II) sulfate solution completes the copper cycle.

In this reaction, magnesium serves as a **reducing agent** (a substance that provides electrons to another substance—i.e., $Cu^{2+} + 2e^- \rightarrow Cu$). Magnesium, being a more active metal than copper, reduces copper(II) ion from the copper(II) sulfate solution to copper metal and forms water-soluble magnesium sulfate, $MgSO_4$, completing the chemistry of copper cycle.

$$CuSO_4(aq) + Mg(s) \rightarrow Cu(s) + MgSO_4(aq) \qquad (3.8)$$

The net ionic equation for the reaction is

$$Cu^{2+}(aq) + Mg(s) \rightarrow Cu(s) + Mg^{2+}(aq) \qquad (3.9)$$

Magnesium metal also reacts with sulfuric acid. Therefore, when magnesium metal is added to the acidic copper(II) sulfate solution, a second reaction occurs that produces hydrogen gas, H_2, and additional magnesium sulfate:

$$Mg(s) + H_2SO_4(aq) \rightarrow H_2(g) + MgSO_4(aq) \qquad (3.10)$$

The net ionic equation for this reaction is

$$Mg(s) + 2\,H^+(aq) \rightarrow Mg^{2+}(aq) + H_2(g) \qquad (3.11)$$

Therefore hydrogen gas bubbles are observed during this reaction step of the cycle. This reaction also removes any excess magnesium metal that remains after the copper metal has been recovered.

EXPERIMENTAL PROCEDURE

Procedure Overview: Copper metal is successively treated with nitric acid, sodium hydroxide, heat, sulfuric acid, and magnesium in a cycle of chemical reactions to regenerate the copper metal. The percent recovery is determined.

You will need to obtain instructor approval after each step in the Experimental Procedure. Perform the experiment with a partner. At each circled superscript⊝ in the procedure, *stop* and record your observation on the **Report Sheet**. Discuss your observations with your lab partner and your instructor.

A. Copper Metal to Copper(II) Nitrate

Perform the series of reactions in a test tube that is compatible with your laboratory centrifuge. Consult with your laboratory instructor.

1. **Prepare the copper metal sample.** Obtain a *less than* 0.02-g sample of Cu wool. Measure the mass (± 0.001 g) of the selected test tube.[1] Roll and place the Cu wool into the test tube and then measure and record the mass of the test tube and copper sample.

2. **Reaction of the copper metal.** Hold the test tube with a test tube clamp for the remainder of the experiment—do *not* use your fingers.

   Perform this step in the fume hood because of the evolution of toxic $NO_2(g)$. (**Caution:** *Do not inhale the evolved nitrogen dioxide gas.*) Using a dropper bottle or a dropper pipet, add drops (≤ 10 drops) of *conc* HNO_3 to the copper sample until no further evidence of a chemical reaction is observed. Do not add an excess! (**Caution:** *Concentrated HNO_3 is very corrosive. Do not allow it to touch the skin.*)

   At this point, the Cu metal has completely reacted. What is the color of the gas? Add 10 drops of deionized water. Show the resulting solution to your laboratory instructor for approval① and save the solution for Part B.

B. Copper(II) Nitrate to Copper(II) Hydroxide

1. **Preparation of copper(II) hydroxide.** Agitate or continuously stir with a stirring rod the solution from Part A.2 while slowly adding ~10 drops of 6 *M* NaOH. (**Caution:** *Wash with water immediately if the* NaOH *comes into contact with the skin.*) This forms the $Cu(OH)_2$ precipitate. After the first 10 drops are added, add ~10 more drops of 6 *M* NaOH. Using a wash bottle and deionized water, rinse the stirring rod, allowing the rinse water to go into the test tube. Centrifuge the solution for 30 seconds (ask your instructor for instructions in operating the centrifuge).

2. **A complete precipitation.** Test for a complete precipitation of $Cu(OH)_2$ by adding 2–3 more drops of 6 *M* NaOH to the **supernatant**. If additional precipitate forms, add 4–5 more drops and again centrifuge. Repeat the test until no further formation of the $Cu(OH)_2$ occurs. The solution should appear colorless, and the precipitate should be light blue. Obtain your laboratory instructor's approval② and save for Part C.

Supernatant: the clear solution in the test tube

---

[1]Consult with your instructor.

C. Copper(II) Hydroxide to Copper(II) Oxide

Cool flame: an adjusted Bunsen flame having a low supply of fuel

1. **Heat the sample.** Decant (pour off) and discard the supernatant from the test tube. *Carefully (**very carefully!**) and slowly heat the test tube with a **cool flame**[2] until the $Cu(OH)_2$ precipitate changes color. **Read footnote 2!** You need *not* heat the contents to dryness. Avoid ejection (and projection) of your copper compound by *not* holding the test tube over the direct flame for a prolonged period of time. If the contents of the test tube are ejected, you will need to restart the Experimental Procedure at Part A. Obtain your instructor's approval[3] and save for Part D.

D. Copper(II) Oxide to Copper(II) Sulfate

1. **Dissolution of copper(II) oxide.** To the solid CuO in the test tube from Part C, add drops (≤ 20 drops, 1 mL) of 6 M H_2SO_4 with agitation until the CuO dissolves. (**Caution:** *Do not let sulfuric acid touch the skin!*) (Slight heating *may* be necessary, but be careful not to eject the contents!) The solution's sky-blue appearance is evidence of the presence of soluble $CuSO_4$. Obtain your instructor's approval[4] and save for Part E.

E. Copper(II) Sulfate to Copper Metal

1. **Formation of copper metal.**

   a. Using fine steel wool (or sandpaper), polish about 5–7 cm of Mg ribbon. Cut or tear the ribbon into 1-cm lengths. Dilute the solution from Part D with deionized water until the test tube is half-full. Add a 1-cm Mg strip to the solution. When the Mg strip has reacted (disappeared), add a second Mg strip and so on until the blue has disappeared from the solution. Describe what is happening. What is the coating on the magnesium ribbon? What is the gas?[5]

   b. If a white, milky precipitate forms [from the formation of magnesium hydroxide, $Mg(OH)_2$], add several drops of 6 M H_2SO_4. (**Caution:** *Avoid skin contact.*) Break up the red-brown Cu coating on the Mg ribbon with a stirring rod. *After* breaking up the Cu metal *and* after adding several pieces of Mg ribbon, centrifuge the mixture.

2. **Washing.**

   a. Add drops of 6 M H_2SO_4 to react any excess Mg ribbon. (**Caution:** *Avoid skin contact.*) Do this by breaking up the Cu metal with a stirring rod to expose the Mg ribbon, coated with Cu metal, to the H_2SO_4 solution. Centrifuge for 30 seconds, decant, and discard the supernatant. Be careful to keep the Cu metal in the test tube.

   b. Wash the red-brown Cu metal with three 1-mL portions of deionized water.[3] Rinse the stirring rod in the test tube. Centrifuge, decant, and discard each washing.

3. **Determination of the mass of recovered copper.** *Very gently* dry the Cu in the test tube over a *cool* flame (**see footnote 2**). Allow the tube and contents to cool and determine the mass (± 0.001 g). Repeat the heating procedure until a reproducibility in mass of $\pm 1\%$ is obtained. Record the mass of Cu recovered in the experiment.

> *Disposal:* All solutions used in the procedure can be disposed of in the Waste Salts container. Dispose of the copper metal in the Waste Solids container. Check with your instructor.

CLEANUP: Rinse all glassware twice with tap water and twice with deionized water. Discard all rinses in the sink.

The Next Step

Many alloys other than coinage alloys have varying amounts of copper—brass, for example. What are some other methods for determining the amount of copper in a sample—gravimetrically, spectrophotometrically (see *Experiment 35*), or volumetrically (see *Experiments 23, 24, or 29*—also copper(II) ion reacts with iodide ion to produce I_3^-)?

---

[2]From *Technique 13C*, "If you can feel the heat of the flame with the hand holding the test tube clamp, the flame is too hot!"

[3]Wash the Cu metal by adding water, stirring the mixture with a stirring rod, and allowing the mixture to settle.

Experiment 3 *Prelaboratory Assignment*

Chemistry of Copper

Date _____ Lab Sec. _____ Name _____ Desk No. _____

1. Review net-ionic equations 3.2, 3.4, 3.7, 3.9, and 3.11.
   a. Three of the equations represent oxidation–reduction reactions. Identify the three equations and indicate the oxidizing agent in each.

   b. One of the equations represents an acid–base reaction. Identify the equation and indicate the base.

2. Copper forms many different compounds in this experiment.
   a. Experimental Procedure, Part A. Identify the *oxidizing agent* in the conversion of copper metal to copper(II) ion.

   b. Experimental Procedure, Part E. Identify the *oxidizing agent* in the conversion of copper(II) ion to copper metal.

   c. Experimental Procedure, Part D. Classify the type of reaction for the conversion of copper(II) oxide to copper(II) sulfate.

3. A number of **Caution** chemicals and solutions are used in this experiment. Refer to the Experimental Procedure and the corresponding sections to identify the specific chemical or solution that must be handled with care.

Experimental Procedure	Precautionary Chemical/Solution
Part A.2	
Part A.2	
Part B.1	
Part D.1	
Part E.1	

4. Experimental Procedure, Part A.2. What volume, in drops, of 16 M (*conc*) HNO_3 is required to react with 0.0214 g of Cu metal? See equation 3.1. Assume 20 drops per milliliter.

5. Experimental Procedure, Parts C.1 and E.3. Extreme caution *must* be observed when heating a solution in a test tube.
   a. What criterion indicates that you are heating the solution in the test tube with a "cool flame"?

   b. At what angle should the test tube be held while moving the test tube circularly in and out of the cool flame?

   c. What is the consequence of not using this technique properly?

6. a. What function does a centrifuge perform?

   b. Describe the technique for balancing a centrifuge when centrifuging a sample.

7. A 0.0194-g sample of copper metal is recycled through the series of reactions in this experiment. If 0.0169 g of copper is then recovered after the series of reactions in this experiment, what is the percent recovery of the copper metal?

Chemistry of Copper

Date _____ Lab Sec. _____ Name _____ Desk No. _____

Data for Copper Cycle	*Trial 1*	*Trial 2*	*Trial 3*
1. Mass of test tube (*g*)	_____	_____	_____
2. Mass of test tube (*g*) + copper (*g*)	_____	_____	_____
3. Mass of copper sample (*g*)	▨▨▨▨▨	▨▨▨▨▨	▨▨▨▨▨

Synthesis of	**Observation**	**Instructor Approval**	**Balanced Equation**
①A. $Cu(NO_3)_2$ (*aq*)	_____	_____	_____
②B. $Cu(OH)_2$ (*s*)	_____	_____	_____
③C. CuO (*s*)	_____	_____	_____
④D. $CuSO_4$ (*aq*)	_____	_____	_____

⑤E. Copper(II) sulfate to copper metal. Write a full description of the reactions that occurred. Include a balanced equation in your discussion.

4. Mass of test tube and recovered copper (*g*)   1st mass (*g*)   _____   _____   _____

   2nd mass (*g*)   _____   _____   _____

   3rd mass (*g*)   _____   _____   _____

5. Final mass of Cu recovered (*g*)   _____   _____   _____

6. Percent recovery, $\dfrac{\text{mass Cu (recovered)}}{\text{mass Cu (original)}} \times 100$

7. Average percent recovery

8. Account for the percent recovery being equal to or less than 100%.

Laboratory Questions

Circle the questions that have been assigned.

1. Part A.2 What is the formula *and* the color of the gas that is evolved?

2. Part B.1. When the NaOH solution is added, $Cu(OH)_2$ does not precipitate immediately. What else present in the reaction mixture from Part A reacts with the NaOH before the copper(II) ion? Explain.

3. Part C.1. The sample in Part B was *not* centrifuged. Why? Perhaps the student chemist had to be across campus for another appointment. Because of the student's "other priorities" the percent recovery of copper in the experiment will decrease. Explain why.

4. Part D.1. All of the CuO does *not* react with the sulfuric acid. Will the reported percent recovery of copper in the experiment be too high or too low? Explain.

5. Part E. Sulfuric acid has a dual role in the chemistry. What are its two roles in the recovery of the copper metal?

6. Part E.2. Jacob couldn't find the 6 *M* H_2SO_4, so instead substituted the 6 *M* HNO_3 that was available. What change was most likely observed as a result of this decision? Explain.

7. Part E. Errors in experimental technique can lead to the percent recovery of copper being *too high*—one such error may occur in Part E.2 and another in Part E.3. Cite those two errors and explain what should be done to ensure that those errors do not occur in the recovery.

Experiment 4

Inorganic Compounds and Metathesis Reactions

Drops of a potassium hydroxide solution added to an iron(III) chloride solution produces insoluble iron(III) hydroxide.

- To characterize the physical appearance of common laboratory chemicals
- To systematically observe and express the stages of a **metathesis reaction**
- To determine the solubilities of some salts by studying metathesis reactions

OBJECTIVES

Metathesis reaction: the interchange of ions between two compounds involved in a reaction

The following techniques are used in the Experimental Procedure

TECHNIQUES

INTRODUCTION

Stoichiometry: a study of a chemical reaction using a balanced equation

By now you have learned to name and write the formulas for a large number of inorganic compounds. In addition you should also be familiar with balanced equations and **stoichiometry.** But names, formulas, and equations have little meaning unless there is some tangible relationship to chemicals and chemical reactions. To a chemist, sulfur is not just an element with the symbol S that reacts with oxygen to form sulfur dioxide, but rather a yellow solid that can be held in the hand and burns in air with a blue flame, producing a choking irritant called sulfur dioxide.

In this experiment you will "look" at some laboratory chemicals with the intent that a mental association develops between a compound's formula and its physical appearance. You will also conduct a number of chemical reactions, observe some of the chemical properties of chemicals, and make conclusions on the basis of your observations.

In Part A, a number of compounds are identified by their formulas, names, physical states, colors, crystal characteristics (if a solid), and solubilities in water.

In Part B, the chemical reactions of some ionic compounds are studied in an aqueous solution. In these chemical reactions two ionic compounds, as reactants, are dissolved in solution whereby the ions are free to exchange partners to form products. A chemical reaction (an exchange of ionic partners) is observed if a chemical change is evident, such as the formation of a precipitate or the evolution of a gas. These chemical reactions are called **metathesis** (or double displacement) **reactions.**

To systematically interpret the progress of a metathesis reaction, a sequence of observations and equation writing steps are followed. Using the **salts** silver nitrate and sodium chloride as reactants, these steps are as follows:

Salt: an ionic compound

1. **Define the Reactants.** Write the formulas of the reactants.

$$AgNO_3 + NaCl \qquad (4.1)$$

Figure 4.1 The progression of a reaction between solutions of silver nitrate and sodium chloride.

2. **Determine the Products and Write the Molecular Equation.** The formulas of the products are written by exchanging the cations with the anions of the reactants. A *balanced* **molecular equation** for the proposed metathesis reaction is

$$AgNO_3 + NaCl \rightarrow AgCl + NaNO_3 \tag{4.2}$$

It is this molecular equation that is studied in detail in the laboratory—what is the nature of each of these substances in aqueous solution?

3. **Formulas of Reactants in Solution.** The physical states of the reactants in solution *before mixing* are observed; for example, are the salts soluble or insoluble? What is their *actual* appearance? The formulas of the salts are written accordingly, either as separated hydrated ions or as a solid.

Both silver nitrate and sodium chloride are soluble salts (Figure 4.1a). The cations and anions of the two salts move about the aqueous solution as separate hydrated species; each is written as (*aq*).

$$Ag^+(aq) + NO_3^-(aq) + Na^+(aq) + Cl^-(aq) \rightarrow \tag{4.3}$$

4. **Evidence of Reaction.** On combination of the ions from the two aqueous solutions into a single system, an observation determines whether or not a reaction has occurred between the ions. A chemical reaction is observed when

- a precipitate forms
- a gas is evolved
- heat is evolved or absorbed
- a color change occurs
- a change in acidity (or basicity) occurs
- light is emitted

In this system, the formation of the white precipitate of silver chloride is observed (Figure 4.1b).

5. **Formulas of Products in Solution.** The formulas of the products are then written as they appear in the aqueous solution after the mixing (Figure 4.1c). A precipitate is written as (*s*), and an ion remaining in solution is written as (*aq*).

$$\rightarrow AgCl(s) + Na^+(aq) + NO_3^-(aq) \tag{4.4}$$

6. **Ionic Equation.** The reactants (from Step 3) and the products (from Step 5) are combined to form a balanced **ionic equation** that represents each species as it actually exists in the aqueous solution.

$$Ag^+(aq) + NO_3^-(aq) + Na^+(aq) + Cl^-(aq) \rightarrow$$
$$AgCl(s) + Na^+(aq) + NO_3^-(aq) \tag{4.5}$$

7. **Net Ionic Equation.** A final equation, called the **net ionic equation,** includes only those ions responsible for the observed reaction. The ions present, but not involved in the observed reaction, are considered **spectator ions** and do not appear in a net ionic equation. The sodium and nitrate ions are not involved in any observable reaction.

$$Ag^+(aq) + Cl^-(aq) \rightarrow AgCl(s) \qquad (4.6)$$

Similar molecular equations, ionic equations, and net ionic equations are written for a number of chemical systems in Part B of this experiment.

Procedure Overview: An array of laboratory chemicals are observed and described. Eleven metathesis reactions are observed, and appropriate formulas and equations are systematically written to express the nature of each species in solution.

EXPERIMENTAL PROCEDURE

A broad selection of chemical compounds in test tubes or laboratory dishes (Figure 4.2) are located on the display table. Describe the color and **crystal characteristics** (if a solid) of each chemical; also predict the water solubility[1] of each chemical. Use the Report Sheet as a format for reporting your observations and predictions.

Attempt to group some of the compounds on the basis of color, crystal characteristics, and/or solubility.

A. Identification

Crystal characteristics: shape (powder, granular, etc.), brightness, and wet or dry status

This experiment requires either a set of 12 clean, small test tubes or a 24-well plate. Consult with your instructor. If you use test tubes, label them in accordance with the well numbers in Table 4.1.

1. **Test Solutions.** Set up the test tubes (Figure 4.3) or the 24-well plate (Figure 4.4) with the reactant solutions or preparations listed in Table 4.1. Volumes of solutions only need to be approximate.[2] Your instructor may substitute, add, or delete chemicals from the table.

2. **Systematic Procedure for Studying Reactions.** Pairs of reactant solutions are combined according to Figure 4.4. Record your stepwise analysis of each reaction on the Report Sheet using the steps outlined in the Introduction. Be sure to look for any evidence of a chemical change occurring.

B. Systematic Study of Metathesis Reactions

Table 4.1 An Organization of the Reactants for a Series of Metathesis Reactions

Test Tube No. or Well No.	Reactant Solution or Preparation
A1	Several crystals of $CaCO_3$
A2	2 mL of 3.0 M HCl and several drops of universal indicator[3]
A3	2 mL of 3.0 M NaOH
A4	Several crystals of $FeCl_3 \cdot 6H_2O$ in 2 mL of water *or* 2 mL of 0.1 M $FeCl_3$
A5	Several crystals of $CoCl_2 \cdot 6H_2O$ in 2 mL of water *or* 2 mL of 0.1 M $CoCl_2$
A6	Several crystals of $AgNO_3$ in 2 mL of water *or* 2 mL of 0.1 M $AgNO_3$
B3	Several crystals of NH_4Cl
B6	Several crystals of Na_2CO_3 in 2 mL of water *or* 2 mL of 0.1 M Na_2CO_3
C4	Several crystals of $NiCl_2 \cdot 6H_2O$ in 2 mL of water *or* 2 mL of 0.1 M $NiCl_2$
C5	Several crystals of $Na_3PO_4 \cdot 12H_2O$ in 2 mL of water *or* 2 mL of 0.1 M Na_3PO_4
C6	Several crystals of $CuSO_4 \cdot 5H_2O$ in 2 mL of water *or* 2 mL of 0.1 M $CuSO_4$
D6	Several crystals of $BaCl_2 \cdot 2H_2O$ in 2 mL of water *or* 2 mL of 0.1 M $BaCl_2$

Figure 4.2 A view of the nature of substances.

[1]The predicted solubility is based on the rules in Appendix G.
[2]The volume of a small (75-mm) test tube is about 3 mL; the volume of each well is about 3.4 mL.
[3]Universal indicator is a mixture of acid–base indicators that gradually changes color, depending on the acidity of the solution.

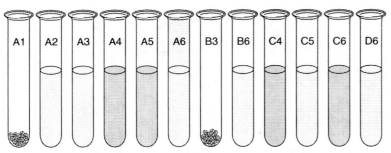

Figure 4.3 The arrangement of 12 small, labeled test tubes for test solutions.

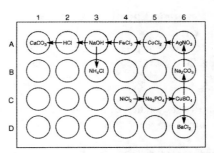

Figure 4.4 The arrangement of the test solutions in a 24-well plate.

Use clean dropping pipets or Beral pipets to slowly make the following solution transfers:

a. Transfer approximately one-half of solution A2 to A1 in (test tube/well) A1.

b. Transfer one-third of solution A3 to the remainder of solution A2 in (test tube/well) A2.

c. Transfer one-third of solution A3 to B3 in (test tube/well) B3. (Warm the test tube in your hand or the bottom of the well with your finger and smell cautiously. Test the fumes with wet, red litmus.)

d. Transfer one-half of solution A4 to the remainder of solution A3 in (test tube/well) A3.

e. Transfer one-half of solution A5 to the remainder of solution A4 in (test tube/well) A4.

f. Transfer one-half of solution A6 to the remainder of solution A5 in (test tube/well) A5.

g. Transfer one-half of solution B6 to the remainder of solution A6 in (test tube/well) A6.

h. Transfer one-third of solution C6 to the remainder of solution B6 in (test tube/well) B6.

i. Transfer one-third of solution C6 to solution D6 in (test tube/well) D6.

j. Transfer one-half of solution C5 to the remainder of solution C6 in (test tube/well) C6.

k. Transfer one-half of solution C4 to the remainder of solution C5 in (test tube/well) C5.

3. **Unknown Salt.** To obtain an unknown salt, submit a *clean*, small test tube to your laboratory instructor. Using your acquired knowledge from Part B.2, identify the cation and anion of the unknown.

Disposal: Dispose of the waste solutions, as identified by your instructor, in the "Waste Liquids" container.

CLEANUP: Rinse the test tubes or well plate with tap water twice and with deionized water twice. Discard each rinse in the sink, followed by a generous amount of tap water.

Experiment 4 *Prelaboratory Assignment*

Inorganic Compounds and Metathesis Reactions

Date _____ Lab Sec. _____ Name _____ Desk No. _____

1. a. Copper(II) sulfate dissolves in water to form a blue solution. What species are present in solution, i.e., what is actually swimming around in solution? Write the formulas.

   b. Sodium carbonate dissolves in water to form a colorless solution. What species are present in solution? Write the formulas.

   c. When solutions of copper(II) sulfate and sodium carbonate are mixed, blue copper(II) carbonate precipitates. What species remain in solution? (These are the spectator ions.) What is the color of the solution? [Assume that stoichiometric amounts of copper(II) sulfate and sodium carbonate are mixed.] Write the formulas.

2. a. An aqueous solution of sodium hydroxide is labeled 0.010 M NaOH. What are the molar concentrations of NaOH, Na^+, and OH^- in the aqueous solution? Explain.

   b. An aqueous solution of calcium chloride is labeled 0.010 M $CaCl_2$. What are the molar concentrations of $CaCl_2$, Ca^{2+}, and Cl^- in the aqueous solution? Explain.

3. Sodium phosphate dodecahydrate, $Na_3PO_4 \cdot 12H_2O$, is a crystalline salt that is water soluble. Describe what is present in an aqueous solution of sodium phosphate dodecahydrate.

4. When aqueous solutions of ferrous sulfate and barium chloride are mixed, a white precipitate forms. With time the aqueous solution turns a red-orange color.
   a. Refer to Appendix G. What is the white precipitate? Write the formula.

   b. Write a balanced equation using only those ions that are involved in the formation of the white precipitate (this is a net ionic equation).

   *c. Explain why the aqueous solution turns a red-orange color with time.

5. Write molecular equations for each of the following metathesis reactions:

   a. $AgNO_3(aq) + ZnI_2(aq) \rightarrow$

   b. $CuSO_4(aq) + K_3PO_4(aq) \rightarrow$

   c. $K_2CO_3(aq) + CaCl_2(aq) \rightarrow$

   d. $Na_2SO_3(aq) + HCl(aq) \rightarrow$

   e. $Ni(NO_3)_2(aq) + K_2C_2O_4(aq) \rightarrow$

6. List five observations, appealing to your senses, that indicate a chemical reaction has occurred. In each case, identify an example where you have experienced that observation.

	Observation	Example
a.		
b.		
c.		
d.		
e.		

Experiment 4 *Report Sheet*

Inorganic Compounds and Metathesis Reactions

Date _____ Lab Sec. _____ Name _____ Desk No. _____

A. Identification

On a separate sheet of paper, construct a table with the headings shown below. Fill in the table as described in the Experimental Procedure. Submit this data sheet along with your Report Sheet.

	Formula	Name	Physical State (g, l, s)	Color	Characteristics	Predicted Solubility in Water (Appendix G)
Ex.	NaCl	Sodium chloride	Solid	White	Small, shiny, dry	Soluble
1	____	_____	_____	_____	_____	_____
2	____	_____	_____	_____	_____	_____
3	____	_____	_____	_____	_____	_____

B. Metathesis Reactions (Double-Displacement Reactions)

Use the seven steps presented in the Introduction as a guide to writing formulas and equations as you observe the stages of a chemical reaction.

Step	Formulas, Observations, Equations	Step	Formulas, Observations, Equations
1	Formulas of reactants	5	Formulas of products in solution
2	Molecular equation	6	Ionic equation
3	Formulas of reactants in solution	7	Net ionic equation
4	Evidence of reaction		

On a separate sheet of paper, use this 7-step format to write the formulas, observations, and equations for the systems described in Part B.2. Submit this data sheet along with the Report Sheet.

a. $CaCO_3 + HCl \rightarrow$

b. $HCl + NaOH \rightarrow$

c. $NH_4Cl + NaOH \rightarrow$

d. $NaOH + FeCl_3 \rightarrow$

e. $FeCl_3 + CoCl_2 \rightarrow$

f. $CoCl_2 + AgNO_3 \rightarrow$

g. $AgNO_3 + Na_2CO_3 \rightarrow$

h. $Na_2CO_3 + CuSO_4 \rightarrow$

i. $BaCl_2 + CuSO_4 \rightarrow$

j. $CuSO_4 + Na_3PO_4 \rightarrow$

k. $Na_3PO_4 + NiCl_2 \rightarrow$

On the basis of your observations in Part B.2, summarize your data in the following table:

cations \ anions	SO_4^{2-}	CO_3^{2-}	OH^-	PO_4^{3-}	NO_3^-	Cl^-
Cations forming insoluble salts						
Cations forming soluble salts						

Unknown salt. Identification of cation and anion. Unknown No. _____

What is the cation? _____ Justify your conclusion.

What is the anion? _____ Justify your conclusion.

Laboratory Questions

Circle the questions that have been assigned.

1. Parts A and B. A wide range of chemicals was observed and studied in this experiment. General conclusions can be made regarding the following:
   a. Identify the color of most copper containing salts.
   b. Identify the color of most nickel containing salts.
   c. Identify the color of most cobalt containing salts.
   d. Colored salts generally have a cation from which section of the periodic table?
   e. Several chloride salts were observed. What is the contributing color of the chloride ion (and of most other anions)?

2. Part A. Distinguish between the general appearance of those salts that are hydrated and those that are not. In which section of the periodic table are cations found that are commonly hydrated?

3. Part B. Review the observed reactions for the mixtures created. Identify the *general* solubility (soluble or insoluble) of salts containing the following ions:
   a. Cl^-
   b. CO_3^{2-}
   c. PO_4^{3-}
   d. Na^+
   e. NO_3^-

4. Part B. On the basis of the limited data from this experiment, what predictions of solubility (soluble or insoluble) would you make regarding the following?
   a. transition metal hydroxides
   b. alkali metal chlorides
   c. transition metal chlorides
   d. transition metal sulfates
   e. transition metal carbonates
   f. transition metal phosphates

5. a. Carbon dioxide gas bubbles from a reaction mixture of an acid and carbonate ion. Write a net ionic equation showing the reaction.
   b. Sulfite salts have properties similar to those of carbonate salts. Predict the reaction, using a net ionic equation, of sulfite salts with acid.
   c. Ammonia is always evolved when an ammonium salt is placed into a basic solution. Write a net ionic equation showing the reaction.

Experiment 5

A Volumetric Analysis

A titrimetric analysis requires the careful addition of titrant.

OBJECTIVES

- To prepare and standardize a sodium hydroxide solution
- To determine the molar concentration of a strong acid

TECHNIQUES

The following techniques are used in the Experimental Procedure:

INTRODUCTION

A chemical analysis that is performed primarily with the aid of volumetric glassware (e.g., pipets, burets, volumetric flasks) is called a **volumetric analysis.** For a volumetric analysis procedure, a known quantity or a carefully measured amount of one substance reacts with a to-be-determined amount of another substance with the reaction occurring in aqueous solution. The volumes of all solutions are carefully measured with volumetric glassware.

The known amount of the substance for an analysis is generally measured and available in two ways:

1. As a **primary standard**—An accurate mass (and thus, moles) of a solid substance is measured on a balance, dissolved in water, and then reacted with the substance being analyzed.

2. As a **standard solution**—A measured number of moles of substance is present in a measured volume of solution, generally expressed as the molar concentration (or molarity) of the substance. A measured volume of the standard solution then reacts with the substance being analyzed.

Primary standard: a substance that has a known high degree of purity, a relatively large molar mass, is nonhygroscopic, and reacts in a predictable way

Standard solution: a solution having a very well known concentration of a solute

The reaction of the known substance with the substance to be analyzed, occurring in aqueous solution, is generally conducted by a titration procedure.

The titration procedure requires a buret to dispense a liquid, called the **titrant,** into a flask containing the **analyte** (Figure 5.1*a*, page 90). For the acid–base titration studied in Part B of this experiment, the titrant is a standard solution of sodium hydroxide and the analyte is an acid.

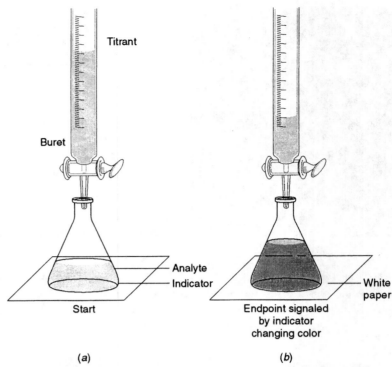

Figure 5.1 (a) Titrant in the buret is dispensed into the analyte until (b) the indicator changes color at its endpoint.

A reaction is complete when **stoichiometric amounts** of the reacting substances are combined. In a titration this is the **stoichiometric point.**[1] In this experiment, the stoichiometric point for the acid–base titration is detected using a phenolphthalein **indicator.** Phenolphthalein is colorless in an acidic solution but pink in a basic solution. The point in the titration at which the phenolphthalein changes color is called the **endpoint** of the indicator (Figure 5.1*b*). Indicators are selected so that the stoichiometric point in the titration coincides (at approximately the same **pH**) with the endpoint of the indicator.

Standardization of a Sodium Hydroxide Solution

COOH

COO⁻K⁺

potassium hydrogen phthlate

Solid sodium hydroxide is very **hygroscopic;** therefore, its mass cannot be measured to prepare a solution with an accurately known molar concentration (a primary standard solution). To prepare a NaOH solution with a very well known molar concentration, it must be standardized with an acid that *is* a primary standard.

In Part A of this experiment, *dry* potassium hydrogen phthalate, $KHC_8H_4O_4$, is used as the primary acid standard for determining the molar concentration of a sodium hydroxide solution. Potassium hydrogen phthalate is a white, crystalline, acidic solid. It has the properties of a primary standard because of its high purity, relatively high molar mass, and because it is only *very slightly* hygroscopic. The moles of $KHC_8H_4O_4$ used for the analysis is calculated from its measured mass and molar mass (204.44 g/mol):

$$\text{mass (g) } KHC_8H_4O_4 \times \frac{\text{mol } KHC_8H_4O_4}{204.44 \text{ g } KHC_8H_4O_4} = \text{mol } KHC_8H_4O_4 \qquad (5.1)$$

From the balanced equation for the reaction, one mole of $KHC_8H_4O_4$ reacts with one mole of NaOH according to the equation:

$$KHC_8H_4O_4(aq) + NaOH(aq) \rightarrow H_2O(l) + NaKC_8H_4O_4(aq) \qquad (5.2)$$

[1]The stoichiometric point is also called the **equivalence point**, indicating the point at which stoichiometrically equivalent quantities of the reacting substances are combined.

In Part A.4 of the Experimental Procedure, an accurately measured mass of dry potassium hydrogen phthalate is dissolved in deionized water. A prepared NaOH solution in Parts A.1, 3 is then dispensed from a buret into the $KHC_8H_4O_4$ solution until the stoichiometric point is reached, signaled by the colorless to pink change of the phenolphthalein indicator. At this point, the dispensed volume of NaOH is noted and recorded.

The molar concentration of the NaOH solution is calculated by determining the number of moles of NaOH used in the reaction (equation 5.2) and the volume of NaOH dispensed from the buret.

$$\text{molar concentration } (M) \text{ of NaOH } (mol/L) = \frac{\text{mol NaOH}}{\text{L of NaOH solution}} \qquad (5.3)$$

Once the molar concentration of the sodium hydroxide is calculated, the solution is said to be "standardized," and the sodium hydroxide solution is called a **secondary standard** solution.

Molar Concentration of an Acid Solution

In Part B, an unknown molar concentration of an acid solution is determined. The standardized NaOH solution is used to titrate an accurately measured volume of the acid to the stoichiometric point. By knowing the volume and molar concentration of the NaOH, the number of moles of NaOH used for the analysis is

$$\text{volume } (L) \times \text{molar concentration } (mol/L) = \text{mol NaOH} \qquad (5.4)$$

From the stoichiometry of the reaction, the moles of acid neutralized in the reaction can be calculated. If your acid of unknown concentration is a monoprotic acid, HA [as is HCl(aq)], then the mole ratio of acid to NaOH will be 1:1 (equation 5.5). However, if your acid is diprotic, H_2A (as is H_2SO_4), then the mole ratio of acid to NaOH will be 1:2 (equation 5.6). Your instructor will inform you of the acid type: HA or H_2A.

$$HA(aq) + NaOH(aq) \rightarrow NaA(aq) + H_2O(l) \qquad (5.5)$$
$$H_2A(aq) + 2\,NaOH(aq) \rightarrow Na_2A(aq) + 2\,H_2O(l) \qquad (5.6)$$

From the moles of the acid that react and its measured volume, the molar concentration of the acid is calculated:

$$\text{molar concentration of the acid } (mol/L) = \frac{\text{mol acid}}{\text{volume of acid } (L)} \qquad (5.7)$$

EXPERIMENTAL PROCEDURE

Procedure Overview: A NaOH solution is prepared with an approximate concentration. A more accurate molar concentration of the NaOH solution (as the titrant) is determined using dry potassium hydrogen phthalate as a primary standard. The NaOH solution, now a secondary standard solution, is then used to determine the "unknown" molar concentration of an acid solution.

Check with your laboratory instructor; stockroom personnel may have completed Parts A.1, A.2, and/or A.3 (or all of Part A). Begin the Experimental Procedure with the steps that follow those already completed by the stockroom personnel.

A. The Standardization of a Sodium Hydroxide Solution

You are to complete at least three good trials ($\pm 1\%$ reproducibility) in standardizing the NaOH solution. Prepare three clean 125-mL or 250-mL Erlenmeyer flasks for the titration.

You will need to use approximately one liter of boiled, deionized water for this experiment. Start preparing that first.

1. **Prepare the stock NaOH solution.** One week before the scheduled laboratory period, dissolve about 4 g of NaOH (pellets or flakes) (**Caution:** *NaOH is very corrosive—do not allow skin contact. Wash hands thoroughly with water.*) in 5 mL of deionized water in a 150-mm rubber-stoppered test tube. Thoroughly

mix and allow the solution to stand for the precipitation of sodium carbonate, Na_2CO_3.[2]

2. **Dry the primary standard acid.** Dry 2–3 g of $KHC_8H_4O_4$ at 110°C for several hours in a constant-temperature drying oven. Cool the sample in a desiccator.

3. **Prepare the diluted NaOH solution.** Decant about 4 mL of the NaOH solution prepared in Part A.1 into a 500-mL polyethylene bottle (Figure 5.2). (**Caution:** *Concentrated NaOH solution is extremely corrosive and can cause severe skin removal!*) Dilute to 500 mL with previously boiled,[3] deionized water cooled to room temperature. Cap the polyethylene bottle to prevent the absorption of CO_2. Swirl the solution and label the bottle.

   Calculate an *approximate* molar concentration of your diluted NaOH solution.

4. **Prepare the primary standard acid.**

   a. Calculate the mass of $KHC_8H_4O_4$ that will require about 15–20 mL of your diluted NaOH solution to reach the stoichiometric point. Show the calculations on the **Report Sheet**.

   b. Measure this mass (± 0.001 g) of $KHC_8H_4O_4$ on a **tared** piece of weighing paper (Figure 5.3) and transfer it to a clean, labeled Erlenmeyer flask. Similarly, prepare all three samples while you are occupying the balance. Dissolve the $KHC_8H_4O_4$ in about 50 mL of previously boiled, deionized water and add 2 drops of phenolphthalein.

Tared mass: mass of a sample without regard to its container

Figure 5.2 A 500-mL polyethylene bottle for the NaOH solution

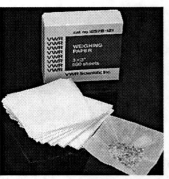

Figure 5.3 Weighing paper for the $KHC_8H_4O_4$ measurements

5. **Prepare a clean buret.** Wash a 50-mL buret and funnel thoroughly with soap and water using a long buret brush. Flush the buret with tap water and rinse several times with deionized water. Rinse the buret with three 5-mL portions of the diluted NaOH solution, making certain that the solution wets the entire inner surface. Drain each rinse through the buret tip. Discard each rinse in the Waste Bases container. Have the instructor approve your buret and titration setup before continuing.

---

[2]Carbon dioxide, CO_2, from the atmosphere is an **acidic anhydride** (meaning that when CO_2 dissolves in water, it forms an acidic solution). The acid CO_2 reacts with the base NaOH to form the less soluble salt, Na_2CO_3.

$$CO_2(g) + 2\ NaOH(aq) \rightarrow Na_2CO_3(s) + H_2O(l)$$

[3]Boiling the water removes traces of CO_2 that would react with the sodium hydroxide in solution.

6. **Fill the buret.** Using a clean funnel, fill the buret with the NaOH solution.[4] After 10–15 seconds, read the volume by viewing the bottom of the meniscus with the aid of a black line drawn on a white card or see Figure 5.4 (the buret can be removed from the stand or moved up or down in the buret clamp to simplify this reading; you need not stand on a lab stool to read the meniscus). Record this initial volume according to the guideline in *Technique 16A.2*, using all certain digits (from the labeled calibration marks on the glassware) *plus* one uncertain digit (the last digit which is the best estimate between the calibration marks). Place a sheet of white paper beneath the Erlenmeyer flask.

7. **Titrate the primary standard acid.** Slowly add the NaOH titrant to the first acid sample prepared in Part A.4. Swirl the flask (with the proper hand[5]) after each addition. Initially, add the NaOH solution in 1- to 2-mL increments. As the stoichiometric point nears, the color fade of the indicator occurs more slowly. Occasionally rinse the wall of the flask with (previously boiled, deionized) water from your wash bottle. Continue addition of the NaOH titrant until the endpoint is reached. *The endpoint in the titration should be within one-half drop of a slight pink color* (see opening photo). The color should persist for 30 seconds. After 10–15 seconds, read (Figure 5.4) and record the final volume of NaOH in the buret.

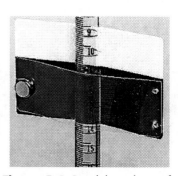

Figure 5.4 Read the volume of titrant with a black background.

8. **Repeat the analysis with the remaining standard acid samples.** Refill the buret and repeat the titration with the remaining two samples prepared in Part A.4.

9. **Do the calculations.** Calculate the molar concentration of the diluted NaOH solution. The molar concentrations of the NaOH solution from the three analyses should be within ±1%. Place a corresponding label on the 500-mL polyethylene bottle.

Disposal: Dispose of the neutralized solutions in the Erlenmeyer flasks in the Waste Acids container.

Three samples of the acid having an unknown concentration are to be analyzed. Ask your instructor for the acid type of your unknown (i.e., HA or H₂A). Prepare three *clean* 125- or 250-mL Erlenmeyer flasks for this determination.

B. Molar Concentration of an Acid Solution

1. **Prepare the acid samples of unknown concentration.** In an Erlenmeyer flask, pipet 25.00 mL of the acid solution. Add 2 drops of phenolphthalein.

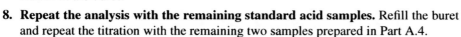

2. **Fill the buret and titrate.** Refill the buret with the (now) standardized NaOH solution and, after 10–15 seconds, read and record the initial volume. Refer to Parts A.6 and A.7. Titrate the acid sample to the phenolphthalein endpoint. Read and record the final volume of titrant.

3. **Repeat.** Similarly titrate the remaining samples of the acid solution.

4. **Calculations.** Calculate the average molar concentration of your acid unknown.

Save. Save your standardized NaOH solution in the *tightly capped 500-mL* polyethylene bottle for *Experiments 10, 17, 18, and/or 19.* Consult with your instructor.

Disposal: Dispose of the neutralized solutions in the Waste Acids container. Consult with your instructor.

---

[4]Be certain all air bubbles are removed from the buret tip.
[5]Check *Technique 16C.3* for this procedure.

CLEANUP: Rinse the buret and pipet several times with tap water and discard through the tip into the sink. Rinse twice with deionized water. Similarly clean the Erlenmeyer flasks.

Check and clean the balance area. All solids should be discarded in the Waste Solid Acids container.

The Next Step

What are the acid concentrations for various noncarbonated soft drinks? the acid of vinegar (*Experiment 10*), the acids used for treating swimming pools? the acid of fruit juices? the antacids (*Experiment 17*), of aspirin (*Experiment 19*). Specifically, what are those acids? Design a procedure for determining the acidity for a select grouping of foods, drinks, or other familiar commercial products.

NOTES AND CALCULATIONS

A Volumetric Analysis

Date _____ Lab Sec. _____ Name _____ Desk No. _____

1. a. Define the analyte in a titration.

b. Is the indicator generally added to the titrant or the analyte in a titration?

2. a. What is the primary standard used in this experiment (name and formula)? Define a primary standard.

b. What is the secondary standard used in this experiment (name and formula)? Define a secondary standard.

3. Distinguish between a stoichiometric point and an endpoint in an acid–base titration.

4. a. How do you know that glassware (e.g., a buret or pipet) is clean?

b. When rinsing a buret after cleaning it with soap and water, should the rinse be dispensed through the buret tip or the top opening of the buret? Explain.

c. Experimental Procedure, Part A.5. In preparing the buret for titration, the final rinse is with the NaOH titrant rather than with deionized water. Explain.

d. Experimental Procedure, Part A.7. How is a "half-drop" of titrant dispensed from a buret?

5. Experimental Procedure, Part A.1. A 4-g mass of NaOH is dissolved in 5 mL of water.
   a. What is the approximate molar concentration of the NaOH?

   b. In Part A.3, a 4-mL aliquot of this solution is diluted to 500 mL of solution. What is the approximate molar concentration of NaOH in the diluted solution? Enter this calculation on your **Report Sheet**. Express this (approximate) molar concentration of NaOH to the correct number of significant figures.

   c. Part A.4. Calculate the mass of $KHC_8H_4O_4$ (molar mass = 204.44 g/mol) that reacts with 15 mL of the NaOH solution in Part A.3. Express this mass $KHC_8H_4O_4$ to the correct number of significant figures and record the calculation on the **Report Sheet**.

6. a. A 0.411-g sample of potassium hydrogen phthalate, $KHC_8H_4O_4$ (molar mass = 204.44 g/mol) is dissolved with 50 mL of deionized water in a 125-mL Erlenmeyer flask. The sample is titrated to the phenolphthalein endpoint with 15.17 mL of a sodium hydroxide solution. What is the molar concentration of the NaOH solution? Express the molar concentration of NaOH to the correct number of significant figures.

   b. A 25.00-mL aliquot of a nitric acid solution of unknown concentration is pipetted into a 125-mL Erlenmeyer flask and 2 drops of phenolphthalein are added. The *above* sodium hydroxide solution (the titrant) is used to titrate the nitric acid solution (the analyte). If 16.77 mL of the titrant is dispensed from a buret in causing a color change of the phenolphthalein, what is the molar concentration of the nitric acid (a monoprotic acid) solution? Express the molar concentration of HNO_3 to the correct number of significant figures.

A Volumetric Analysis

Date _____ Lab Sec. _____ Name _____ Desk No. _____

Maintain at least three significant figures when recording data and performing calculations.

A. Standardization of a Sodium Hydroxide Solution

Calculate the approximate molar concentration of diluted NaOH solution (Part A.3).

Calculate the approximate mass of $KHC_8H_4O_4$ for the standardization of the NaOH solution (Part A.4).

	Trial 1	*Trial 2*	*Trial 3*
1. Tared mass of $KHC_8H_4O_4$ (*g*)	_____	_____	_____
2. Molar mass of $KHC_8H_4O_4$		204.44 g/mol	
3. Moles of $KHC_8H_4O_4$ (*mol*)			
Titration apparatus approval		_____	
4. Buret reading of NaOH, *initial* (*mL*)	_____	_____	_____
5. Buret reading of NaOH, *final* (*mL*)	_____	_____	_____
6. Volume of NaOH dispensed (*mL*)			
7. Molar concentration of NaOH (*mol/L*)			
8. Average molar concentration of NaOH (*mol/L*)			
9. Standard deviation of molar concentration		*Appendix B*	
10. Relative standard deviation of molar concentration (*%RSD*)		*Appendix B*	

B. Molar Concentration of an Acid Solution

Acid type: _____ Unknown No. _____

Balanced equation for neutralization of acid with NaOH.

	Sample 1	Sample 2	Sample 3
1. Volume of acid solution (*mL*)	25.0	25.0	25.0
2. Buret reading of NaOH, *initial* (*mL*)			
3. Buret reading of NaOH, *final* (*mL*)			
4. Volume of NaOH dispensed (*mL*)			
5. Molar concentration of NaOH (*mol/L*), Part A			
6. Moles of NaOH dispensed (*mol*)			
7. Molar concentration of acid solution (*mol/L*)			
8. Average molar concentration of acid solution (*mol/L*)			
9. Standard deviation of molar concentration		**Appendix B**	
10. Relative standard deviation of molar concentration (*%RSD*)		**Appendix B**	

Laboratory Questions

Circle the questions that have been assigned.

1. Part A.2. Pure potassium hydrogen phthalate is used for the standardization of the sodium hydroxide solution. Suppose that the potassium hydrogen phthalate is *not* completely dry. Will the reported molar concentration of the sodium hydroxide solution be too high, too low, or unaffected because of the moistness of the potassium hydrogen phthalate? Explain.

2. Part A.3. The student forgot to prepare any boiled, deionized water for the preparation of the NaOH solution and *then* forgot to cap the bottle. Will the concentration of the NaOH solution be greater than, less than, or unaffected by this carelessness? Explain.

3. Part A.7. A drop of the NaOH titrant adheres to the side of the buret (because of a dirty buret) between the initial and final readings for the titration. As a result of the "clean glass" error, will the molar concentration of the NaOH solution be reported as too high or too low? Explain.

4. Part A. The mass of $KHC_8H_4O_4$ is measured to the nearest milligram; however, the volume of water in which it is dissolved is *never* of concern—water is even added to the wall of the Erlenmeyer flask during the titration. Explain why water added to the $KHC_8H_4O_4$ has no effect on the data, whereas water added to the NaOH solution may drastically affect the data.

5. Part B.2. The wall of the Erlenmeyer flask is occasionally rinsed with water from the wash bottle (see Part A.7) during the analysis of the acid solution. Will this technique result in the molar concentration of the acid solution being reported as too high, too low, or unaffected? Explain.

6. Parts A.7 and B.2. For the standardization of the NaOH solution in Part A.7, the endpoint was consistently reproduced to a faint pink color. However, the endpoint for the titration of the acid solution in Part B.2 was consistently reproduced to a dark pink color. Will the reported molar concentration of the acid solution be too high, too low, or unaffected by the differences in the colors of the endpoints. Explain.

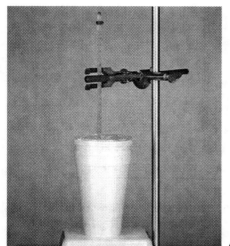

Calorimetry

A set of nested coffee cups is a good constant pressure calorimeter.

- To determine the specific heat of a metal
- To determine the enthalpy of neutralization for a strong acid–strong base reaction
- To determine the enthalpy of solution for the dissolution of a salt

TECHNIQUES

The following techniques are used in the Experimental Procedure:

INTRODUCTION

Accompanying all chemical and physical changes is a transfer of heat (energy); heat may be either evolved (exothermic) or absorbed (endothermic). A **calorimeter** is the laboratory apparatus that is used to measure the quantity and direction of heat flow accompanying a chemical or physical change. The heat change in chemical reactions is quantitatively expressed as the **enthalpy (or heat) of reaction,** ΔH, at constant pressure. ΔH values are negative for exothermic reactions and positive for endothermic reactions.

ΔH values are often expressed as J/mol or kJ/mol

    Three quantitative measurements of heat are detailed in this experiment: measurements of the specific heat of a metal, the heat change accompanying an acid–base reaction, and the heat change associated with the dissolution of a salt in water.

Specific Heat of a Metal

The energy (heat, expressed in joules, J) required to change the temperature of one gram of a substance by 1°C is the **specific heat**[1] of that substance:

$$\text{specific heat} \left(\frac{J}{g \cdot {}^\circ C}\right) = \frac{\text{energy} (J)}{\text{mass} (g) \times \Delta T ({}^\circ C)} \qquad (6.1)$$

or, rearranging for energy,

$$\text{energy} (J) = \text{specific heat} \left(\frac{J}{g \cdot {}^\circ C}\right) \times \text{mass} (g) \times \Delta T ({}^\circ C) \qquad (6.2)$$

    ΔT is the temperature change of the substance. Although the specific heat of a substance changes slightly with temperature, for our purposes, we assume it is constant over the temperature changes of this experiment.

    The specific heat of a metal that does not react with water is determined by (1) heating a measured mass of the metal, M, to a known (higher) temperature; (2) placing it into a measured amount of water at a known (lower) temperature; and (3) measuring the final equilibrium temperature of the system after the two are combined.

---

[1] The specific heat of a substance is an intensive property (independent of sample size), as are its melting point, boiling point, density, and so on.

The following equations, based on the law of conservation of energy, show the calculations for determining the specific heat of a metal. Considering the direction of energy flow by the conventional sign notation of energy loss being "negative" and energy gain being "positive," then

$$-\text{energy }(J)\text{ lost by metal}_M = \text{energy }(J)\text{ gained by water}_{H_2O} \qquad (6.3)$$

Substituting from equation 6.2,

$$-\text{specific heat}_M \times \text{mass}_M \times \Delta T_M = \text{specific heat}_{H_2O} \times \text{mass}_{H_2O} \times \Delta T_{H_2O} \quad (6.4)$$

Rearranging equation 6.4 to solve for the specific heat of the metal$_M$ gives

Equation 6.4 is often written as $-c_{p,M} \times m_M \times \Delta T_M = c_{p,H_2O} \times m_{H_2O} \times \Delta T_{H_2O}$

$$\text{specific heat}_M = -\frac{\text{specific heat}_{H_2O} \times \text{mass}_{H_2O} \times \Delta T_{H_2O}}{\text{mass}_M \times \Delta T_M} \qquad (6.5)$$

In the equation, the temperature change for either substance is defined as the difference between the final temperature, T_f, and the initial temperature, T_i, of the substance:

$$\Delta T = T_f - T_i \qquad (6.6)$$

These equations assume no heat loss to the calorimeter when the metal and the water are combined. The specific heat of water is 4.18 J/g •°C.

Enthalpy (Heat) of Neutralization of an Acid–Base Reaction

Enthalpy of neutralization: energy released per mole of water formed in an acid–base reaction—an exothermic quantity

The negative sign in equation 6.8 is a result of heat "loss" by the acid–base reaction system.

The reaction of a strong acid with a strong base is an exothermic reaction that produces water and heat as products.

$$H_3O^+(aq) + OH^-(aq) \rightarrow 2\ H_2O(l) + \text{heat} \qquad (6.7)$$

The **enthalpy (heat) of neutralization**, ΔH_n, is determined by (1) assuming the density and the specific heat for the acid and base solutions are equal to that of water and (2) measuring the temperature change, ΔT (equation 6.6), when the two are mixed:

$$\text{enthalpy change, } \Delta H_n = -\text{specific heat}_{H_2O} \times combined\ \text{masses}_{acid + base} \times \Delta T \quad (6.8)$$

ΔH_n is generally expressed in units of kJ/mol of water that forms from the reaction. The mass (grams) of the solution equals the *combined* masses of the acid and base solutions.

Enthalpy (Heat) of Solution for the Dissolution of a Salt

Lattice energy: energy required to vaporize one mole of salt into its gaseous ions—an endothermic quantity

Hydration energy: energy released when one mole of a gaseous ion is attracted to and surrounded by water molecules forming one mole of hydrated ion in aqueous solution—an exothermic quantity

When a salt dissolves in water, energy is either absorbed or evolved, depending on the magnitude of the salt's lattice energy and the hydration energy of its ions. For the dissolution of KI:

$$KI(s) \xrightarrow{H_2O} K^+(aq) + I^-(aq) \qquad \Delta H_s = +13\text{ kJ/mol} \qquad (6.9)$$

The **lattice energy** (an endothermic quantity) of a salt, ΔH_{LE}, and the **hydration energy** (an exothermic quantity), ΔH_{hyd}, of its composite ions account for the amount of heat evolved or absorbed when one mole of the salt dissolves in water. The **enthalpy (heat) of solution**, ΔH_s, is the sum of these two terms (for KI, see Figure 6.1).

$$\Delta H_s = \Delta H_{LE} + \Delta H_{hyd} \qquad (6.10)$$

Whereas ΔH_{LE} and ΔH_{hyd} are difficult to measure in the laboratory, ΔH_s is easily measured. A temperature rise for the dissolution of a salt, indicating an exothermic process, means that the ΔH_{hyd} is greater than the ΔH_{LE} for the salt; conversely, a temperature decrease in the dissolution of the salt indicates that ΔH_{LE} is greater than ΔH_{hyd} and ΔH_s is positive.

The enthalpy of solution for the dissolution of a salt, ΔH_s, is determined experimentally by adding the heat changes of the salt and the water when the two are mixed. ΔH_s is expressed in units of kilojoules per mole of salt.

$$\text{total enthalpy change per mole, } \Delta H_s = \frac{(-\text{energy change}_{H_2O}) + (-\text{energy change}_{salt})}{\text{mole}_{salt}}$$

$$(6.11)$$

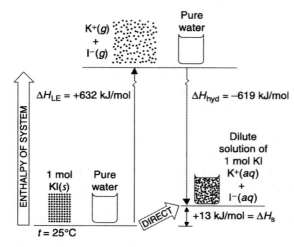

Figure 6.1 Energy changes in the dissolving of solid KI in water

$$\Delta H_s = \frac{(-\text{specific heat}_{H_2O} \times \text{mass}_{H_2O} \times \Delta T_{H_2O}) + (-\text{specific heat}_{salt} \times \text{mass}_{salt} \times \Delta T_{salt})}{\text{mole}_{salt}}$$

$$(6.12)$$

Refer to equation 6.6 for an interpretation of ΔT. The specific heats of some salts are listed in Table 6.1.

Table 6.1 Specific Heat of Some Salts

Salt	Formula	Specific Heat $(J/g \cdot °C)$
Ammonium chloride	NH_4Cl	1.57
Ammonium nitrate	NH_4NO_3	1.74
Ammonium sulfate	$(NH_4)_2SO_4$	1.409
Calcium chloride	$CaCl_2$	0.657
Lithium chloride	$LiCl$	1.13
Sodium carbonate	Na_2CO_3	1.06
Sodium hydroxide	$NaOH$	1.49
Sodium sulfate	Na_2SO_4	0.903
Sodium thiosulfate pentahydrate	$Na_2S_2O_3 \cdot 5H_2O$	1.45
Potassium bromide	KBr	0.439
Potassium nitrate	KNO_3	0.95

EXPERIMENTAL PROCEDURE

Procedure Overview: Three different experiments are completed in a "double" coffee cup calorimeter. Each experiment requires careful mass, volume, and temperature measurements before and after the mixing of the respective components. Calculations are based on an interpretation of plotted data.

Ask your instructor which parts of this experiment you are to complete.

You and a partner are to complete at least two trials for each part assigned. The temperature versus time curves to be plotted in Parts A.5, B.4, and C.4 can be established by using a thermal probe that is connected directly to either a calculator or a computer with the appropriate software. If this thermal sensing and/or recording apparatus is available in the laboratory, consult with your instructor for its use and adaptation to the experiment. The probe merely replaces the glass or digital thermometer in Figure 6.4, page 103.

A. Specific Heat of a Metal

The temperature is to be recorded with the correct number of significant figures.

Use a stirring rod to assist in the gentle transfer of the metal into the water of the calorimeter.

Prepare a boiling water bath in a 400-mL beaker as shown in Figure 6.2.

1. **Prepare the metal.** Obtain 10–30 g of an unknown dry metal[2] from your instructor. Record the number of the unknown metal on the ***Report Sheet***. Use weighing paper to measure its mass on your assigned balance. Transfer the metal to a dry, 200-mm test tube. Place the 200-mm test tube in a 400-mL beaker filled with water well above the level of the metal sample in the test tube (Figure 6.2). Heat the water to boiling and maintain this temperature for at least 5 minutes so that the metal reaches thermal equilibrium with the boiling water. Proceed to Part A.2 while the water is heating.

2. **Prepare the water in the calorimeter.** The apparatus for the calorimetry experiment appears in Figure 6.4. Obtain two 6- or 8-oz Styrofoam coffee cups, a plastic lid, stirrer, and a 110° glass or digital thermometer. Thoroughly clean the Styrofoam cups with several rinses of deionized water. Measure and record the combined mass (± 0.01 g) of the calorimeter (the two Styrofoam cups, the plastic lid, and the stirrer).

   Using a graduated cylinder, add ~20.0 mL of water and measure the mass of the calorimeter *plus* water. Secure the glass or digital (Figure 6.3) thermometer with a clamp and position the bulb or thermal sensor below the water surface. (**Caution:** *Carefully handle a glass thermometer. If the thermometer is accidentally broken, notify your instructor immediately.*)

3. **Measure and record the temperatures of the metal and water.** Once thermal equilibrium has been reached in Parts A.1 and A.2, measure and record the temperatures of the *boiling* water from Part A.1 *and* the water in the calorimeter from Part A.2. Record the temperatures using all certain digits *plus* one uncertain digit.

4. **Transfer the hot metal to the cool water and record the data.** Remove the test tube from the boiling water and *quickly* transfer *only* the metal to the water in the calorimeter.[3] Replace the lid and swirl the contents gently. Record the water temperature as a function of time (about 5-second intervals for 1 minute and then 15-second intervals for ~5 minutes) on the table at the end of the ***Report Sheet***.

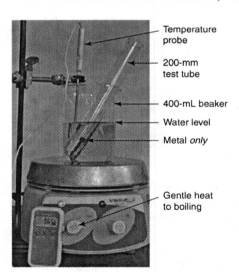

— Temperature probe

— 200-mm test tube

— 400-mL beaker

— Water level

— Metal *only*

— Gentle heat to boiling

Figure 6.2 Placement of the metal in the dry test tube below the water surface in the beaker. A Bunsen flame may replace the hot plate.

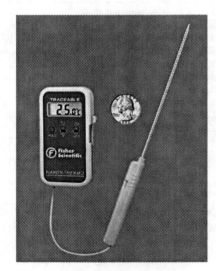

Figure 6.3 A modern digital thermometer can be substituted for a glass thermometer.

[2]Ask your instructor to determine the approximate mass of metal to use for the experiment.
[3]Be careful *not* to splash out any of the water in the calorimeter. If you do, you will need to repeat the entire procedure. Also, be sure that the metal is fully submerged in the calorimeter.

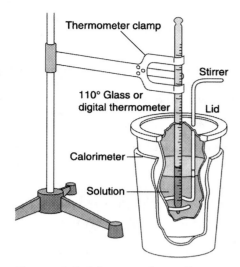

Thermometer clamp

Stirrer

110° Glass or
digital thermometer

Lid

Calorimeter

Solution

Figure 6.4 Schematic of a "coffee cup" calorimeter (see opening photo)

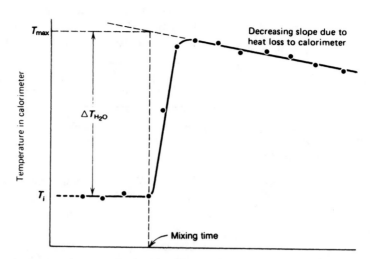

T_{max}

ΔT_{H_2O}

T_i

Temperature in calorimeter

Decreasing slope due to heat loss to calorimeter

Mixing time

Figure 6.5 Extrapolation of temperature versus time data (not to scale) for an exothermic process

5. **Plot the data.** Plot the temperature (y-axis) versus time (x-axis) on the top half of a sheet of linear graph paper or by using appropriate software. The maximum temperature is the intersection point of two lines: (1) the best line drawn through the data points on the cooling portion of the curve and (2) a line drawn perpendicular to the time axis at the mixing time [when the metal is added to the water (Figure 6.5)].[4] Have your instructor approve your graph.

Appendix C

6. **Do it again.** Repeat Parts A.1 through A.5 for the same *dry* metal sample. Plot the data on the bottom half of the same sheet of linear graph paper.

Disposal: Return the metal to the appropriately labeled container, as advised by your instructor.

Obtain 110 mL of 1.1 M HCl, 110 mL of 1.1 M HNO$_3$ and 210 mL of standardized 1.0 M NaOH from the stock reagents.

B. Enthalpy (Heat) of Neutralization for an Acid–Base Reaction

1. **Measure the volume and temperature of the HCl.** Measure 50.0 mL of 1.1 M HCl in a *clean* graduated cylinder. Measure and record its temperature.

2. **Measure the volume and temperature of the NaOH.** Using a second *clean* graduated cylinder, transfer 50.0 mL of a **standard** 1.0 M NaOH **solution** to the *dry* calorimeter (see Figure 6.4). Record the temperature and exact molar concentration of the NaOH solution.

Standard solution: a solution with a very accurately measured concentration of a solute

3. **Collect the data.** Carefully but quickly add the acid to the base, replace the calorimeter lid, and swirl gently. Read and record the temperature and time every 5 seconds for 1 minute and thereafter every 15 seconds for ~5 minutes.

4. **Plot the data.** Plot the temperature (y-axis) versus time (x-axis) on the top half of a sheet of linear graph paper or by using appropriate software. Determine the maximum temperature as was done in Part A.5. Have your instructor approve your graph.

Appendix C

5. **Do it again.** Repeat the acid–base experiment, Parts B.1 through B.4. Plot the data on the bottom half of the same sheet of graph paper.

---

[4]The maximum temperature is never recorded because of some, albeit very small, heat loss to the calorimeter wall.

6. **Change the acid and repeat the neutralization reaction.** Repeat Parts B.1 through B.5, substituting 1.1 M HNO_3 for 1.1 M HCl. On the ***Report Sheet***, compare the ΔH_n values for the two strong acid–strong base reactions.

> *Disposal:* Discard the neutralized solutions contained in the calorimeter into the Waste Acids container. Rinse the calorimeter twice with deionized water.

C. Enthalpy (Heat) of Solution for the Dissolution of a Salt

Measure the mass of salt for each of the separate trials (Part C.5) while occupying the balance.

1. **Prepare the salt.** On weighing paper, measure about 5.0 g (± 0.001 g) of the assigned salt. Record the name of the salt and its mass on the ***Report Sheet***.

2. **Prepare the calorimeter.** Measure the mass of the *dry* calorimeter. Using your clean graduated cylinder, add ~20.0 mL of deionized water to the calorimeter. Measure the combined mass of the calorimeter and water. Secure the thermometer with a clamp and position the bulb or thermal sensor below the water surface (see Figure 6.4) and record its temperature.

3. **Collect the temperature data.** Carefully add (do not spill) the salt to the calorimeter, replace the lid, and swirl gently. Read and record the temperature and time at 5-second intervals for 1 minute and thereafter every 15 seconds for ~5 minutes.

Appendix C

4. **Plot the data.** Plot the temperature (*y*-axis) versus time (*x*-axis) on the top half of a sheet of linear graph paper or by using appropriate software. Determine the maximum (for an exothermic process) or minimum (for an endothermic process) temperature as was done in Part A.5. Have your instructor approve your graph.

5. **Do it again.** With a fresh sample, repeat the dissolution of your assigned salt, Parts C.1 through C.4. Plot the data on the bottom half of the same sheet of linear graph paper.

> *Disposal:* Discard the salt solution into the Waste Salts container, followed by additional tap water. Consult with your instructor.

CLEANUP: Rinse the coffee cups twice with tap water and twice with deionized water, insert the thermometer into its carrying case, and return them.

The Next Step

$$\text{Calorimeter constant} = \frac{\text{energy change}}{^\circ C},$$

the heat lost to or gained by the calorimeter per degree Celsius temperature change.

Heat is evolved or absorbed in all chemical reactions. (1) Since heat is transferred to/from the calorimeter, design an experiment to determine the **calorimeter constant** (called its *heat capacity*) for a calorimeter. (2) An analysis of the combustion of different fuels is an interesting yet challenging project. Design an apparatus and develop a procedure for the thermal analysis (kilojoules/gram) of various combustible materials—for example, alcohol, gasoline, coal, or wood.

Experiment 6 *Prelaboratory Assignment*

Calorimetry

Date _____ Lab Sec. _____ Name _____ Desk No. _____

1. A 20.94-g sample of a metal is heated to 99.4°C in a hot water bath until thermal equilibrium is reached. The metal sample is quickly transferred to 100.0 mL of water at 22.0°C contained in a calorimeter. The thermal equilibrium temperature of the metal sample plus water mixture is 24.6°C. What is the specific heat of the metal? Express the specific heat with the correct number of significant figures.

2. **a.** Experimental Procedure, Part A.1. What is the procedure for heating a metal to an exact but measured temperature?

   b. Experimental Procedure, Part A.1. How can bumping be avoided when heating water in a beaker?

3. Experimental Procedure, Parts A.4, 5.
   a. When a metal at a higher temperature is transferred to water at a lower temperature, heat is inevitably lost to the calorimeter (Figure 6.4). Will this unmeasured heat loss increase or decrease the calculated value of the specific heat of the metal? Explain. See equation 6.5.

   b. Explain why the extrapolated temperature is used to determine the maximum temperature of the mixture rather than the highest recorded temperature in the experiment. See Figure 6.5.

4. Experimental Procedure, Part B. Three student chemists measured 50.0 mL of 1.00 M NaOH in separate Styrofoam coffee cup calorimeters (Part B). Brett added 50.0 mL of 1.10 M HCl to his solution of NaOH; Dale added 45.5 mL of 1.10 M HCl (equal moles) to his NaOH solution. Lyndsay added 50.0 mL of 1.00 M HCl to her NaOH solution. Each student recorded the temperature change and calculated the enthalpy of neutralization.

   Identify the student who observes a temperature change that will be different from that observed by the other two chemists. Explain why and how (higher or lower) the temperature will be different.

5. Experimental Procedure, Part C. Angelina observes a temperature increase when her salt dissolves in water.
   a. Is the lattice energy for the salt greater or less than the hydration energy for the salt? Explain.

   b. Will the solubility of the salt increase or decrease with temperature increases? Explain.

6. A 5.00-g sample of KBr at 25.0°C dissolves in 25.0 mL of water also at 25.0°C. The final equilibrium temperature of the resulting solution is 18.1°C. What is the enthalpy of solution, ΔH_s, of KBr expressed in kilojoules per mole? See equation 6.12.

Calorimetry

Date _____ Lab Sec. _____ Name _____ Desk No. _____

A. Specific Heat of a Metal

Unknown No. _____   *Trial 1*   *Trial 2*

  1. Mass of metal (*g*) _____ _____

  2. Temperature of metal (boiling water) (°*C*) _____ _____

  3. Mass of calorimeter (*g*) _____ _____

  4. Mass of calorimeter + water (*g*) _____ _____

  5. Mass of water (*g*) _____ _____

  6. Temperature of water in calorimeter (°*C*) _____ _____

  7. Maximum temperature of metal and water from graph (°*C*) _____ _____

  8. Instructor's approval of graph _____ _____

Calculations for Specific Heat and the Molar Mass of a Metal

  1. Temperature change of water, ΔT (°*C*) _____ _____

  2. Heat *gained* by water (*J*) _____ _____

  3. Temperature change of metal, ΔT (°*C*) _____ _____

  4. Specific heat of metal, equation 6.5 (*J/g•°C*) _____ * _____

  5. Average specific heat of metal (*J/g•°C*) _____

*Show calculations for Trial 1 using the correct number of significant figures.

B. Enthalpy (Heat) of Neutralization for an Acid–Base Reaction

	HCl + NaOH		HNO$_3$ + NaOH	
	Trial 1	*Trial 2*	*Trial 1*	*Trial 2*
1. Volume of acid (*mL*)	_____	_____	_____	_____
2. Temperature of acid (°*C*)	_____	_____	_____	_____
3. Volume of NaOH (*mL*)	_____	_____	_____	_____
4. Temperature of NaOH (°*C*)	_____	_____	_____	_____
5. Exact molar concentration of NaOH (*mol/L*)	_____		_____	
6. Maximum temperature from graph (°*C*)	_____	_____	_____	_____
7. Instructor's approval of graph	_____	_____	_____	_____

Calculations for Enthalpy (Heat) of Neutralization for an Acid–Base Reaction

	HCl + NaOH		HNO$_3$ + NaOH	
1. *Average* initial temperature of acid and NaOH (°*C*)				
2. Temperature change, ΔT (°*C*)				
3. Volume of final mixture (*mL*)				
4. Mass of final mixture (*g*) (Assume the density of the solution is 1.0 g/mL.)				
5. Specific heat of mixture	4.18 J/g•°C		4.18 J/g•°C	
6. Heat evolved (*J*)				
7. Moles of OH⁻ reacted, the limiting reactant (*mol*)				
8. Moles of H$_2$O formed (*mol*)				
9. ΔH_n (*kJ/mol H$_2$O*), equation 6.8		*		
10. Average ΔH_n (*kJ/mol H$_2$O*)				

*Show calculations for Trial 1 using the correct number of significant figures.

Comment on your two values of ΔH_n.

C. Enthalpy (Heat) of Solution for the Dissolution of a Salt

	Trial 1	*Trial 2*
Name of salt _____		
1. Mass of salt (*g*)	_____	_____
2. Moles of salt (*mol*)		
3. Mass of calorimeter (*g*)	_____	_____
4. Mass of calorimeter + water (*g*)	_____	_____
5. Mass of water (*g*)		
6. Initial temperature of water (°C)	_____	_____
7. Final temperature of mixture from graph (°C)	_____	_____
8. Instructor's approval of graph	_____	_____

Calculations for Enthalpy (Heat) of Solution for the Dissolution of a Salt

	Trial 1	*Trial 2*
1. Change in temperature of solution, ΔT (°C)		
2. Heat change of water (*J*)		
3. Heat change of salt (*J*) (Obtain its specific heat from Table 6.1.)		
4. *Total* enthalpy change, equation 6.11 (*J*)		
5. ΔH_s (*J/mol salt*), equation 6.12	*	
6. Average ΔH_s (*J/mol salt*)		

*Show calculations for Trial 1. Report the result with the correct number of significant figures.

Specific Heat of a Metal				Enthalpy (Heat) of Neutralization for an Acid–Base Reaction								Enthalpy (Heat) of Solution for the Dissolution of a Salt			
Trial 1		Trial 2		Trial 1		Trial 2		Trial 1		Trial 2		Trial 1		Trial 2	
Time	Temp	Time	Temp	Time	Temp	Time	Temp	Time	Temp	Time	Temp	Time	Temp	Time	Temp

Laboratory Questions

Circle the questions that have been assigned.

1. Part A.1. The 200-mm test tube also contained some water (besides the metal) that was subsequently added to the calorimeter (in Part A.4). Considering a higher specific heat for water, will the temperature change in the calorimeter be higher, lower, or unaffected by this technique error? Explain.

2. Part A.4. When a student chemist transferred the metal to the calorimeter, some water splashed out of the calorimeter. Will this technique error result in the specific heat of the metal being reported as too high or too low? Explain.

3. Part B. The enthalpy of neutralization for *all* strong acid–strong base reactions should be the same within experimental error. Explain. Will that also be the case for all weak acid–strong base reactions? Explain.

4. Part B. Heat is lost to the Styrofoam calorimeter. Assuming a 6.22°C temperature change for the reaction of HCl(*aq*) with NaOH(*aq*), calculate the heat loss to the inner 2.35-g Styrofoam cup. The specific heat of Styrofoam is 1.34 J/g•°C.

5. Part B.3. Jacob carelessly added only 40.0 mL (instead of the recommended 50.0 mL) of 1.1 *M* HCl to the 50.0 mL of 1.0 *M* NaOH. Explain the consequence of the error.

6. Part B.3. The chemist used a thermometer that was miscalibrated by 2°C over the entire thermometer scale. Will this factory error cause the reported energy of neutralization, ΔH_n, to be higher, lower, or unaffected? Explain.

7. Part C.3. If some of the salt remains adhered to the weighing paper (and therefore is *not* transferred to the calorimeter), will the enthalpy of solution for the salt be reported too high or too low? Explain.

8. Part C. The dissolution of ammonium nitrate, NH_4NO_3, in water is an endothermic process. Since the calorimeter is *not* a perfect insulator, will the enthalpy of solution, ΔH_s, for ammonium nitrate be reported as too high or too low if this heat change is ignored? Explain.

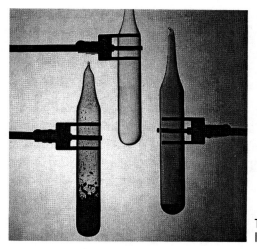

Periodic Table and Periodic Law

The halogens are, from left to right, solid iodine crystals, chlorine gas, and liquid bromine.

OBJECTIVES

- To become more familiar with the periodic table
- To observe and to generalize the trends of various atomic properties within groups and periods of elements
- To observe from experiment the trends of the chemical properties within groups and periods of elements

TECHNIQUES

The following techniques are used in the Experimental Procedure:

INTRODUCTION

Similarities between the chemical and physical properties of elements were well known early in the nineteenth century. Several reports of grouping elements with like properties provided the background from which the modern periodic table finally evolved.

However, it was in 1869, nearly simultaneously, when *two* masterful organizations of all known elements were revealed, one by Dmitri Mendeleev from Russia and the other from Lothar Meyer from Germany. From their independent research, their arrangement of the elements established the modern periodic table. Mendeleev showed that with the elements arranged in order of increasing atomic mass, their *chemical* properties recur periodically. When Meyer arranged the elements in order of increasing atomic mass, he found that their *physical* properties recur periodically. The two tables, however, were virtually identical. Because he drafted his table earlier in 1869 and because his table included "blanks" for yet-to-be-discovered elements to fit, Mendeleev is considered the "father" of the modern periodic table.

In 1913, H. G. J. Moseley's study of the X-ray spectra of the elements refined the periodic table to its current status: **When the elements are arranged in order of increasing atomic *number*, certain chemical and physical properties repeat periodically.** See the inside back cover for a modern version of the periodic table. Photos of most all of the elements can be seen on www.periodictabletable.com.

The periodic table continues to expand with the synthesis of new elements (the transactinides[1]), primarily at the Lawrence Livermore National Laboratory (California), the Joint Institute for Nuclear Research (Dubna, Russia), and the Institute for Heavy-Ion

Dmitri Mendeleev (1834–1907)

Atomic number: the number of protons in the nucleus

[1]en.wikipedia.org/wiki/Transactinide_element

Glenn T. Seaborg (1912–1999)

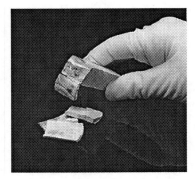

Sodium metal is a shiny, but very reactive metal, typical of Group 1A elements.

Properties of Chlorine

Atomic number	17
Molar mass	35.453 g/mol
Density at 293 K	3.214 g/L
Molar volume	22.7 cm³/mol
Melting point	172.22 K
Boiling point	239.2 K
Heat of fusion	3.203 kJ/mol
Heat of vaporization	10.20 kJ/mol
First ionization energy	1251.1 kJ/mol
Second ionization energy	2297.3 kJ/mol
Third ionization energy	3821.8 kJ/mol
Electronegativity	3.16
Electron affinity	349 kJ/mol
Specific heat	0.48 J/g·K
Heat of atomization	121 kJ/mol atoms
Atomic radius	100 pm
Ionic radius (−1 ion)	167 pm
Thermal conductivity	0.01 J/m·s·K

Research (Darmstadt, Germany). The most recent confirmation (in 2010) is the synthesis of element 117, an element that now completes the seventh row of elements in the periodic table. Glenn T. Seaborg was the most prominent of the U.S. chemists involved in the synthesis of the *transuranium* elements. He was the recipient of the 1951 Nobel Prize in chemistry and was honored with the naming of element 106, Seaborgium.

In the periodic table, each horizontal row of elements is a **period**, and each column is a **group** (or **family**). All elements within a group have similar chemical and physical properties. Common terms associated with various sections of the periodic table are

- Representative elements: Group "A" elements
- Transition elements: Groups 3–12
- Inner-transition elements: the lanthanide (atomic numbers 58–71) and actinide (atomic numbers 90–103) series
- Metallic elements: elements to the left of the "stairstep line" that runs diagonally from B to At
- Nonmetallic elements: elements to the right of the "stairstep line"
- Metalloids: elements that lie adjacent to the "stairstep line," excluding Al
- Post-transition metals (or Poor metals): metals to the right of the transition metals
- Alkali metals: Group 1A elements
- Alkaline earth metals: Group 2A elements
- Chalcogens: Group 6A elements
- Halogens: Group 7A elements
- Noble gases: Group 8A elements
- Rare earth metals: the lanthanide series of elements
- Coinage metals: Cu, Ag, Au
- Noble metals: Ru, Os, Rh, Ir, Pd, Pt, Ag, Au, Hg

The periodicity of a physical property for a series of elements can be shown by plotting the experimental value of the property versus increasing atomic number. Physical properties studied in this experiment are the following.

- Ionization energy (Figure 7.1): the energy required to remove an electron from a gaseous atom
- Atomic radius (Figure 7.2): the radius of an atom of the element
- Electron affinity (Figure 7.3): the *energy released* when a neutral gaseous atom accepts an electron
- Density (Figure 7.4): the mass of a substance per unit volume

For a very complete look at the properties and periodic trends of the elements, go to www.webelements.com.

Other physical properties that show trends in groups and periods of elements are listed for chlorine in the table.

Trends in the *chemical* properties of the boldface elements are studied in this experiment.

2	Li	Be	B	C	N	O	**F**
3	**Na**	**Mg**	**Al**	Si	P	S	**Cl**
4	K	**Ca**	Ga	Ge	As	Se	**Br**
5	Rb	**Sr**	In	Sn	Sb	Te	**I**

In this experiment, the relative acidic and/or basic strength of the hydroxides or oxides in the third period of the periodic table, the relative chemical reactivity of the halogens, and the relative solubility of the hydroxides and sulfates of magnesium, calcium, and strontium are observed through a series of qualitative tests. Observe closely the results of each test before generalizing your information.[2]

---

[2]For trends in chemical properties, go to http://en.wikipedia.org/wiki/category:chemistry

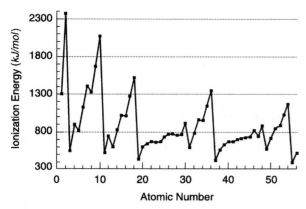

Figure 7.1 Ionization energies (*kJ/mol*) plotted against atomic number

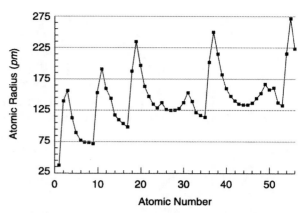

Figure 7.2 Atomic radii (*pm*) plotted against atomic number

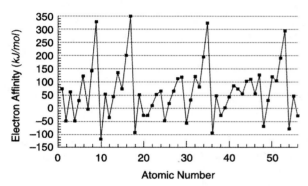

Figure 7.3 Electron affinities (*kJ/mol*) plotted against atomic number, defined here as energy released

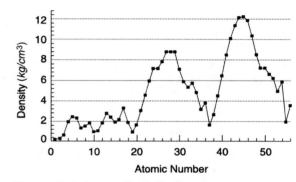

Figure 7.4 Density (*kg/m³*) plotted against atomic number

Procedure Overview: General trends in the physical properties of the elements are observed and studied in Figures 7.1–7.4. Experimental observations of the physical and chemical properties of a number of representative elements are made. Special attention is paid to the chemical properties of the halogens.

Ask your instructor about the working relationship, individuals or partners, for Part A. For Parts B, C, and D, perform the experiment with a partner. At each circled superscript (1–18) in the procedure, *stop* and record your observation on the *Report Sheet*. Discuss your observations with your lab partner and your instructor.

EXPERIMENTAL PROCEDURE

Figures 7.1 through 7.4 plot the experimental data of four physical properties of the elements as a function of their atomic number. While actual values cannot be readily obtained from the graphical data, the periodic trends are easily seen. All values requested for the analyses of the graphical data need only be given as your "best possible" estimates from the figure.

The periodic trends for the elements are analyzed through a series of questions on the *Report Sheet*.

A. Periodic Trends in Physical Properties (Dry Lab)

Prepare a hot water bath for Part B.3.

1. **Samples of elements.** Samples of the third period elements sodium, magnesium, aluminum, silicon, and sulfur are on the reagent table. Note that the Na metal is stored under a nonaqueous liquid to prevent rapid air oxidation. Polish the Mg and

B. The Appearance of Some Representative Elements

Tap–tap–tap
w/ "little" finger

Figure 7.5 Shake the contents of the test tube with the little finger.

Al metal strips with steel wool for better viewing. Record your observations on the *Report Sheet*.

Since some chlorine, bromine, and iodine vapors may escape the test tubes in Parts B.2–4 and C.1–3, *you may want to conduct the experiments in the fume hood.* Consult with your laboratory instructor.

2. **Chlorine.** In a clean, 150-mm test tube, place 2 mL of a 5% sodium hypochlorite, NaClO, solution (commercial laundry bleach) and 10 drops of cyclohexane. Agitate the mixture (Figure 7.5). Which layer is the cyclohexane layer?[3]

Add ~10 drops of 6 *M* HCl. (**Caution:** 6 *M* HCl *is very corrosive. Wash immediately from the skin.*) Swirl or agitate the mixture (with a stirring rod) so that the HCl mixes with the NaClO solution. Note the color of the chlorine in the cyclohexane layer. Record your observation.① Do not discard—save for Part C.1.

3. **Bromine.** In a second, clean test tube, place 2 mL of 3 *M* KBr solution and 3 drops of cyclohexane. Add 5–10 drops of 8 *M* HNO₃. (**Caution:** HNO₃ *attacks skin tissue; flush the affected area immediately with water.*) Agitate or swirl the mixture so that the 8 *M* HNO₃ mixes with the KBr solution. Place the test tube in a hot water bath to increase the reaction rate. Note the color of the bromine in the cyclohexane layer. Record,② but do not discard—save for Part C.2.

4. **Iodine.** Repeat Part B.3 in a third test tube, substituting 3 *M* KI for 3 *M* KBr. Record. Compare the appearance of the three halogens dissolved in the cyclohexane.③ Save for Part C.3.

C. The Chemical Properties of the Halogens

Pinch: a solid mass about the size of a grain of rice

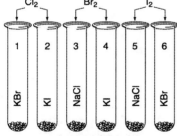

Figure 7.6 Six labeled test tubes to test the relative reactivity of the halogens

For Parts C.1–3, six clean, small (~75-mm), test tubes[4] are required. Summarize your observations at the conclusion of Part C.3 on the *Report Sheet*. Number each test tube (Figure 7.6).

1. **Chlorine and its reactions with bromide and iodide ions.** Clean two small test tubes; add a **pinch** (on the end of a spatula) of solid KBr to the *first* test tube and a pinch of KI to the *second*. Use a dropping pipet to withdraw the chlorine/cyclohexane layer from Part B.2 and add an (approximately) equal portion to the two test tubes. Swirl or agitate the solution, observe, and record. Write appropriate net ionic equations.④

2. **Bromine and its reactions with chloride and iodide ions.** Add a pinch of solid NaCl to a *third*, small clean test tube and a pinch of KI to the *fourth* test tube. Use a dropping pipet to withdraw the bromine/cyclohexane layer from Part B.3 and add an (approximately) equal portion to the two test tubes. Swirl or agitate the solution, observe, and record. Write appropriate net ionic equations.⑤

3. **Iodine and its reactions with chloride and bromide ions.** Add a pinch of solid NaCl to a *fifth*, small clean test tube and a pinch of KBr to the *sixth* test tube. Use a dropping pipet to withdraw the iodine/cyclohexane layer from Part B.4 and add an (approximately) equal portion to the two test tubes. Swirl or agitate the solution, observe, and record. Write appropriate net ionic equations.⑥

What can you conclude about the relative chemical reactivity of the halogens?

> *Disposal:* Dispose of the waste water/halogen mixtures in the Waste Halogens container.

---

[3]Mineral oil, or any colorless cooking oil, may be substituted for cyclohexane.
[4]A 24-well plate may be substituted for the small test tubes.

Twelve clean, small (~75-mm) test tubes[5] are required for the chemical reactions observed in Part D. Number each test tube (Figure 7.7).

D. The Chemical Properties of the Halides

Appendix G

1. **The reactions of the halides with various metal ions.** Label 12 clean, small test tubes and transfer the following to each:

   - Test tubes 1, 2, and 3: a pinch of NaF and 10 drops of water
   - Test tubes 4, 5, and 6: a pinch of NaCl and 10 drops of water
   - Test tubes 7, 8, and 9: a pinch of KBr and 10 drops of water
   - Test tubes 10, 11, and 12: a pinch of KI and 10 drops of water

   a. Slowly add 10 drops of 2 M Ca(NO$_3$)$_2$ to test tubes 1, 4, 7, and 10. Observe closely and over a period of time. Vary the color of the background of the test tubes for observation.⑦

   b. Slowly add 10 drops of 0.1 M AgNO$_3$ to test tubes 2, 5, 8, and 11. Observe. After about 1 minute, add 10 drops of 3 M NH$_3$.⑧

   c. Add 1 drop of 6 M HNO$_3$ (**Caution!**) and slowly add 10 drops of 0.1 M Fe(NO$_3$)$_3$ to test tubes 3, 6, 9, and 12. Observe closely and over a period of time.⑨

   d. Summarize your observations of the chemical activity for the halides with the Ca^{2+}, Ag$^+$, and Fe^{3+} ions.

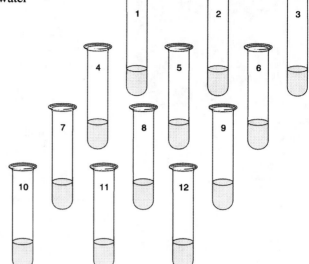

Figure 7.7 Twelve labeled test tubes to test the reactivity of the halides.

Disposal: Dispose of the waste water/halogen mixtures in the Waste Halogens container.

CLEANUP: Rinse the test tubes with copious amounts of tap water and twice with deionized water. Discard the rinses in the sink.

---

1. **Sodium.**[6] *Instructor Demonstration Only.* Wrap a pea-sized piece of sodium metal in aluminum foil. Fill a 200-mm Pyrex test tube with water, add 2 drops of phenolphthalein,[7] and invert the test tube in a beaker of water (Figure 7.8, page 116). Set the beaker and test tube behind a safety shield. Punch 5–10 holes with a pin in the aluminum foil.

   With a pair of tongs or tweezers, place the wrapped sodium metal in the mouth of the test tube, keeping it under water. What is the evolved gas? Test the gas by holding the mouth of the inverted test tube over a Bunsen flame.⑩ A loud pop indicates the presence of hydrogen gas. Account for the appearance of the color change in the solution.⑪

E. Chemical Reactivity of Some Representative Elements

---

[5]A 24-well plate may be substituted for the small test tubes.
[6]Calcium metal can be substituted for sodium metal with the same results.
[7]Phenolphthalein is an acid–base indicator; it is colorless in an acidic solution but pink in a basic solution.

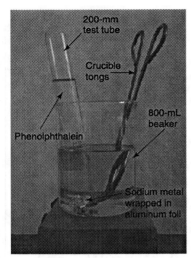

Figure 7.8
Collection of
hydrogen gas from
the reaction of
sodium and water

2. **Magnesium and aluminum.**

   a. *Reaction with acid.* Polish 5-cm strips of Mg and Al metal; cut 5-mm pieces and place them into separate small test tubes. Add ~10 drops of 3 *M* HCl to each test tube. (**Caution:** *Do not allow the HCl to touch the skin. Wash the affected area immediately.*) Which metal reacts more rapidly?⑫ What is the gas that is evolved?⑬

   b. *Reaction with base.* Add (and count) drops of 6 *M* NaOH to each test tube until a precipitate appears. Continue to add NaOH to the test tube containing the aluminum ion until a change in appearance occurs. Add the same number of drops to the test tube containing the magnesium ion. Record your observations.[8] ⑭

   Add drops of 6 *M* HCl until both solutions are again colorless. Observe closely as each drop is added. Record and explain.

3. **Solubilities of alkaline-earth cations.**

   a. *Solubility of the hydroxides.* Place 10 drops of 0.1 *M* $MgCl_2$, 0.1 *M* $CaCl_2$, and 0.1 *M* $Sr(NO_3)_2$ in three separate, clean test tubes. Count and add drops of 0.050 *M* NaOH until a cloudiness appears in each test tube. Predict the trend in the solubility of the hydroxides of the Group 2A cations.⑮

   b. *Solubility of the sulfates.* Place 10 drops of 0.1 *M* $MgCl_2$, 0.1 *M* $CaCl_2$, and 0.1 *M* $Sr(NO_3)_2$ in three separate, clean test tubes. Count and add drops of 0.10 *M* Na_2SO_4 until a cloudiness appears in each test tube. Predict the trend in the solubility of the sulfates of the Group 2A cations.⑯

4. **Sulfurous acid and sulfuric acid.** Because of the possible evolution of a foul-smelling gas, you may want to conduct this part of the experiment in the fume hood. Consult with your instructor.

   a. Place a double pinch of solid sodium sulfite, Na_2SO_3, into a clean small or medium-sized test tube. Add 5–10 drops of 6 *M* HCl. Test the evolved gas with wet blue litmus paper. Write a balanced equation for the reaction.⑰

   b. Repeat the test, substituting solid sodium sulfate, Na_2SO_4, for the Na_2SO_3. Account for any differences or similarities in your observations.⑱

Disposal: Discard the solutions as directed by your instructor.

CLEANUP: Rinse the test tubes twice with tap water and with deionized water. Discard the rinses in the sink.

The Next Step

The periodic trends for many chemical and physical properties of the elements can be found on the Internet. There are many Web sites, and the data are plotted for many properties using various coordinates. A first reference is www.acs.org. Seek a data plot, for example, of atomic radii versus ionization energy or for any properties as listed in the table for chlorine in the Introduction.

---

[8]Magnesium ion precipitates as magnesium hydroxide, $Mg(OH)_2$; aluminum ion also precipitates as the hydroxide, $Al(OH)_3$ but redissolves in an excess of OH^- to produce $Al(OH)_4^-$, the aluminate ion.

Periodic Table and Periodic Law

Date _____ Lab Sec. _____ Name _____ Desk No. _____

1. On the blank periodic table, *clearly* indicate six of the following element sections, using your own color code.

   a. Representative elements
   b. Transition elements
   c. Inner-transition elements
   d. Chalcogens
   e. Coinage metals
   f. Metalloids
   g. Post-transition metals

   h. Alkali metals
   i. Alkaline earth metals
   j. Halogens
   k. Noble gases
   l. Noble metals
   m. Lanthanide series
   n. Actinide series

Periodic Table

2. Sketch in the stairstep line that separates the metals from the nonmetals on the periodic table.

3. Identify the atomic numbers of the elements that would be called the *transactinide* elements.

4. Classify each of the following elements according to the categories of elements identified in question 1:

a. Magnesium _____

b. Plutonium _____

c. Argon _____

d. Zirconium _____

e. Bromine _____

f. Potassium _____

g. Element 118 _____

h. Silver _____

i. Lead _____

j. Titanium _____

5. Refer to Figure 7.1. Which of the following has the highest ionization energy?

a. carbon or oxygen _____

b. phosphorus or sulfur _____

c. magnesium or aluminum _____

d. magnesium or calcium _____

6. Refer to Figure 7.2. Which of the following has the largest atomic radius?

a. carbon or oxygen _____

b. phosphorus or sulfur _____

c. magnesium or aluminum _____

d. magnesium or calcium _____

Compare your answers for questions 5 and 6. What correlation can be made?

7. a. Proceeding from left to right across a period of the periodic table, the elements become (more, less) metallic.

b. Proceeding from top to bottom in a group of the periodic table, the elements become (more, less) metallic.

8. Consider the generic equation for the reaction of the halogens, X_2 and Y_2:

$$X_2(g) + 2Y^-(aq) \rightarrow 2X^-(aq) + Y_2(g)$$

Is X_2 or Y_2 the more reactive halogen? Explain.

9. a. Experimental Procedure, Part B.2. What commercially available compound is used to generate Cl_2 in the experiment?

b. Experimental Procedure, Part B. The observation for the presence of the elemental form of the halogens is in a solvent other than water. Identify the solvent.

c. Experimental Procedure, Part E.3. Identify the tests used to observe the periodic trends in the chemical properties of the alkaline–earth metal ions.

Periodic Table and Periodic Law

Date _____ Lab Sec. _____ Name _____ Desk No. _____

A. Periodic Trends in Physical Properties (Dry Lab)

Consult with your laboratory instructor as to the procedure and schedule for submitting your responses to the following questions about periodic trends.

1. Figure 7.1: Graphical data for the ionization energies of the elements show sawtooth trends across the periods of the elements.
   a. Locate the noble gas group of elements. What appears to be the periodic trend in ionization energies down the noble gas group (i.e., with increasing atomic number)?
   b. Scanning the graphical data for elements adjacent to and then further removed from the halogens, what *general statement* can summarize the trend in the ionization energies when moving down a group of elements?
   c. Which element has the highest ionization energy?
   d. What *general statement* can summarize the trend in the ionization energies when moving across a period of elements?

2. Figure 7.2: Graphical data for the atomic radii of the elements show generally decreasing trends across a period of elements. The noble gases are an anomaly.
   a. Which *group* of elements has the largest atomic radii?
   b. Moving down a group of elements (increasing atomic number), what is the general trend for atomic radii?
   c. Which element has the largest atomic radius?
   d. What *general statement* can summarize the correlation of ionization energies to atomic radii for the elements?

3. Figure 7.3: Graphical data for the electron affinities of the elements show a number of irregularities, but a general increasing trend in values exists across a period of elements.
   a. Which *group* of elements has the highest electron affinities?
   b. Is the trend in electron affinities repetitive for Periods 2 and 3? Cite examples.
   c. Which element has the highest electron affinity?
   d. Is there a correlation of electron affinities to atomic radii for the elements? If so, what is it? Cite examples.

4. Figure 7.4 shows repeated trends in density for the periods of elements.
   a. What is the general trend in densities for Periods 2 and 3?
   b. What is the trend in the densities moving down a group of elements?
   c. Which section of the periodic table (see Introduction) has elements with greater densities?
   d. Which element has the greatest density?

B. The Appearance of Some Representative Elements

Element	Physical State (*g, l, s*)	Physical Appearance and Other Observations	Color
Na	_____	_____	_____
Mg	_____	_____	_____
Al	_____	_____	_____
Si	_____	_____	_____
S_8	_____	_____	_____
①Cl_2	_____	_____	_____
②Br_2	_____	_____	_____
③I_2	_____	_____	_____

C. The Chemical Properties of the Halogens

Observations in the cyclohexane layer

	$Cl_2$④	$Br_2$⑤	$I_2$⑥	Net Ionic Equation(s)
KCl	XX*	_____	_____	_____
KBr	_____	XX	_____	_____
KI	_____	_____	XX	_____

*No reaction mixture.

What can you conclude about the relative reactivity of Cl_2, Br_2, and I_2?

D. The Chemical Properties of the Halides

1. The Reactions of the Halides with Various Metal Ions
   Describe the appearance of each mixture in tubes 1–12.

	⑦$Ca(NO_3)_2$(*aq*)	⑧$AgNO_3$(*aq*)	⑨$Fe(NO_3)_3$(*aq*)
(Test tube no.)	(1)	(2)	(3)
NaF(*aq*)	_____	_____	_____
(Test tube no.)	(4)	(5)	(6)
NaCl(*aq*)	_____	_____	_____
(Test tube no.)	(7)	(8)	(9)
NaBr(*aq*)	_____	_____	_____
(Test tube no.)	(10)	(11)	(12)
NaI(*aq*)	_____	_____	_____

From the observed data, answer the following questions.

    a. Which of the metal fluorides are insoluble? _____

    b. Which of the metal chlorides are insoluble? _____

    c. Which of the metal bromides are insoluble? _____

    d. Which of the metal iodides are insoluble? _____

E. Chemical Reactivity of Some Representative Elements

  1. Sodium (or Calcium)

    a. ⑩Name the gas evolved in the reaction of Na with water: _____

    b. ⑪What is produced from the reaction of Na with water as indicated by the action of phenolphthalein?

    c. Write the chemical equation for the reaction of Na with water:

  2. Magnesium and Aluminum

    a. ⑫Which metal reacts more rapidly with HCl? _____

      ⑬What is the gas that is evolved when Mg and Al react with HCl? _____

    b. Reaction of metal ion with NaOH

⑭Observations	6 *M* NaOH	Excess 6 *M* NaOH
Mg^{2+} (drops to precipitate)	_____	_____
Al^{3+} (drops to precipitate)	_____	_____

    c. Explain the differences in chemical behavior of the magnesium and aluminum hydroxides. Use chemical equations in your discussion.

  3. Solubilities of Alkaline-Earth Cations

Observations	⑮0.050 *M* NaOH	⑯0.10 *M* Na_2SO_4
Mg^{2+} (drops to precipitate)	_____	_____
Ca^{2+} (drops to precipitate)	_____	_____
Sr^{2+} (drops to precipitate)	_____	_____

List the hydroxide salts in order of increasing solubility: _____ < _____ < _____

List the sulfate salts in order of increasing solubility: _____ < _____ < _____

What can you conclude about the general trend in solubilities of the Group 2A metal hydroxides and sulfates?

4. Sulfurous Acid and Sulfuric Acid

    a. ⑰What does the litmus test indicate about the chemical stability of sulfurous acid?

    b. What is the gas that is generated? _____

    c. Write an equation for the decomposition of sulfurous acid.

    d. ⑱What does the litmus test indicate about the chemical stability of sulfuric acid? _____

    e. What chemical property differentiates sulfurous acid from sulfuric acid?

Laboratory Questions

Circle the questions that have been assigned.

1. Part A. Considering the trends in ionization energies, would you expect sodium or potassium to be more reactive? Explain.

2. Part A. Considering the trends in atomic radii, would you expect cesium or radon to have the larger radius? Explain.

3. Part A. Compare the ionization energies of sodium and rubidium and then compare the electron affinities of chlorine and iodine. Which of the following chemical combinations of the elements would be the most exothermic—Na and CI, Na and I, Rb and CI, or Rb and I? Explain.

4. Part C. Chlorine is used extensively as a disinfectant and bleaching agent. Without regard to adverse effects or costs, would bromine be a more or less effective disinfectant and bleaching agent? Explain.

5. Part C. Is fluorine gas predicted to be more or less reactive than chlorine gas? Explain.

6. Part C. Not much is known of the chemistry of astatine. Would you expect astatine to more or less reactive than iodine? Explain.

7. Part E.2. Predict the reactivity of silicon metal relative to that of magnesium and aluminum. Explain.

8. Part E.3.
    a. Is barium hydroxide predicted to be more or less soluble that $Ca(OH)_2$? Explain.
    b. Is barium sulfate predicted to be more or less soluble that $CaSO_4$? Explain.

Atomic and Molecular Structure

Metallic cations heated to high temperatures produce characteristic colors that appear in the starbursts.

OBJECTIVES

- To view and calibrate visible line spectra
- To identify an element from its visible line spectrum
- To identify a compound from its infrared spectrum
- To predict the three-dimensional structure of molecules and molecular ions

INTRODUCTION

Visible light, as we know it, is responsible for the colors of nature—blue skies, green trees, red roses, orange-red rocks, and brown deer. Our eyes are able to sense and distinguish the subtleties and the intensities of those colors through a complex naturally designed detection system—our eyes. The beauty of nature is a result of the interaction of sunlight with matter. Since all matter consists of atoms and molecules, it is obvious that sunlight, in some way, interacts with them to produce nature's colors.

Within molecules of compounds are electrons, vibrating bonds, and rotating atoms, all of which can absorb energy. Because every compound is different, every molecule of a given compound possesses its own unique set of electronic, vibrational, and rotational **energy states,** which are said to be **quantized.** When incident electromagnetic (EM) radiation falls on a *molecule,* the radiation absorbed (the absorbed light) is an energy equal to the difference between two energy states, placing the molecule in an excited state. The remainder of the EM radiation passes through the molecule unaffected.

Atoms of elements interact with EM radiation in much the same way, except there are no bonds to vibrate or atoms to rotate. Only electronic energy states are available for energy absorption.

EM radiation is energy as well as light, and light has wavelengths and frequencies. The relationship between the energy, *E,* and its **wavelength,** λ, and **frequency,** *ν*, is expressed by the equation:

$$E = \frac{hc}{\lambda} = h\nu \qquad (D3.1)$$

where *h* is Planck's constant, 6.63×10^{-34} J•s/photon; *c* equals the velocity of the EM radiation, 3.00×10^8 m/s; λ is the wavelength of the EM radiation in meters; and *ν* (pronounced "new") is its frequency in reciprocal seconds (s^{-1}).

EM radiation includes not only the wavelengths of the visible region (400 to 700 nm) but also those that are shorter (e.g., the ultraviolet and X-ray regions) and longer (e.g., the infrared, microwave, and radio wave regions). See Figure D3.1, page 124. From Equation D3.1, shorter wavelength EM radiation has higher energy.

When an atom or molecule absorbs EM radiation from the visible region of the spectrum, it is usually an electron that is excited from a lower to a higher energy state.

Energy state: the amount of energy confined within an atom or molecule, which can be changed by the absorption or emission of discrete (quantized) amounts of energy

Quantized: only a definitive amount (of energy)

Wavelength: the distance between two crests of a wave

Frequency: the number of crests that pass a given point per second

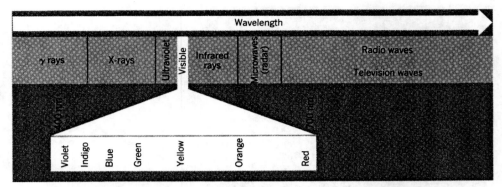

Figure D3.1 Visible light (400–700 nm) is a small part of the electromagnetic spectrum.

White light: EM radiation containing all wavelengths of visible light

Spectrophotometer: an instrument used to detect and monitor the interaction of electromagnetic radiation with matter. The instrument has an EM radiation source, a grating to sort wavelengths, a sample cell, and an EM radiation detector.

When **white light** passes through a sample, our eyes (and the EM detector of a **spectrophotometer**) detect the wavelengths of visible light *not* absorbed—that is, the transmitted light. Therefore, the colors we see are *complementary* to the ones absorbed. If, for example, the atom or molecule absorbs energy exclusively from the violet region of the visible spectrum, the transmitted light (and the substance) appears yellow (violet's complementary color) (Figure D3.2) In reality, atoms and molecules of a substance absorb a range of wavelengths, some wavelengths more so than others, resulting in a mix of transmitted colors leading to various shades of colors.

Table D3.1 lists the colors corresponding to wavelength regions of light (and their complements) in the visible region of the EM spectrum.

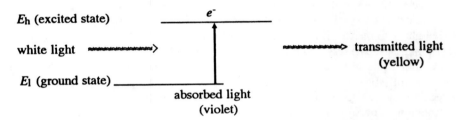

Figure D3.2 White light that is *not* absorbed is the transmitted light that we detect with our eyes.

Atomic Structure

Photon: a particlelike quantity of electromagnetic radiation, often associated with electron transitions

When an atom of an element absorbs EM radiation, it is the electrons that absorb energy to reach excited states. When the electrons return to the lowest energy state (the **ground state**) by various pathways, the same amount of energy absorbed is now emitted as **photons.**[1] The photons have unique energies and wavelengths that represent the difference in the energy states of the atom.

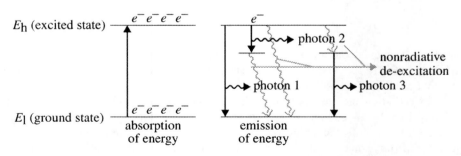

[1]Many electrons "de-excite" to the ground state by only nonradiative pathways, others through a combination of photons *and* nonradiative pathways.

Table D3.1 Color and Wavelengths in the Visible Region of the Electromagnetic Spectrum

Color Absorbed	Wavelength (*nm*)	Color Transmitted
Red	750–610	Green-blue
Orange	610–595	Blue-green
Yellow	595–580	Violet
Green	580–500	Red-violet
Blue	500–435	Orange-yellow
Violet	435–380	Yellow

Because electrons can have a large number of excited states, a large collection of excited-state electrons returning to the ground state produces an array of photons. When these emitted photons pass through a prism, an emission **line spectrum** is produced; each line in the spectrum corresponds to photons of fixed energy and wavelength. The line spectrum for hydrogen is shown in Figure D3.3.

Each element exhibits its own characteristic line spectrum because of the unique electronic energy states in its atoms. For example, the 11 electrons in sodium have a different set of electron energy states than do the 80 electrons in mercury. Therefore, when an electron in an excited state of a sodium atom moves to a lower energy state, the emitted photon has a different energy and wavelength from one that is emitted when an electron de-excites (i.e., moves to a lower energy state) in a mercury atom.

The different wavelengths of the emitted photons produce different yet characteristic colors of light. Light emitted from an excited sodium atom is characteristically yellow-orange, but mercury emits a blue light. Flame tests (*Experiment 38*) and exploding aerial fireworks attest to the uniqueness of the electronic energy states of the atoms for different elements.

Much of the modern theory of atomic structure, which we call *quantum theory* or *quantum mechanics*, is based on the emission spectra of the elements.

Molecular Structure

The structures of molecules are much more complex than those of atoms. Molecules may contain thousands of atoms, each in a unique (energy and three-dimensional) environment. Since each molecule is unique, so must be its energy levels for EM

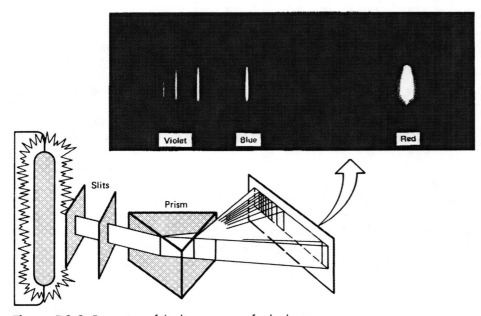

Figure D3.3 Formation of the line spectrum for hydrogen

Table D3.2 Infrared Absorption Bands for Specific Atoms in Bond Arrangements in Molecules

Atoms in Bonds	Wavenumbers	Wavelengths
O—H	3,700 to 3,500 cm^{-1}	2.7 to 2.9 μm
C—H	3,000 to 2,800 cm^{-1}	3.3 to 3.6 μm
C=O	1,800 to 1,600 cm^{-1}	5.6 to 6.2 μm
C—O	1,200 to 1,050 cm^{-1}	8.3 to 9.5 μm
C—C	1,670 to 1,640 cm^{-1}	6.0 to 6.1 μm

absorption. Using EM radiation to elucidate the three-dimensional structure of a molecule can be painstakingly tedious, especially for the structures of the "living" (biochemical) molecules, such as DNA and hemoglobin. Oftentimes, EM radiation is only one of many tools used to determine the molecular structure of a compound.

Infrared EM radiation is used as a probe for the identification of specific atom arrangements in molecules. For example, the O—H bond, as in water and alcohols, absorbs infrared radiation for a principal vibrational energy transition between 3,700 and 3,500 **cm^{-1}** or wavelengths of 2.7 to 2.9 μm. Other characteristic infrared absorption bands for specific atom arrangements in molecules are listed in Table D3.2.

A first view of an infrared spectrum of a molecule seems confusing as more absorption bands appear than what might be anticipated from looking at the structure of the molecule and Table D3.2. Other absorptions occur as a result of multiatom interactions (stretches, bends, etc.) or orientations, but the primary bands appear as expected. Therefore, in an analysis of an infrared spectrum, a search of the primary bands in Table D3.2 is first and foremost.

For other molecules and molecular ions, other regions of EM radiation are most effective. For example, the $FeNCS^{2+}$ ion has a major absorption of radiation at 447 nm, and this property is used to measure its concentration in an aqueous solution in *Experiments 34 and 35*—the higher the concentration, the more EM radiation that is absorbed.

*cm^{-1}: Infrared spectroscopists often indicate absorption bands in units of reciprocal centimeters, called **wavenumbers,** rather than as wavelengths.*

Lewis Theory

Valence electrons: electrons in the highest energy state (outermost shell) of an atom in the ground state

Isoelectronic: two atoms are isoelectronic if they have the same number of electrons.

Gilbert Newton Lewis
(1875–1946)

In 1916, G. N. Lewis developed a theory that focused on the significance of **valence electrons** in chemical reactions and in bonding. He proposed the **octet rule** in which atoms form bonds by losing, gaining, or sharing valence electrons until each atom of the molecule has the same number of valence electrons (eight) as the nearest noble gas in the periodic table. The resulting arrangement of atoms formed the Lewis structure of the compound.

The Lewis structure for water shows that by sharing the one valence electron on each of the hydrogen atoms with the six valence electrons on the oxygen atom, all three atoms obtain the same number of valence electrons as the nearest noble gas. Thus, in water the hydrogen atoms are **isoelectronic** with helium atoms and the oxygen atom is isoelectronic with the neon atom.

The Lewis structures for ions are written similarly, except that electrons are removed from (for cations) or added to (for anions) the structure to account for the ion's charge.

An extension of the Lewis structure also exists for molecules or molecular ions in which the central atom is of Period 3 or greater. While the peripheral atoms retain the noble gas configuration, the central atom often extends its valence electrons to accommodate additional electron pairs. As a consequence the central atom accommodates more than eight valence electrons, an extension of the octet rule. For example, the six valence electrons of sulfur bond to four fluorine atoms in forming SF_4. To do so, four of the six valence electrons on sulfur share with the four fluorine atoms and two remain nonbonding—now 10 valence electrons exist for the bonded sulfur atom.

Although a Lewis structure accounts for the bonding based on the valence electrons on each atom, it does not predict the three-dimensional structure for a molecule. The development of the **valence shell electron pair repulsion** (VSEPR) theory provides insight into the three-dimensional structure of the molecule.

VSEPR theory proposes that the structure of a molecule is determined by the repulsive interaction of electron pairs in the valence shell of its central atom. The three-dimensional orientation is such that the distance between the electron pairs is maximized and the electron pair–electron pair interactions are minimized. A construction of the Lewis structure of a molecule provides the first link in predicting the molecular structure.

Methane, CH_4, has four bonding electron pairs in the valence shell of its carbon atom (the central atom in the molecule). Repulsive interactions between these four electron pairs are minimized when the electron pairs are positioned at the vertices of a tetrahedron with H—C—H bond angles of 109.5°. On the basis of the VSEPR theory, one can generalize that all molecules (or molecular ions) having four electron pairs in the valence shell of its central atom have a tetrahedral arrangement of these electron pairs with approximate bond angles of 109.5°. The nitrogen atom in ammonia, NH_3, and the oxygen atom in water, H_2O, also have four electron pairs in their valence shell!

The preferred arrangement of the bonding and nonbonding electron pairs around the central atom gives rise to the corresponding structure of a molecule. The three-dimensional structures for numerous molecules and molecular ions can be grouped into a few basic structures. Based on a correct Lewis structure, a VSEPR formula summarizes the number and type (bonding and nonbonding) of electron pairs in the compound or ion. The VSEPR formula uses the following notations:

A refers to the central atom.

X_m refers to m number of bonding pairs of electrons on A.

E_n refers to n number of nonbonding pairs of electrons on A.

If a molecule has the formula AX_mE_n, it means there are $m + n$ electron pairs in the valence shell of A, the central atom of the molecule; m are bonding and n are nonbonding electron pairs. For example, CH_4, SiF_4, $GeCl_4$, PH_4^+, and PO_4^{3-} all have a VSEPR formula of AX_4. Thus, they all have the same three-dimensional structure, that of a tetrahedral structure.

It should be noted here that valence electrons on the central atom contributing to a multiple bond do not affect the geometry of a molecule. For example in SO_2, the VSEPR formula is AX_2E, and the geometric shape of the molecule is V-shaped. See Table D3.3. Further applications are presented in more advanced chemistry courses.[2]

Valence Shell Electron Pair Repulsion (VSEPR) Theory of the Structures of Molecules and Molecular Ions

Table D3.3 VSEPR and Geometric Shapes of Molecules and Molecular Ions

Valence Shell Electron Pairs	Bonding Electron Pairs	Nonbonding Electron Pairs	VSEPR Formula	Three-Dimensional Structure	Bond Angle	Geometric Shape	Examples
2	2	0	AX_2		180°	Linear	$HgCl_2$, $BeCl_2$
3	3	0	AX_3		120°	Planar triangular	BF_3, $In(CH_3)_3$
	2	1	AX_2E		<120°	V-shaped	$SnCl_2$, $PbBr_2$
4	4	0	AX_4		109.5°	Tetrahedral	CH_4, $SnCl_4$
	3	1	AX_3E		<109.5°	Trigonal pyramidal	NH_3, PCl_3, H_3O^+
	2	2	AX_2E_2		<109.5°	Bent	H_2O, OF_2, SCl_2
5	5	0	AX_5		90°/120°	Trigonal bipyramidal	PCl_5, $NbCl_5$
	4	1	AX_4E		>90°	Irregular tetrahedral	SF_4, $TeCl_4$
	3	2	AX_3E_2		<90°	T-shaped	ICl_3
	2	3	AX_2E_3		180°	Linear	ICl_2^-, XeF_2
6	6	0	AX_6		90°	Octahedral	SF_6
	5	1	AX_5E		>90°	Square pyramidal	BrF_5
	4	2	AX_4E_2		90°	Square planar	ICl_4^-, XeF_4

[2]For more information on VSEPR theory and structure, go to http://winter.group.shef.ac.uk/vsepr.

Table D3.3 presents a summary of the VSEPR theory for predicting the geometric shape and approximate bond angles of a molecule or molecular ion based on the five basic VSEPR three-dimensional structures of molecules and molecular ions.

Let us refer back to SF_4, the molecule with the extended valence shell on the central atom. The sulfur atom has four bonding electron pairs ($m = 4$) and one nonbonding pair ($n = 1$). This gives a VSEPR formula of AX_4E_1, predicting a geometric shape of irregular tetrahedral (sometimes also called *seesaw*) with bond angles greater than 90°. Molecular models will enable you to envision these properties of SF_4.

DRY LAB PROCEDURE

In Part A, the visible spectra of a number of elements are studied (see color plate on back cover of this manual). The wavelengths of the spectra are to be calibrated relative to the mercury spectrum at the bottom of color plate. The most intense lines of the mercury spectrum are listed in Table D3.4.

In Part B, a spectrum from the color plate will be assigned, and, with reference to Table D3.5, the element producing the line spectrum will be identified.

In Part C, a molecule will be assigned and, with reference to Table D3.2, a spectra will be matched to the molecule.

In Part D, a number of simple molecules and molecular ions will be assigned, and their three-dimensional structure and approximate bond angles will be determined. The Lewis structure and the VSEPR adaptation of the Lewis structure are used for analysis.

Discuss with your instructor which parts of the Dry Lab Procedure are to be completed and by when. If there is no advanced preparation and you are to complete all parts, you may be rushed for time.

A. The Mercury Spectrum

1. **The color plate.** Notice the various experimental emission line spectra on the color plate (back cover). A continuous spectrum appears at the top, the line spectra for various elements appear in the middle, and the Hg spectrum appears at the bottom.

2. **Calibrate the spectra of the color plate.** Use a ruler to mark off a linear wavelength scale across the bottom of the color plate such that the experimental wavelengths of the mercury spectrum correlate with those in Table D3.4.

   Extend the linear wavelength scale perpendicularly and upward across spectra on the color plate, thus creating a wavelength grid for calibrating all of the emission spectra. A wax marker or "permanent" felt tip pen may be required for marking the wavelength grid.

   Have your instructor approve your calibration of the spectra on the color plate. See the ***Report Sheet***.

Table D3.4 Wavelengths of the Visible Lines in the Mercury Spectrum

Violet	404.7 nm
Violet	407.8 nm
Blue	435.8 nm
Yellow	546.1 nm
Orange	577.0 nm
Orange	579.1 nm

B. The Spectra of Elements

1. **Hydrogen spectrum.** Use Figure D3.3, page 125, to identify which of the emission spectra on the color plate on the back cover is that of hydrogen. Justify your selection.

2. **Unknown spectra.** Your instructor will assign to you one or two emission spectra from the color plate. Analyze each spectrum by locating the most intense wavelengths in the assigned emission spectrum. Compare the wavelengths of the most intense lines with the data in Table D3.5. Identify the element having the assigned spectrum.

C. Infrared Spectra of Compounds

1. **Match of molecule with infrared spectrum.** Your instructor will assign one or more compounds on page 130 for which you are to determine its infrared spectrum. The absorption bands characteristic of atoms in bonds are listed in Table D3.2, page 126, to assist in the match.

Table D3.5 Wavelengths and Relative Intensities of the Emission Spectra of Several Elements

Element	Wavelength (nm)	Relative Intensity	Element	Wavelength (nm)	Relative Intensity	Element	Wavelength (nm)	Relative Intensity
Argon	451.1	100	Helium	388.9	500	Rubidium	420.2	1,000
	560.7	35		396.5	20		421.6	500
	591.2	50		402.6	50		536.3	40
	603.2	70		412.1	12		543.2	75
	604.3	35		438.8	10		572.4	60
	641.6	70		447.1	200		607.1	75
	667.8	100		468.6	30		620.6	75
	675.2	150		471.3	30		630.0	120
	696.5	10,000		492.2	20	Sodium	466.5	120
	703.0	150		501.5	100		466.9	200
	706.7	10,000		587.5	500		497.9	200
	706.9	100		587.6	100		498.3	400
Barium	435.0	80		667.8	100		568.2	280
	553.5	1,000	Neon	585.2	500		568.8	560
	580.0	100		587.2	100		589.0	80,000
	582.6	150		588.2	100		589.6	40,000
	601.9	100		594.5	100		616.1	240
	606.3	200		596.5	100	Thallium	377.6	12,000
	611.1	300		597.4	100		436.0	2
	648.3	150		597.6	120		535.0	18,000
	649.9	300		603.0	100		655.0	16
	652.7	150		607.4	100		671.4	6
	659.5	3,000		614.3	100	Zinc	468.0	300
	665.4	150		616.4	120		472.2	400
Cadmium	467.8	200		618.2	250		481.1	400
	479.9	300		621.7	150		507.0	15
	508.6	1,000		626.6	150		518.2	200
	610.0	300		633.4	100		577.7	10
	643.8	2,000		638.3	120		623.8	8
Cesium	455.5	1,000		640.2	200		636.2	1,000
	459.3	460		650.7	150		647.9	10
	546.6	60		660.0	150		692.8	15
	566.4	210	Potassium	404.4	18			
	584.5	300		404.7	17			
	601.0	640		536.0	14			
	621.3	1,000		578.2	16			
	635.5	320		580.1	17			
	658.7	490		580.2	15			
	672.3	3,300		583.2	17			
				691.1	19			

D. Structure of Molecules and Molecular Ions

1. **Five basic structures.** Using an appropriate set of molecular models, construct the five basic three-dimensional structures shown in Table D3.3, page 127. Because of the possible limited availability of molecular models, some sharing with other chemists may be necessary. Consult with your laboratory instructor.

2. **Determine three-dimensional structures.** On the *Report Sheet* are selections of suggested molecules and molecular ions for which their three-dimensional structures (geometric shapes) and approximate bond angles are to be determined. Ask your instructor which are to be completed. Set up the table as suggested on the *Report Sheet* for your assigned molecules/molecular ions. Refer to your "built" five basic VSEPR structures as you analyze each molecule/molecular ion.

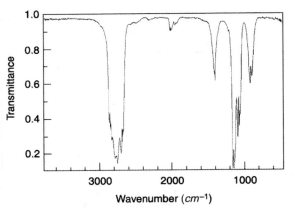

Figure D3.5A

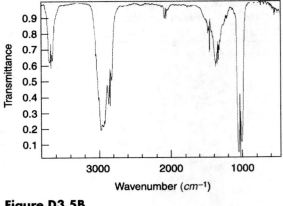

Figure D3.5B

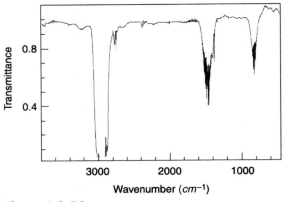

Figure D3.5C

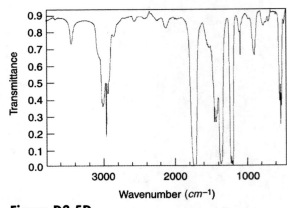

Figure D3.5D

$H_3C \!-\! CH_3$
ethane

$H_3C \!-\! OH$
methanol

$H_3C \!-\! O \!-\! CH_3$
dimethyl ether

acetone

The Next Step

What you complete in this experiment are techniques/tools for atomic and molecular structural analysis. Chemists, biologists, and biochemists are very interested in the identification and structures of compounds. Electromagnetic radiation is just one of those avenues for determination.

Atomic and Molecular Structure

Date _____ Lab Sec. _____ Name _____ Desk No. _____

A. The Mercury Spectrum

Instructor's approval of the calibration of the color plate (back cover) _____

B. The Spectra of Elements

1. Spectrum number _____ is the emission line spectrum for hydrogen on the color plate.

    What are the wavelengths and colors of the emission lines of its visible spectrum?

2. Identification of Spectra
    a. Spectrum number _____

        Intense lines in the spectrum: _____ nm; _____ nm; _____ nm; _____ nm; _____ nm; _____ nm; _____ nm

        Element producing the spectrum _____

    b. Spectrum number _____

        Intense lines in the spectrum: _____ nm; _____ nm; _____ nm; _____ nm; _____ nm; _____ nm; _____ nm

        Element producing the spectrum _____

C. Match of Molecule with Infrared Spectrum

Complete the following table.

Molecule Assigned	Atom-in-Bond Arrangements	Absorption Bands (cm^{-1})	Infrared Spectrum Figure No.
_____	_____	_____	_____
_____	_____	_____	_____
_____	_____	_____	_____

D. Structure of Molecules and Molecular Ions

On a separate sheet of paper, set up the following table (with eight columns) for each of the molecules/molecular ions that are assigned to you/your group. The central atom of the molecule/molecular ion is italicized.

Molecule or Molecular Ion	Lewis Structure	Valence Shell Electron Pairs	Bonding Electron Pairs	Nonbonding Electron Pairs	VSEPR Formula	Approx. Bond Angle	Geometric Shape
1. CH_4	H H:C:H H	4	4	0	AX_4	109.5°	tetrahedral
2. SF_4							
3. H_2O							

1. Complete the table (as outlined above) for the following molecules/molecular ions, all of which obey the Lewis octet rule. Complete those that are assigned by your laboratory instructor.
   a. H_3O^+
   b. NH_3
   c. NH_4^+
   d. CH_3^-
   e. SnH_4
   f. BF_4^-
   g. PO_4^{3-}
   h. PF_3
   i. AsH_3
   j. SiF_4
   k. H_2S
   l. NH_2^-

2. Complete the table (as outlined above) for the following molecules/molecular ions, *none* of which obey the Lewis octet rule. Complete those that are assigned by your laboratory instructor.
   a. GaI_3
   b. PCl_2F_3
   c. BrF_3
   d. XeF_2
   e. XeF_4
   f. $XeOF_2$
   g. $XeOF_4$
   h. SbF_6^-
   i. SF_6
   j. SnF_6^{2-}
   k. IF_4^-
   l. IF_4^+

3. Complete the table (as outlined above) for the following molecules/molecular ions. No adherence to the Lewis octet rule is indicated. Complete those that are assigned by your laboratory instructor.
   a. AsF_3
   b. ClO_2^-
   c. CF_3Cl
   d. SnF_2
   e. SnF_4
   f. PF_4^+
   g. PF_5
   h. SO_4^{2-}
   i. CN_2^{2-}
   j. KrF_2
   k. TeF_6
   l. AsF_5

4. Complete the table (as outlined above) for the following molecules/molecular ions. For molecules or molecular ions with two or more atoms considered as central atoms, consider each atom separately in the analysis according to Table D3.3. Complete those that are assigned by your laboratory instructor.
   a. $OPCl_3$
   b. H_2CCH_2
   c. $CH_3NH_3^+$
   d. Cl_3CCF_3
   e. Cl_2O
   f. $ClCN$
   g. $COCl_2$
   h. $OCCCO$
   i. CO_2
   j. O_3
   k. NO_3^-
   l. $TeF_2(CH_3)_4$

Dry Lab Questions

Circle the questions that have been assigned.

1. What experimental evidence leads scientists to believe that only quantized electronic energy states exist in atoms?

2. **a.** What is the wavelength range of the visible spectrum for electromagnetic radiation?

   b. What is the color of the short wavelength region of the visible spectrum?

   c. If a substance absorbed the wavelengths from the short wavelength region of the visible spectrum, what would be its color?

3. Explain why "roses are red and violets are blue."

4. **a.** Is the energy absorption associated with bands in an infrared spectrum of higher or lower energy than the lines appearing in a visible line spectrum? Explain.

   b. Identify the type of energy transition occurring in a molecule that causes a band to appear in an infrared spectrum.

   c. Identify the type of energy transition occurring in an atom that causes a line to appear in a visible line spectrum.

5. Since $FeNCS^{2+}$ has an absorption maximum at 447 nm, what is the color of the $FeNCS^{2+}$ ion in solution?

6. **a.** Write the Lewis structure for XeF_4.

   b. Write the VSEPR formula for XeF_4.

   c. Sketch (or describe) the three-dimensional structure (or geometric shape) of XeF_4.

   d. What are the approximate F–Xe–F bond angles in XeF_4?

7. Glycine, the simplest of the amino acids, has the formula, $CH_2(NH_2)COOH$, and the Lewis structure at right.

   a. Write the VSEPR formula for the nitrogen atom as the central atom in glycine.

$$\begin{array}{ccc} H & & :O: \\ | & & \| \\ H-C & - & C - \ddot{O} - H \\ | & & \\ :N & - & H \\ | & & \\ H & & \end{array}$$

   b. Based on VSEPR theory, what is the approximate C—N—H bond angle in glycine? Explain.

   c. What is the approximate O—C—O bond angle in glycine? Explain.

   d. Identify at least two absorption bands (and corresponding cm^{-1}) that would likely appear in the infrared spectrum of glycine.

Molar Mass of a Solid

A thermometer is secured with a thermometer clamp to guard against breakage.

- To observe and measure the effect of a solute on the freezing point of a solvent
- To determine the molar mass (molecular weight) of a nonvolatile, nonelectrolyte solute

The following techniques are used in the Experimental Procedure:

A pure liquid, such as water or ethanol, has characteristic physical properties: the melting point, boiling point, density, vapor pressure, viscosity, surface tension, and additional data listed in handbooks of chemistry. The addition of a soluble solute to the liquid forms a homogeneous mixture called a **solution.** The solvent of the solution assumes physical properties that are no longer definite but dependent on the amount of solute added. The vapor pressure of the solvent decreases, the freezing point of the solvent decreases, the boiling point of the solvent increases, and the osmotic pressure of the solvent increases. The degree of the change depends on the *number* of solute particles that have dissolved, *not* on the chemical identity of the solute. These four physical properties that depend on the number of solute particles dissolved in a solvent are called **colligative properties.**

For example, one mole of glucose or urea (neither of which dissociates in water) lowers the freezing point of one kilogram of water by 1.86°C; whereas one mole of sodium chloride lowers the freezing point of one kilogram of water by nearly twice that amount (~3.72°C) because, when dissolved in water, it dissociates into Na^+ and Cl^- providing *twice* as many moles of solute particles per mole of solute as do glucose or urea.

When freezing ice cream at home, a salt–ice water mixture provides a lower temperature bath than an ice/water mixture alone. Antifreeze (ethylene glycol, Figure 8.1) added to the cooling system of an automobile reduces the probability of freeze-up in the winter and boiling over in the summer because the antifreeze/water solution has a lower freezing point and a higher boiling point than pure water.

These changes in the properties of pure water that result from the presence of a **nonvolatile solute** are portrayed by the phase diagram in Figure 8.2, page 136, a plot of vapor pressure versus temperature. The solid lines refer to the equilibrium conditions between the respective phases for pure water; the dashed lines represent the same conditions for an aqueous solution.

Figure 8.1 Ethylene glycol is a major component of most antifreeze solutions.

Colligative properties: properties of a solvent that result from the presence of the number of solute particles in the solution and not their chemical composition

Nonvolatile solute: a solute that does not have a measurable vapor pressure

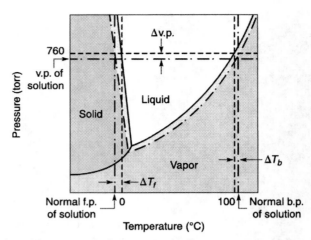

Figure 8.2 Phase diagram (not shown to scale) for water (—) and for an aqueous solution (–·–·–).

The **vapor pressure** of water is 760 torr at its boiling point of 100°C. When a nonvolatile solute dissolves in water to form a solution, solute molecules occupy a part of the surface area. This inhibits movement of some water molecules into the vapor state, causing a **vapor pressure lowering** of the water (Δ*v.p.* in Figure 8.2), lower than 760 torr. With the vapor pressure less than 760 torr, the solution (more specifically, the water in the solution) no longer boils at 100°C. For the solution to boil, the vapor pressure must be increased to 760 torr; boiling can resume only if the temperature is increased above 100°C. This **boiling point elevation** (ΔT_b in Figure 8.2) of the water is due to the presence of the solute.

A solute added to water also affects its freezing point. The normal freezing point of water is 0°C, but in the presence of a solute, the temperature must be lowered below 0°C before freezing occurs (the energy of the water molecules must be lowered to increase the magnitude of the intermolecular forces so that the water molecules "stick" together to form a solid); this is called a **freezing point depression** of the water (ΔT_f in Figure 8.2).

The changes in the freezing point, ΔT_f, and the boiling point, ΔT_b, are directly proportional to the molality, *m*, of the solute in solution. The proportionality is a constant, characteristic of the actual solvent. For water, the freezing point constant, k_f, is 1.86°C·kg/mol, and the boiling point constant, k_b, is 0.512°C·kg/mol.

$$\Delta T_f = |T_{f, \text{solvent}} - T_{f, \text{solution}}| = k_f m \qquad (8.1)$$

$$\Delta T_b = |T_{b, \text{solvent}} - T_{b, \text{solution}}| = k_b m \qquad (8.2)$$

In equations 8.1 and 8.2, T_f represents the freezing point and T_b represents the boiling point of the respective system. $|T_{f, \text{solvent}} - T_{f, \text{solution}}|$ represents the absolute temperature difference in the freezing point change. **Molality** is defined as

$$\text{molality}, m = \frac{\text{mol solute}}{\text{kg solvent}} = \frac{(\text{mass/molar mass})}{\text{kg solvent}} \qquad (8.3)$$

k_f and k_b values for various solvents are listed in Table 8.1.

In this experiment, the freezing points of a selected pure solvent and of a solute–solvent mixture are measured. The freezing point lowering (difference), the k_f data from Table 8.1 for the solvent, and equations 8.1 and 8.3 are used to calculate the moles of solute dissolved in solution and, from its measured mass, the molar mass of the solute.

The freezing points of the solvent and the solution are obtained from a **cooling curve**—a plot of temperature versus time. An ideal plot of the data appears in Figure 8.3. The cooling curve for a pure solvent reaches a plateau at its freezing point:

Table 8.1 Molal Freezing Point and Boiling Point Constants for Several Solvents

Substance	Freezing Point (°C)	$k_f\left(\dfrac{°C \cdot kg}{mol}\right)$	Boiling Point (°C)	$k_b\left(\dfrac{°C \cdot kg}{mol}\right)$
H_2O	0.0	1.86	100.0	0.512
Cyclohexane	—	20.0	80.7	2.69
Naphthalene	80.2	6.9	—	—
Camphor	179	39.7	—	—
Acetic acid	17	3.90	118.2	2.93
t-Butanol	25.5	9.1	—	—

Extrapolation of the plateau to the temperature axis determines its freezing point. The cooling curve for the solution does *not* reach a plateau but continues to decrease slowly as the solvent freezes out of solution. Its freezing point is determined at the intersection of two straight lines drawn through the data points above and below the freezing point (Figure 8.3).

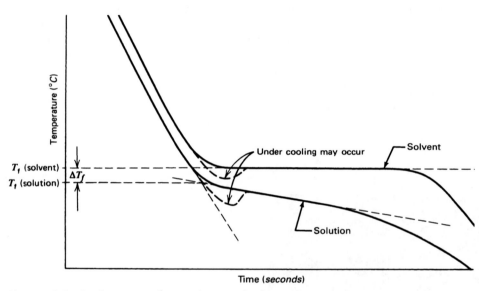

Figure 8.3 Cooling curves for a solvent and solution

Procedure Overview: Cyclohexane is the solvent selected for this experiment although other solvents may be just as effective for the determination of the molar mass of a solute. Another solvent[1] may be used at the discretion of the laboratory instructor. Consult with your instructor. The freezing points of cyclohexane and a cyclohexane *solution* are determined from plots of temperature versus time. The mass of the solute is measured before it is dissolved in a known mass of cyclohexane.

Obtain about 15 mL of cyclohexane. You'll use the cyclohexane throughout the experiment. Your laboratory instructor will issue you about 1 g of unknown solute. Record the unknown number of the solute on the **Report Sheet**.

The cooling curve to be plotted in Part A.4 can be established by using a thermal probe that is connected directly to either a calculator or computer with the appropriate software. If this thermal sensing/recording apparatus is available in the laboratory, consult with your instructor for its use and adaptation to the experiment. The probe merely replaces the glass or digital thermometer in Figure 8.4, page 138.

EXPERIMENTAL PROCEDURE

---

[1]t-Butanol is a suitable substitute for cyclohexane in this experiment.

A. Freezing Point of Cyclohexane (Solvent)

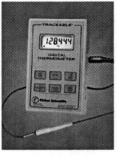

A modern digital thermometer

Appendix C

1. **Prepare the ice–water bath.** Assemble the apparatus shown in Figure 8.4. A 400-mL beaker is placed inside a 600-mL beaker, the latter being an outside insulating beaker. You may want to place a paper towel between the beakers to further insulate the ice–water bath. Place about 300 mL of an ice–water slurry into the 400-mL beaker.[2]

   Obtain a digital or glass thermometer, mount it with a thermometer clamp to the ring stand, and position the thermometer in the test tube. (**Caution:** *If the thermometer is a glass thermometer, handle the thermometer carefully. If the thermometer is accidentally broken, notify your instructor immediately.*)

2. **Prepare the cyclohexane.** Determine the mass (±0.01 g)[3] of a *clean, dry* 200-mm test tube in a 250-mL beaker (Figure 8.5). Add approximately 12 mL of cyclohexane (**Caution:** *Cyclohexane is flammable—keep away from flames; cyclohexane is a mucous irritant—do not inhale*) to the test tube. Place the test tube containing the cyclohexane into the ice–water bath (Figure 8.4). Secure the test tube with a utility clamp. Insert the thermometer probe and a wire stirrer into the test tube. *Secure the thermometer* so that the thermometer bulb or thermal sensor is completely submerged into the cyclohexane.

3. **Record data for the freezing point of cyclohexane.** While stirring with the wire stirrer, record the temperature at timed intervals (15 or 30 seconds) on the second page of the ***Report Sheet***. The temperature remains virtually constant at the freezing point until the solidification is complete. Continue collecting data until the temperature begins to drop again.

4. **Plot the data.** On linear graph paper or by using appropriate software, plot the temperature (°C, vertical axis) versus time (*sec*, horizontal axis) to obtain the cooling curve for cyclohexane. Have your instructor approve your graph.

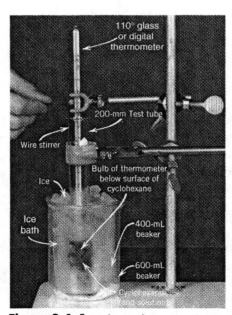
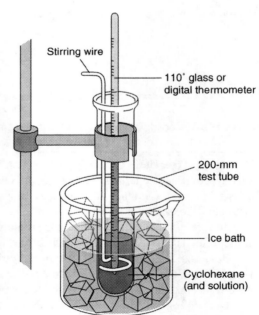

Figure 8.4 Freezing point apparatus

---

[2]Rock salt may be added to further lower the temperature of the ice–water bath.
[3]Use a balance with ±0.001 g sensitivity, if available.

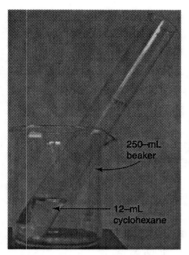

Figure 8.5 Determining the mass of beaker and test tube before (Part A.2) and after adding cyclohexane (Part B.1)

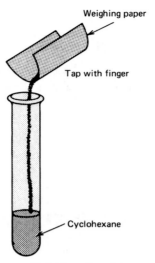

Figure 8.6 Transfer of the unknown solid solute to the test tube containing cyclohexane

Three freezing point trials for the cyclohexane solution are to be completed. Successive amounts of unknown sample are added to the cyclohexane in Parts B.4 and B.5.

B. Freezing Point of Cyclohexane plus Unknown Solute

1. **Measure the mass of solvent and solid solute.** Dry the outside of the test tube containing the cyclohexane and measure its mass in the same 250-mL beaker. On weighing paper, tare the mass of 0.1–0.3 g of unknown solid solute (ask your instructor for the approximate mass to use) and record. Quantitatively transfer the solute to the cyclohexane in the 200-mm test tube (Figure 8.6).[4]

2. **Record data for the freezing point of solution.** Determine the freezing point of this solution in the same way as that of the solvent (Part A.3). Record the time and temperature data on page 2 of the *Report Sheet*. When the solution nears the freezing point of the pure cyclohexane, record the temperature at more frequent time intervals (~15 seconds). A "break" in the curve occurs as the freezing begins, although it may not be as sharp as that for the pure cyclohexane.

3. **Plot the data on the same graph.** Plot the temperature versus time data on the *same* graph (and same coordinates) as those for the pure cyclohexane (Part A.4). Draw straight lines through the data points above and below the freezing point (see Figure 8.3); the intersection of the two straight lines is the freezing point of the solution.

Appendix C

4. **Repeat with additional solute.** Remove the test tube and solution from the ice–water bath. Add an additional 0.1–0.3 g of unknown solid solute using the *same procedure* as in Part B.1. Repeat the freezing-point determination and again plot the temperature versus time data on the same graph (Parts B.2 and B.3). The total mass of solute in solution is the sum from the first and second trials.

5. **Again. Repeat with additional solute.** Repeat Part B.4 with an additional 0.1–0.2 g of unknown solid solute, using the *same procedure* as in Part B.1. Repeat the freezing-point determination and again plot the temperature versus time data on the same graph (Parts B.2–4). The total mass of solute in solution is the sum for the masses added in Parts B.1, B.4 and B.5. You now should have four plots on the same graph.

---

[4]In the transfer, be certain that *none* of the solid solute adheres to the test tube wall. If some does, roll the test tube until the solute dissolves.

6. **Obtain instructor's approval.** Have your instructor approve the three temperature versus time graphs (Parts B.3–5) that have been added to your first temperature versus time graph (Part A.4) for the pure cyclohexane.

Disposal: Dispose of the waste cyclohexane and cyclohexane solution in the Waste Organic Liquids container.

CLEANUP: Safely store and return the thermometer. Rinse the test tube once with acetone; discard the rinse in the Waste Organic Liquids container.

C. Calculations

1. From the plotted data, determine ΔT_f for Trial 1, Trial 2, and Trial 3. Refer to the plotted cooling curves (see Figure 8.3).
2. From k_f (Table 8.1), the mass (in kg) of the cyclohexane, and the measured ΔT_f, calculate the moles of solute for each trial. See equations 8.1 and 8.3.
3. Determine the molar mass of the solute for each trial (remember the mass of the solute for each trial is different).
4. What is the average molar mass of your unknown solute?
5. Calculate the standard deviation and the relative standard deviation (%RSD) for the molar mass of the solute.

The Next Step

Salts dissociate in water. (1) Design an experiment to determine the percent dissociation for a selection of salts in water—consider various concentrations of the salt solutions. Explain your data. (2) Determine the total concentration of dissolved solids in a water sample using this technique and compare your results to the data in *Experiment 3*.

NOTES AND CALCULATIONS

Experiment 8 *Prelaboratory Assignment*

Molar Mass of a Solid

Date _____ Lab Sec. _____ Name _____ Desk No. _____

1. This experiment is more about understanding the colligative properties of a solution rather than the determination of the molar mass of a solid.
   a. Define colligative properties.

   b. Which of the following solutes has the greatest effect on the colligative properties for a given mass of pure water? Explain.
      (i)   0.01 mol of $CaCl_2$ (an electrolyte)
      (ii) 0.01 mol of KNO_3 (an electrolyte)
      (iii) 0.01 mol of $CO(NH_2)_2$ (a nonelectrolyte)

2. A 0.194-g sample of a nonvolatile solid solute dissolves in 9.82 g of cyclohexane. The change in the freezing point of the solution is 2.94°C.
   a. What is the molality of the solute in the solution. See Table 8.1 and equations 8.1 and 8.3.

   b. Calculate the molar mass of the solute to the correct number of significant figures.

   c. The same mass of solute is dissolved in 9.82 g of *t*-butanol instead of cyclohexane. What is the expected freezing-point *change* of this solution? See Table 8.1.

3. Explain why ice cubes formed from water of a glacier freeze at a higher temperature than ice cubes formed from water of an underground aquifer.

4. Two students prepare two cyclohexane solutions having the same freezing point. Student 1 uses 26.6 g of cyclohexane solvent, and student 2 uses 24.1 g of cyclohexane solvent. Which student has the greater number of moles of solute? Show calculations.

5. Two solutions are prepared using the *same* solute:
   Solution A: 0.27 g of the solute dissolves in 27.4 g of *t*-butanol
   Solution B: 0.23 g of the solute dissolves in 24.8 g of cyclohexane
   Which solution has the greatest freezing point change? Show calculations and explain.

6. Experimental Procedure.
   a. How many (total) data plots are to be completed for this experiment? Account for each.

   b. What information is to be extracted from each data plot?

Experiment *8 Report Sheet*

Molar Mass of a Solid

Date _____ Lab Sec. _____ Name _____ Desk No. _____

A. Freezing Point of Cyclohexane (Solvent)

1. Mass of beaker, test tube (*g*) _____

2. Freezing point, from cooling curve (°C) _____

3. Instructor's approval of graph _____

B. Freezing Point of Cyclohexane plus Unknown Solute

	Trial 1 **(Parts B.1, B.3)**	**Trial 2** **(Part B.4)**	**Trial 3** **(Part B.5)**
Unknown solute no. _____			

1. Mass of beaker, test tube, cyclohexane (*g*) _____

2. Mass of cyclohexane (*g*) _____

3. Tared mass of added solute (*g*) _____ _____ _____

4. Freezing point, from cooling curve (°C) _____ _____ _____

5. Instructor's approval of graph _____

Calculations

1. k_f for cyclohexane (pure solvent)   20.0 °C • kg/mol

2. Freezing-point *change*, ΔT_f (°C)

3. Mass of cyclohexane in solution (*kg*)

4. Moles of solute, *total* (*mol*)

5. Mass of solute in solution, *total* (*g*)

6. Molar mass of solute (*g/mol*)   *

7. Average molar mass of solute

8. Standard deviation of molar mass   *Appendix B*

9. Relative standard deviation of molar mass (*%RSD*)   *Appendix B*

*Show calculation(s) for Trial 2 on the next page.

*Calculations for Trial 2.

A. Cyclohexane		B. Cyclohexane + Unknown Solute					
Time	Temp	Trial 1		Trial 2		Trial 3	
		Time	Temp	Time	Temp	Time	Temp

Continue recording data on your own paper and submit it with the *Report Sheet*.

Laboratory Questions

Circle the questions that have been assigned.

1. Part A.3. Some of the cyclohexane solvent vaporized during the temperature versus time measurement. Will this loss of cyclohexane result in its freezing point being recorded as too high, too low, or unaffected? Explain.

2. Part A.3. The digital thermometer is miscalibrated by +0.15°C over its entire range. If the same thermometer is used in Part B.2, will the reported moles of solute in the solution be too high, too low, or unaffected? Explain.

3. Part B.1. Some of the solid solute adheres to the side of the test tube during the freezing point determination of the solution in Part B.2. As a result of the oversight, will the reported molar mass of the solute be too high, too low, or unaffected? Explain.

4. Part B.2. Some of the cyclohexane solvent vaporized during the temperature versus time measurement. Will this loss of cyclohexane result in the freezing point of the solution being recorded as too high, too low, or unaffected? Explain.

5. Part B.2. The solute dissociates slightly in the solvent. How will the slight dissociation affect the reported molar mass of the solute—too high, too low, or unaffected? Explain.

*6. Part B.3, Figure 8.3. The temperature versus time data plot (Figure 8.3) shows no change in temperature at the freezing point for a pure solvent; however, the temperature at the freezing point for a solution steadily decreases until the solution has completely solidified. Account for this decreasing temperature.

7. Part C.1. Interpretation of the data plots consistently shows that the freezing points of three solutions are too high. As a result of this "misreading of the data," will the reported molar mass of the solute be too high, too low, or unaffected? Explain.

144 Molar Mass of a Solid

Experiment 9

Hard Water Analysis

Deposits of hardening ions (generally calcium carbonate deposits) can reduce the flow of water in plumbing.

OBJECTIVES

- To learn the cause and effects of hard water
- To determine the hardness of a water sample

TECHNIQUES

The following techniques are used in the Experimental Procedure:

INTRODUCTION

Hardening ions present in natural waters are the result of slightly acidic rainwater flowing over mineral deposits of varying compositions; the acidic rainwater[1] reacts with the *very* slightly soluble carbonate salts of calcium and magnesium and with various iron-containing rocks. A partial dissolution of these salts releases the ions into the water supply, which may be **surface water** or groundwater.

$$CO_2(aq) + H_2O(l) + CaCO_3(s) \rightarrow Ca^{2+}(aq) + 2\ HCO_3^-(aq) \qquad (9.1)$$

Surface water: water that is collected from a watershed—for example, lakes, rivers, and streams

Hardening ions such as Ca^{2+}, Mg^{2+}, and Fe^{2+} (and other divalent, 2^+, ions) form insoluble compounds with soaps and cause many detergents to be less effective. Soaps, which are sodium salts of fatty acids such as sodium stearate, $C_{17}H_{35}CO_2^-Na^+$, are very effective cleansing agents so long as they remain soluble; the presence of the hardening ions however causes the formation of a gray, insoluble soap scum such as $(C_{17}H_{35}CO_2)_2Ca$:

$$2\ C_{17}H_{35}CO_2^-Na^+(aq) + Ca^{2+}(aq) \rightarrow (C_{17}H_{35}CO_2)_2Ca(s) + 2\ Na^+(aq) \quad (9.2)$$

This gray precipitate appears as a bathtub ring and also clings to clothes, causing white clothes to appear gray. Dishes and glasses may have spots, shower stalls and lavatories may have a sticky film, clothes may feel rough and scratchy, hair may be dull and unmanageable, and your skin may be irritated and sticky because of hard water.

Hard water is also responsible for the appearance and undesirable formation of "boiler scale" on tea kettles and pots used for heating water. The boiler scale is a poor conductor of heat and thus reduces the efficiency of transferring heat. Boiler scale also builds on the inside of hot water pipes, causing a decrease in the flow of water (see opening photo); in extreme cases, this buildup causes the pipe to burst.

Boiler scale consists primarily of the carbonate salts of the hardening ions and is formed according to

$$Ca^{2+}(aq) + 2\ HCO_3^-(aq) \xrightarrow{\Delta} CaCO_3(s) + CO_2(g) + H_2O(l) \qquad (9.3)$$

---

[1]CO_2 dissolved in rainwater makes rainwater slightly acidic:

$$CO_2(g) + 2\ H_2O(l) \rightarrow H_3O^+(aq) + HCO_3^-(aq)$$

The greater the $CO_2(g)$ levels in the atmosphere due to fossil fuel combustion, the more acidic will be the rainwater.

Figure 9.1 Stalactite and stalagmite formations are present in regions having large deposits of limestone, a major contributor of hardening ions. Colored formations are often due to trace amounts of Fe^{2+}, Mn^{2+}, or Sr^{2+}, also hardening ions.

Table 9.1 Hardness Classification of Water*

Hardness (*ppm CaCO₃*)	Classification
<17.1 ppm	Soft water
17.1 ppm–60 ppm	Slightly hard water
60 ppm–120 ppm	Moderately hard water
120 ppm–180 ppm	Hard water
>180 ppm	Very hard water

*U.S. Department of Interior and the Water Quality Association

Notice that this reaction is just the reverse of the reaction for the formation of hard water (equation 9.1). The same two reactions are also key to the formation of stalactites and stalagmites for caves located in regions with large limestone deposits (Figure 9.1).

Because of the relatively large natural abundance of limestone deposits and other calcium minerals, such as gypsum, $CaSO_4 \cdot 2H_2O$, it is not surprising that Ca^{2+} ion, in conjunction with Mg^{2+}, is a major component of the dissolved solids in hard water.

Hard water, however, is not a health hazard. In fact, the presence of Ca^{2+} and Mg^{2+} in hard water can be considered dietary supplements to the point of providing their daily recommended allowance (RDA). Some research studies (though disputed) have also indicated a positive correlation between water hardness and decreased heart disease.

The concentration of the hardening ions in a water sample is commonly expressed as though the hardness is due exclusively to $CaCO_3$. Hardness is commonly expressed as mg $CaCO_3$/L, which is also ppm $CaCO_3$,[2]—or grains per gallon, gpg $CaCO_3$, where 1 gpg $CaCO_3$ = 17.1 mg $CaCO_3$/L. A general classification of hard waters is listed in Table 9.1.

Theory of Analysis

Complex ion: generally a cation of a metal ion to which is bonded a number of molecules or anions (see Experiment 36)

Titrant: the solution placed in the buret in a titrimetric analysis

Analyte: the solution containing the substance being analyzed, generally in the receiving flask in a titration setup

Na⁺⁻O   O⁻ Na⁺
O=C   C=O
H₂C   CH₂
  N
  CH₂
  CH₂
  N
H₂C   CH₂
O=C   C=O
OH   OH
Na_2H_2Y

In this experiment, a titration technique is used to measure the combined hardening divalent ion concentrations (primarily Ca^{2+} and Mg^{2+}) in a water sample. The titrant is the disodium salt of ethylenediaminetetraacetic acid (abbreviated Na_2H_2Y).[3]

In aqueous solution, Na_2H_2Y dissociates into Na^+ and H_2Y^{2-} ions. The H_2Y^{2-} ion reacts with the hardening ions, Ca^{2+} and Mg^{2+}, to form very stable **complex ions,** especially in a solution buffered at a pH of about 10. An ammonia–ammonium ion buffer is often used for this pH adjustment in the analysis.

As H_2Y^{2-} **titrant** is added to the **analyte,** it complexes with the "free" Ca^{2+} and Mg^{2+} of the water sample to form the respective complex ions:

$$Ca^{2+}(aq) + H_2Y^{2-}(aq) \rightarrow [CaY]^{2-}(aq) + 2\,H^+(aq) \qquad (9.4a)$$

$$Mg^{2+}(aq) + H_2Y^{2-}(aq) \rightarrow [MgY]^{2-}(aq) + 2\,H^+(aq) \qquad (9.4b)$$

From the balanced equations, it is apparent that once the molar concentration of the Na_2H_2Y solution is known, the moles of hardening ions in a water sample can be calculated, a 1:1 stoichiometric ratio:

$$\text{volume } H_2Y^{2-} \times \text{molar concentration of } H_2Y^{2-} = \text{moles } H_2Y^{2-}$$
$$= \text{moles hardening ions} \qquad (9.5)$$

The hardening ions, for reporting purposes, are assumed to be exclusively Ca^{2+} from the dissolving of $CaCO_3$. Since one mole of Ca^{2+} forms from one mole of $CaCO_3$, the hardness of the water sample expressed as mg $CaCO_3$ per liter of sample is

$$\text{moles hardening ions} = \text{moles } Ca^{2+} = \text{moles of } CaCO_3 \qquad (9.6)$$

$$\text{ppm } CaCO_3 \left(\frac{mg\ CaCO_3}{L\ \text{sample}} \right) = \frac{\text{mol } CaCO_3}{L\ \text{sample}} \times \frac{100.1\ \text{g } CaCO_3}{\text{mol}} \times \frac{mg}{10^{-3}g} \qquad (9.7)$$

[2]ppm means "parts per million"—1 mg of $CaCO_3$ in 1,000,000 mg (or 1 kg) solution is 1 ppm $CaCO_3$. Assuming the density of the solution is 1 g/mL (or 1 kg/L), then 1,000,000 mg solution = 1 L solution. Therefore, 1 mg/L is an expression of ppm.

[3]**E**thylene**d**iamine**te**tra**a**cetic acid is often simply referred to as EDTA with an abbreviated formula of H_4Y.

A special indicator is used to detect the endpoint in the titration. Called Eriochrome Black T (EBT),[4] it forms complex ions with the Ca^{2+} and Mg^{2+} ions, but binds more strongly to Mg^{2+} ions. Because only a small amount of EBT is added, only Mg^{2+} complexes; no Ca^{2+} ion complexes to EBT—therefore, most all of the hardening ions remain "free" in solution. The EBT indicator is sky blue in solution but forms a wine-red complex with Mg^{2+}:

$$Mg^{2+}(aq) + EBT(aq) \rightleftharpoons [Mg\text{-}EBT]^{2+}(aq) \qquad (9.8)$$
$$\text{sky blue} \qquad \text{wine red}$$

Eriochrome Black T

Therefore, before any H_2Y^{2-} titrant is added for the analysis, the analyte is wine red because of the $[Mg\text{-}EBT]^{2+}$ complex ion.

As the H_2Y^{2-} titrant is added, all of the "free" Ca^{2+} and Mg^{2+} ions in the water sample become complexed just prior to the endpoint; thereafter, the H_2Y^{2-} removes the trace amount of Mg^{2+} from the wine-red $[Mg\text{-}EBT]^{2+}$ complex. At this point, the solution changes from the wine-red color back to the original sky-blue color of the EBT indicator to reach the endpoint. All hardening ions have been complexed with H_2Y^{2-}:

$$[Mg^{2+}\text{-}EBT]^{2+}(aq) + H_2Y^{2-}(aq) \rightarrow [MgY]^{2-}(aq) + 2\,H^+(aq) + EBT(aq) \quad (9.9)$$
$$\text{wine red} \qquad\qquad\qquad\qquad\qquad\qquad\qquad \text{sky blue}$$

Therefore, the presence of Mg^{2+} in the sample is a must in order for the color change from wine red to sky blue to be observed. To ensure the appearance of the endpoint, oftentimes a small amount of Mg^{2+} as $[MgY]^{2-}$ is initially added to the analyte along with the EBT indicator to form the wine-red color of $[Mg\text{-}EBT]^{2+}$.

> The mechanism for the process of adding both $[MgY]^{2-}$ and EBT is as follows: The $[MgY]^{2-}$ dissociates in the analyte because the Y^{4-} (as H_2Y^{2-} in water) is more strongly bonded to the Ca^{2+} of the sample; the "freed" Mg^{2+} then combines with the EBT to form the wine-red color (equation 9.8). The complexing of the "free" Ca^{2+} and Mg^{2+} with the H_2Y^{2-} titrant continues until both are depleted. At that point, the H_2Y^{2-} reacts with the $[Mg\text{-}EBT]^{2+}$ in the sample until the endpoint is reached (equation 9.9).
>
> Because Mg^{2+} and Y^{4-} (as H_2Y^{2-}) are freed initially from the added $[MgY]^{2-}$, but later consumed at the endpoint, no additional H_2Y^{2-} titrant is required for the analysis of hardness in the water sample.

The standardization of a Na_2H_2Y solution is determined by its reaction with a known amount of calcium ion in a (primary) standard Ca^{2+} solution (equation 9.4a). The measured aliquot of the standard Ca^{2+} solution is buffered to a pH of 10 and titrated with the Na_2H_2Y solution to the Eriochrome Black T *sky blue* endpoint (equation 9.9). To achieve the endpoint, a small amount of Mg^{2+} in the form of $[MgY]^{2-}$ is added to the standard Ca^{2+} solution.

Note that the standardization of the Na_2H_2Y solution with a standard Ca^{2+} solution in Part A is reversed in Part B, where the (now) standardized Na_2H_2Y solution is used to determine the concentration of Ca^{2+} (and other hardening ions) in a sample.

Procedure Overview: A (primary) standard solution of Ca^{2+} is used to standardize a prepared ~0.01 M Na_2H_2Y solution. The (secondary) standardized Na_2H_2Y solution is subsequently used to titrate the hardening ions of a water sample to the Eriochrome Black T (or calmagite) indicator endpoint.

The standardized Na_2H_2Y solution may have already been prepared by stockroom personnel. If so, obtain 100 mL of the solution and proceed to Part B. Consult with your instructor.

Three trials are to be completed for the standardization of the ~0.01 M Na_2H_2Y solution. Initially prepare three clean 125-mL Erlenmeyer flasks for Part A.3.

---

[4]Calmagite may be substituted for Eriochrome Black T as an indicator. The same wine-red to sky-blue endpoint is observed. Ask your instructor.

Read and record the volume in the buret to the correct number of significant figures.

1. **Measure of the mass of the Na_2H_2Y solution.** Calculate the mass of $Na_2H_2Y \cdot 2H_2O$ (molar mass = 372.24 g/mol) required to prepare 250 mL of a 0.01 M Na_2H_2Y solution. See *Prelaboratory Assignment* question 2 and show this calculation on the *Report Sheet*. Measure this mass on weighing paper, transfer it to a 250-mL volumetric flask containing 100 mL of deionized water, swirl to dissolve, and dilute to the mark (slight heating may be required).

2. **Prepare a buret for titration.** Rinse a *clean* buret with the Na_2H_2Y solution several times and then fill. Record the volume of the titrant using all certain digits plus one uncertain digit.

3. **Prepare the standard Ca^{2+} solution.** Obtain ~80 mL of a standard Ca^{2+} solution and record its exact molar concentration (~0.01 M). Pipet 25.0 mL of the standard Ca^{2+} solution into a 125-mL Erlenmeyer flask, add 1 mL of buffer (pH = 10) solution, and 2 drops of EBT indicator (containing a small amount of $[MgY]^{2-}$).

4. **Titrate the standard Ca^{2+} solution.** Titrate the standard Ca^{2+} solution with the Na_2H_2Y titrant; swirl continuously. Near the endpoint, slow the rate of addition to drops; the last few drops should be added at 3–5-second intervals. The solution changes from wine red to purple to sky blue—no tinge of the wine-red color should remain; the solution is *blue* at the endpoint. Record the final volume in the buret.

5. **Repeat the titration with the standard Ca^{2+} solution.** Repeat the titrations on the remaining two samples. Calculate the molar concentration of the Na_2H_2Y solution. Save the standard Ca^{2+} solution for Part B.

B. Analysis of Water Sample

Complete three trials for your analysis. The first trial is an indication of the hardness of your water sample. You may want to adjust the volume of water for the analysis of the second and third trials.

1. **Obtain the water sample for analysis**

   a. Obtain about 100 mL of a water sample from your instructor. You may use your own water sample or simply the tap water in the laboratory.

   b. If the water sample is from a lake, stream, or ocean, you will need to gravity filter the sample before the analysis.

   c. If your sample is acidic, add 1 M NH_3 until it is basic to litmus (or pH paper).

2. **Prepare the water sample for analysis.** Pipet 25.0 mL of your (filtered, if necessary) water sample[5] into a 125-mL Erlenmeyer flask, add 1 mL of the buffer (pH = 10) solution, and 2 drops of EBT indicator.

3. **Titrate the water sample.** Titrate the water sample with the standardized Na_2H_2Y until the *blue* endpoint appears (as described in Part A.4). Repeat (twice) the analysis of the water sample to determine its hardness.

Disposal: Dispose of the analyzed solutions in the Waste EDTA container.

The Next Step

(1) Because hardness of a water source varies with temperature, rainfall, seasons, water treatment, and so on design a systematic study of the hardness of a water source as a function of one or more variables. (2) Compare the incoming versus the outgoing water hardness of a continuous water supply. (3) Compare the water hardness of drinking water for adjacent city and county water supplies and account for the differences.

---

[5]If your water is known to have a high hardness, decrease the volume of the water proportionally until it takes about 15 mL of Na_2H_2Y titrant for your second and third trials. Similarly, if your water sample is known to have a low hardness, increase the volume of the water proportionally.

Hard Water Analysis

Date _____ Lab Sec. _____ Name _____ Desk No. _____

1. What cations are responsible for water hardness?

2. Experimental Procedure, Part A.1. Calculate the mass of disodium ethylenediaminetetraacetate (molar mass = 372.24 g/mol) required to prepare 250 mL of a 0.010 M solution. Show the calculation here and on the ***Report Sheet***. Express the mass to the correct number of significant figures.

3. Experimental Procedure, Part A.3. A 25.7-mL volume of a prepared Na_2H_2Y solution titrates 25.0 mL of a standard 0.0107 M Ca^{2+} solution to the Eriochrome Black T endpoint. What is the molar concentration of the Na_2H_2Y solution?

4. a. Which hardening ion, Ca^{2+} or Mg^{2+}, binds more tightly to (forms a stronger complex ion with) the Eriochrome Black T indicator used for today's analysis?

   b. What is the color change at the endpoint?

5. A 50.0-mL water sample requires 16.33 mL of 0.0109 M Na$_2$H$_2$Y to reach the Eriochrome Black T endpoint.

a. Calculate the moles of hardening ions in the water sample.

b. Assuming the hardness is due exclusively to CaCO$_3$, express the hardness concentration in mg CaCO$_3$/L sample. See equation 9.7.

c. What is this hardness concentration expressed in ppm CaCO$_3$?

d. Classify the hardness of this water according to Table 9.1.

6. a. Determine the number of moles of hardening ions present in a 100-mL volume sample that has a hardness of 58 ppm CaCO$_3$. See equations 9.6 and 9.7.

b. What volume of 0.100 M Na$_2$H$_2$Y is needed to reach the Eriochrome Black T endpoint for the analysis of the solution. See equation 9.5.

c. Water hardness is also commonly expressed in units of grains/gallon, where 1 grain/gallon equals 17.1 ppm CaCO$_3$. Express the hardness of this "slightly hard" water sample in grains/gallon.

Hard Water Analysis

Date _____ Lab Sec. _____ Name _____ Desk No. _____

A. A Standard 0.01 *M* Disodium Ethylenediaminetetraacetate, Na_2H_2Y, Solution

Calculate the mass of $Na_2H_2Y \cdot 2H_2O$ required to prepare 250 mL of a 0.01 *M* Na_2H_2Y solution.

	Trial 1	*Trial 2*	*Trial 3*
1. Volume of standard Ca^{2+} solution (*mL*)	25.0	25.0	25.0
2. Concentration of standard Ca^{2+} solution (*mol/L*)			
3. Mol Ca^{2+} = mol Na_2H_2Y (*mol*)			
4. Buret reading, *initial* (*mL*)			
5. Buret reading, *final* (*mL*)			
6. Volume of Na_2H_2Y titrant (*mL*)			
7. Molar concentration of Na_2H_2Y solution (*mol/L*)			
8. Average molar concentration of Na_2H_2Y solution (*mol/L*)			

B. Analysis of Water Sample

	Trial 1	*Trial 2*	*Trial 3*
1. Volume of water sample (*mL*)			
2. Buret reading, *initial* (*mL*)			
3. Buret reading, *final* (*mL*)			
4. Volume of Na_2H_2Y titrant (*mL*)			

5. Mol Na_2H_2Y = mol hardening ions, Ca^{2+} and Mg^{2+} (*mol*)

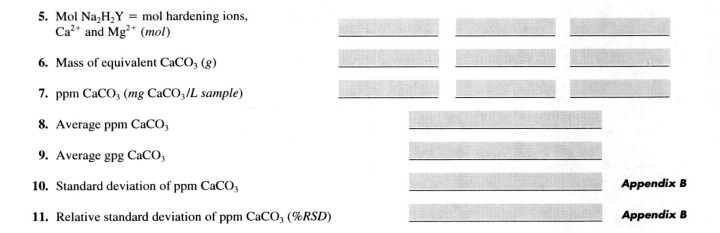

6. Mass of equivalent $CaCO_3$ (*g*)

7. ppm $CaCO_3$ (*mg $CaCO_3$/L sample*)

8. Average ppm $CaCO_3$

9. Average gpg $CaCO_3$

10. Standard deviation of ppm $CaCO_3$ — *Appendix B*

11. Relative standard deviation of ppm $CaCO_3$ (*%RSD*) — *Appendix B*

Laboratory Questions

Circle the questions that have been assigned.

1. Part A.3. State the purpose for the 1 mL of buffer (pH = 10) being added to the standard Ca^{2+} solution.

2. Part A.3. The Eriochrome Black T indicator is mistakenly omitted. What is the color of the analyte (standard Ca^{2+} solution)? Describe the appearance of the analyte with the continued addition of the Na_2H_2Y solution. Explain.

*3. Part A.3. The buffer solution is omitted from the titration procedure, the Eriochrome Black T indicator and a small amount of Mg^{2+} are added, and the standard Ca^{2+} solution is acidic.
   a. What is the color of the solution? Explain.
   b. The Na_2H_2Y solution is dispensed from the buret. What color changes are observed? Explain.

4. Part A.4. Deionized water from the wash bottle is used to wash the side of the Erlenmeyer flask. How does this affect the reported molar concentration of the Na_2H_2Y solution—too high, too low, or unaffected? Explain.

5. Part A.4. The dispensing of the Na_2H_2Y solution from the buret is discontinued when the solution turns purple. Because of this technique error, will the reported molar concentration of the Na_2H_2Y solution be too high, too low, or unaffected? Explain.

6. Part B.3. The dispensing of the Na_2H_2Y solution from the buret is discontinued when the solution turns purple. Because of this technique error, will the reported hardness of the water sample be too high, too low, or unaffected? Explain.

7. Part A.4 and Part B.3. The dispensing of the Na_2H_2Y solution from the buret is discontinued when the solution turns purple. However in Part B.3, the standardized Na_2H_2Y solution is then used to titrate a water sample to the (correct) *blue* endpoint. Will the reported hardness of the water sample be too high, too low, or unaffected? Explain.

*8. Washing soda, $Na_2CO_3 \cdot 10H_2O$ (molar mass = 286 g/mol), is often used to "soften" hard water—that is, to remove hardening ions. Assuming hardness is due to Ca^{2+}, the CO_3^{2-} ion precipitates the Ca^{2+}:

$$Ca^{2+}(aq) + CO_3^{2-}(aq) \rightarrow CaCO_3(s)$$

How many grams and pounds of washing soda are needed to remove the hardness from 500 gallons of water having a hardness of 200 ppm $CaCO_3$ (see Appendix A for conversion factors)?

A Rate Law and Activation Energy

Drops of blood catalyze the decomposition of hydrogen peroxide to water and oxygen gas.

- To determine the rate law for a chemical reaction
- To utilize a graphical analysis of experimental data to
  —determine the order of each reactant in the reaction
  —determine the activation energy for the reaction

TECHNIQUES

The following techniques are used in the Experimental Procedure:

INTRODUCTION

The rate of a chemical reaction is affected by a number of factors, most of which were observed in *Experiment 23*. The rate of a reaction can be expressed in a number of ways, depending on the nature of the reactants being consumed or the products being formed. The rate may be followed as a change in concentration (*mol/L*) of one of the reactants or products per unit of time, the volume of gas produced per unit of time (Figure 10.1), or the change in color (measured as light absorbance) per unit of time, just to cite a few examples.

In Parts A–D of this experiment, a quantitative statement is determined as to how changes in reactant concentrations affect reaction rate at room temperature, the statement being the rate law for the reaction. In Part E, the reaction rate will be determined at different temperatures, allowing us to use the data to calculate the activation energy for the reaction.

To assist in understanding the relationship between reactant concentration and reaction rate, consider the general reaction, $A_2 + 2\,B_2 \rightarrow 2\,AB_2$. The rate of this reaction is related, by some exponential power, to the initial concentration of each reactant. For this reaction, we can write the relationship as

$$\text{rate} = k\,[A_2]^p[B_2]^q \qquad (10.1)$$

This expression is called the **rate law** for the reaction. The value of k, the reaction **rate constant,** varies with temperature but is independent of reactant concentrations.

The superscripts p and q designate the **order** with respect to each reactant and are *always* determined experimentally. For example, if tripling the molar concentration of A_2 while holding the B_2 concentration constant increases the reaction rate by a factor of 9, then $p = 2$. In practice, when the B_2 concentration is in large excess relative to the A_2 concentration, the B_2 concentration remains essentially constant during the course of the reaction; therefore, the change in the reaction rate results from the more significant change in the smaller amount of A_2 in the reaction. An experimental study of the kinetics of any reaction involves determining the values of k, p, and q.

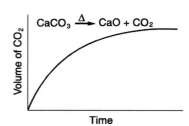

Figure 10.1 The rate of thermal decomposition of calcium carbonate is determined by measuring the volume of evolved carbon dioxide gas versus time.

Rate constant: a proportionality constant relating the rate of a reaction to the initial concentrations of the reactants

Order: the exponential factor by which the concentration of a substance affects reaction rate

In Parts A–D of this experiment, the rate law for the reaction of hydrogen peroxide, H_2O_2, with potassium iodide, KI, is determined.[1] When these reactants are mixed, hydrogen peroxide slowly oxidizes iodide ion to elemental iodine, I_2. In the presence of excess iodide ion, molecular I_2 forms a water-soluble triiodide complex, I_3^- or $[I_2 \bullet I]^-$:

$$3\,I^-(aq) + H_2O_2(aq) + 2\,H_3O^+(aq) \rightarrow I_3^-(aq) + 4\,H_2O(l) \qquad (10.2)$$

The rate of the reaction, governed by the molar concentrations of I^-, H_2O_2, and H_3O^+, is expressed by the rate law:

$$\text{rate} = k\,[I^-]^p[H_2O_2]^q[H_3O^+]^r \qquad (10.3)$$

When the $[H_3O^+]$ is greater than 1×10^{-3} mol/L (pH < 3), the reaction rate is too rapid to measure in the general chemistry laboratory; however, if the $[H_3O^+]$ is *less than* 1×10^{-3} mol/L (pH > 3), the reaction proceeds at a measurable rate. An acetic acid–sodium acetate **buffer** maintains a nearly constant $[H_3O^+]$ at about 1×10^{-5} mol/L (pH = ~5) during the experiment.[2] Since the molar concentration of H_3O^+ is held constant in the buffer solution and does not affect the reaction rate at the pH of the buffer, the rate law for the reaction becomes more simply

$$\text{rate} = k'\,[I^-]^p[H_2O_2]^q \qquad (10.4)$$

where $k' = k\,[H_3O^+]^r$.

In this experiment, Parts B–D, the values of *p*, *q*, and *k'* are determined from the data analysis of Part A for the hydrogen peroxide–iodide ion system. Two sets of experiments are required: One set of experiments is designed to determine the value of *p* and the other to determine the value of *q*.

Determination of *p*, the Order of the Reaction with Respect to Iodide Ion

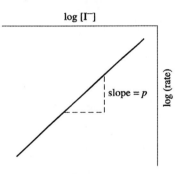

In the first set of experiments, (Table 10.1, kinetic trials 1–4, page 157), the effect that iodide ion has on the reaction rate is observed in several kinetic trials. A "large" excess of hydrogen peroxide in a buffered system maintains the H_2O_2 and H_3O^+ concentrations essentially constant during each trial. Therefore, for this set of experiments, the rate law, equation 10.4, reduces to the form

$$\text{rate} = k'\,[I^-]^p \bullet c \qquad (10.5)$$

c, a constant, equals $[H_2O_2]^q$.

In logarithmic form, equation 10.5 becomes

$$\log(\text{rate}) = \log k' + p\log[I^-] + \log c \qquad (10.6)$$

Combining constants, we have the equation for a straight line:

$$\log(\text{rate}) = p\log[I^-] + C$$
$$y = mx + b \qquad (10.7)$$

C equals $\log k' + \log c$ or $\log k' + \log[H_2O_2]^q$.

Therefore, a plot of log (rate) versus log $[I^-]$ produces a straight line with a slope equal to *p*, the order of the reaction with respect to the molar concentration of iodide ion. See margin figure.

Determination of *q*, the Order of the Reaction with Respect to Hydrogen Peroxide

In the second set of experiments, (Table 10.1, kinetic trials 1, 5–7), the effect that hydrogen peroxide has on the reaction rate is observed in several kinetic trials. A "large"

[1] Your laboratory instructor may substitute $K_2S_2O_8$ for H_2O_2 for this experiment. The balanced equation for the reaction is $S_2O_8^{2-}(aq) + 3\,I^-(aq) \rightarrow 2\,SO_4^{2-}(aq) + I_3^-(aq)$

[2] In general, a combined solution of H_2O_2 and I^- is only very slightly acidic, and the acidity changes little during the reaction. Therefore, the buffer solution may not be absolutely necessary for the reaction. However, to ensure that change in H_3O^+ concentrations is *not* a factor in the reaction rate, the buffer is included as a part of the experiment.

excess of iodide ion in a buffered system maintains the I^- and H_3O^+ concentrations essentially constant during each trial. Under these conditions, the logarithmic form of the rate law (equation 10.4) becomes

$$\log(\text{rate}) = q \log[H_2O_2] + C'$$
$$y = mx + b \qquad (10.8)$$

C' equals $\log k' + \log[I^-]^p$.

A second plot, $\log(\text{rate})$ versus $\log[H_2O_2]$, produces a straight line with a slope equal to q, the order of the reaction with respect to the molar concentration of hydrogen peroxide.

Once the respective orders of I^- and H_2O_2 are determined (from the data plots) and the reaction rate for each trial has been determined, the values of p and q are substituted into equation 10.4 to calculate a specific rate constant, k', for each trial.

Determination of the Specific Rate Constant, k'

Reaction rates are temperature dependent. Higher temperatures increase the kinetic energy of the (reactant) molecules, such that when two reacting molecules collide, they do so with a much greater force (more energy is dispersed within the collision system), causing bonds to rupture, atoms to rearrange, and new bonds (products) to form more rapidly. The energy required for a reaction to occur is called the **activation energy** for the reaction.

Determination of Activation Energy, E_a

The relationship between the reaction rate constant, k', at a measured temperature, $T(K)$, and the activation energy, E_a, is expressed in the Arrhenius equation:

$$k' = Ae^{-E_a/RT} \qquad (10.9)$$

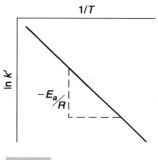

A is a collision parameter for the reaction, and R is the gas constant ($=8.314$ J/mol·K). The logarithmic form of equation 10.9 is

$$\ln k' = \ln A - \frac{E_a}{RT} \quad \text{or} \quad \ln k' = \ln A - \frac{E_a}{R}\left[\frac{1}{T}\right] \qquad (10.10)$$

The latter equation of 10.10 conforms to the equation for a straight line, $y = b + mx$, where a plot of $\ln k'$ versus $1/T$ yields a straight line with a slope of $-E_a/R$ and a y-intercept of $\ln A$.

As the temperature changes, the reaction rate also changes. A substitution of the "new" reaction rate at the "new" temperature into equation 10.4 (with known orders of I^- and H_2O_2) calculates a "new" specific rate constant, k'. A data plot of these new specific rate constants ($\ln k'$) at these new temperatures ($1/T$) allows for the calculation of the activation energy, E_a, for the reaction. In Part E, the temperature of the solutions for kinetic trial 4 (Table 10.1) will be increased or decreased to determine rate constants at these new temperatures.

To follow the progress of the rate of the reaction, two solutions are prepared:

Observing the Rate of the Reaction

- Solution A: a diluted solution of iodide ion, starch, thiosulfate ion ($S_2O_3^{2-}$), and the acetic acid–sodium acetate buffer
- Solution B: the hydrogen peroxide solution

When Solutions A and B are mixed, the H_2O_2 reacts with the I^-:

$$3\,I^-(aq) + H_2O_2(aq) + 2\,H_3O^+(aq) \rightarrow I_3^-(aq) + 4\,H_2O(l) \qquad \text{(repeat of equation 10.2)}$$

To prevent an equilibrium (a back reaction) from occurring in equation 10.2, the presence of thiosulfate ion removes I_3^- as it is formed:

$$2\,S_2O_3^{2-}(aq) + I_3^-(aq) \rightarrow 3\,I^-(aq) + S_4O_6^{2-}(aq) \qquad (10.11)$$

As a result, iodide ion is regenerated in the reaction system; this maintains a constant iodide ion concentration during the course of the reaction until the thiosulfate ion is consumed. When the thiosulfate ion has completely reacted in solution, the generated I_3^- combines with starch, forming a deep-blue I_3^-•starch complex. Its appearance signals a length of time for the reaction (equation 10.2) to occur and the length of time for the disappearance of the thiosulfate ion:

$$I_3^-\,(aq) + \text{starch}\,(aq) \rightarrow I_3^-\text{•starch}\,(aq,\ \text{deep blue}) \qquad (10.12)$$

The time required for a quantitative amount of thiosulfate ion to react is the time lapse for the appearance of the deep-blue solution. During that period a quantitative amount of I_3^- is generated; therefore, the rate of I_3^- production (mol I_3^- /time), and thus the rate of the reaction, is affected *only* by the initial concentrations of H_2O_2 and I^-.

Therefore, the rate of the reaction is followed by measuring the time required to generate a preset number of moles of I_3^-, *not* the time required to deplete the moles of reactants.

For the reaction,

$$\text{rate} = \frac{\Delta \text{ mol } I_3^-}{\Delta t}$$

EXPERIMENTAL PROCEDURE

Procedure Overview: Measured volumes of several solutions having known concentrations of reactants are mixed in a series of trials. The time required for a visible color change to appear in the solution is recorded for the series of trials. The data are collected and plotted (two plots). From the plotted data, the order of the reaction with respect to each reactant is calculated and the rate law for the reaction is derived. After the rate law for the reaction is established, the reaction rate is observed at nonambient temperatures. The plotted data produces a value for the activation energy of the reaction.

Read the entire procedure before beginning the experiment. Student pairs should gather the kinetic data.

A. Determination of Reaction Times

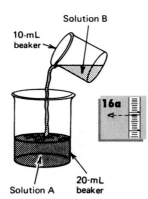

Solution B

10-mL beaker

16a

Solution A   20-mL beaker

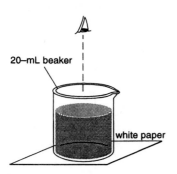

20–mL beaker

white paper

Figure 10.2 Viewing the appearance of the I_3^-•starch complex

1. **Prepare solution A for the kinetic trials.** Table 10.1 summarizes the preparation of the solutions for the kinetic trials. Use previously boiled, deionized water. Measure the volumes of KI and $Na_2S_2O_3$ solutions with *clean*[3] pipets.[4] Burets or pipets can be used for the remaining solutions. At the same time, prepare, all of the solutions A for kinetic trials 1–8 in either clean and *labeled* 20-mL beakers or 150-mm test tubes. Trial 8 is to be of your design.

2. **Prepare solutions for kinetic trial 4.**
   Solution A. Stir the solution in a small 20-mL beaker or 150-mm test tube.
   Solution B. Pipet 3.0 mL of 0.1 *M* H_2O_2 into a clean 10-mL beaker or 150-mm test tube.

3. **Prepare for the reaction.** The reaction begins when the H_2O_2 (solution B) is added to solution A; be prepared to start timing the reaction *in seconds*. Place the beaker on a white sheet of paper so the deep-blue color change is more easily detected (Figure 10.2 or Figure 23.8). As one student mixes the solutions, the other notes the time. All of the solutions should be at ambient temperature before mixing. Record the temperature.

4. **Time the reaction.** Rapidly add solution B to solution A. START TIME and swirl (once) the contents of the mixture. Continued swirling is unnecessary. The appearance of the deep-blue color is sudden. Be ready to STOP TIME. Record the time lapse to the nearest second on the ***Report Sheet***. Repeat if necessary.

Notice! If the time for the color change of trial 4 is less than 10 seconds, STOP. Add an additional 10 mL of boiled, deionized water to each solution A for each kinetic trial (total volume of the reaction mixtures will now be 20 mL instead of 10 mL). A consequence of this dilution will result in a much longer time lapse for a color change in Trial 1—be patient! Consult with your laboratory instructor before the addition of the 10 mL of boiled, deionized water.

---

[3]Cleanliness is important in preparing these solutions because H_2O_2 readily decomposes in the presence of foreign particles. Do *not* dry glassware with paper towels.

$$2\ H_2O_2 \xrightarrow{\text{catalyst}} 2\ H_2O + O_2$$

[4]5-mL *graduated* ($\pm$0.1 mL) pipets are suggested for measuring these volumes.

Table 10.1 Composition of Test Solutions

| Kinetic Trial | Solution A | | | | | Solution B* |
	Boiled, Deionized Water	Buffer**	0.3 M KI	0.02 M $Na_2S_2O_3$	Starch	0.1 M H_2O_2
1	4.0 mL	1.0 mL	1.0 mL	1.0 mL	5 drops	3.0 mL
2	3.0 mL	1.0 mL	2.0 mL	1.0 mL	5 drops	3.0 mL
3	2.0 mL	1.0 mL	3.0 mL	1.0 mL	5 drops	3.0 mL
4	1.0 mL	1.0 mL	4.0 mL	1.0 mL	5 drops	3.0 mL
5	2.0 mL	1.0 mL	1.0 mL	1.0 mL	5 drops	5.0 mL
6	0.0 mL	1.0 mL	1.0 mL	1.0 mL	5 drops	7.0 mL
7	5.0 mL	1.0 mL	1.0 mL	1.0 mL	5 drops	2.0 mL
8†	—	1.0 mL	—	1.0 mL	5 drops	—

*0.1 M $K_2S_2O_8$ may be substituted.
**0.5 M CH_3COOH and 0.5 M $NaCH_3CO_2$.
†You are to select the volumes of solutions for the trial.

5. **Repeat for the remaining kinetic trials.** Mix and time the test solutions for the remaining seven kinetic trials. If the instructor approves, conduct additional kinetic trials, either by repeating those in Table 10.1 or by preparing other combinations of KI and H_2O_2. Make sure that the total diluted volume remains constant at 10 mL.

Disposal: Dispose of the solutions from the kinetic trials in the Waste Iodide Salts container.

CLEANUP: Rinse the beakers or test tubes twice with tap water and discard in the Waste Iodide Salts container. Dispose of two final rinses with deionized water in the sink.

Perform the calculations, carefully *one step at a time*. Appropriate and correctly programmed software would be invaluable for completing this analysis. As you read through this section, complete the appropriate calculation and record it for each test solution on the *Report Sheet*.

B. Calculations for Determining the Rate Law

1. **Moles of I_3^- produced.** Calculate the moles of $S_2O_3^{2-}$ consumed in each kinetic trial. From equation 10.11, the moles of I_3^- that form in the reaction equals one-half the moles of $S_2O_3^{2-}$ that react. This also equals the change in the moles of I_3^-, starting with none at time zero up until a final amount that was produced at the time of the color change. This is designated as "$\Delta(mol\ I_3^-)$" produced.

2. **Reaction rate.** The reaction rate for each kinetic trial is calculated as the ratio of the moles of I_3^- produced, $\Delta(mol\ I_3^-)$, to the time lapse, Δt, for the appearance of the deep-blue color.[5] Compute these reaction rates, $\dfrac{\Delta(mol\ I_3^-)}{\Delta t}$, and the logarithms of the reaction rates (see equations 10.7 and 10.8) for each kinetic trial and enter them on the *Report Sheet*. Because the total volume is a constant for all kinetic trials, we do *not* need to calculate the molar concentrations of the I_3^- produced.

3. **Initial iodide concentrations.** Calculate the initial molar concentration, $[I^-]_0$, and the logarithm of the initial molar concentration, $\log [I^-]_0$, of iodide ion for each kinetic trial.[6] See *Prelaboratory Assignment*, question 4d.

4. **Initial hydrogen peroxide concentrations.** Calculate the initial molar concentration, $[H_2O_2]_0$, and the logarithm of the initial molar concentration, $\log [H_2O_2]_0$, of hydrogen peroxide for each kinetic trial.[7] See *Prelaboratory Assignment*, question 4e.

---

[5]The moles of I_3^- present initially, at time zero, is zero.
[6]Remember, this is *not* 0.3 M I^- because the total volume of the solution is 10 mL after mixing.
[7]Remember, too, this is *not* 0.1 M H_2O_2 because the total volume of the solution is 10 mL after mixing.

C. Determination of the Reaction Order, p and q, for Each Reactant

Appendix C

Appendix C

1. **Determination of p from plot of data.** Plot on the top half of a sheet of linear graph paper or preferably by using appropriate software log (Δmol $I_3^-/\Delta t$), which is log (rate) (y-axis), versus log $[I^-]_0$ (x-axis) at constant hydrogen peroxide concentration. Kinetic trials 1, 2, 3, and 4 have the same H_2O_2 concentration. Draw the best straight line through the four points. Calculate the slope of the straight line. The slope is the order of the reaction, p, with respect to the iodide ion.

2. **Determination of q from plot of data.** Plot on the bottom half of the same sheet of linear graph paper or preferably by using appropriate software log (Δmol $I_3^-/\Delta t$) (y-axis) versus log $[H_2O_2]_0$ (x-axis) at constant iodide ion concentration using kinetic trials 1, 5, 6, and 7. Draw the best straight line through the four points and calculate its slope. The slope of the plot is the order of the reaction, q, with respect to the hydrogen peroxide.

3. **Approval of graphs.** Have your instructor approve both graphs.

D. Determination of k', the Specific Rate Constant for the Reaction

Appendix B

1. **Substitution of p and q into rate law.** Use the values of p and q (from Part C) and the rate law, rate $= \dfrac{\Delta(\text{mol } I_2)}{\Delta t} = k'\,[I^-]^p\,[H_2O_2]^q$, to determine k' for the seven solutions. Calculate the average value of k' with proper units. Also determine the standard deviation and relative standard deviation ($\%RSD$) of k' from your data.

2. **Class data.** Obtain average k' values from other groups in the class. Calculate a standard deviation and relative standard deviation ($\%RSD$) of k' for the class.

E. Determination of Activation Energy

1. **Prepare test solutions.** Refer to Table 10.1, kinetic trial 4. In separate, clean 150-mm test tubes prepare *two* additional sets of solution A and solution B. Place one (solution A/solution B) set in an ice bath. Place the other set in a warm water ($\sim$35°C) bath. Allow thermal equilibrium to be established for each set, about 5 minutes.

    Test solutions prepared at other temperatures are encouraged for additional data points.

2. **Mix solutions A and B.** When thermal equilibrium has been established, quickly pour solution B into solution A, START TIME, and agitate the mixture. When the deep-blue color appears, STOP TIME. Record the time lapse as before. Record the temperature of the water bath and use this time lapse for your calculations. Repeat to check reproducibility and for the other set(s) of solutions.

3. **The reaction rates and "new" rate constants.** The procedure for determining the reaction rates is described in Part B.2. Calculate and record the reaction rates for the (at least) two trials (two temperatures) from Part E.2 and re-record the reaction rate for the (room temperature) kinetic trial 4 in Part A.5. Carefully complete the calculations on the *Report Sheet*.

    Use the reaction rates at the three temperatures (ice, room, and $\sim$35°C temperatures) and the established rate law from Part C to calculate the rate constants, k', at these temperatures. Calculate the natural logarithm of these rate constants.

Appendix C

4. **Plot the data.** Plot ln k' versus $1/T(K)$ for the (at least) three trials at which the experiment was performed. Remember to express temperature in kelvins and $R = 8.314$ J/mol·K.

5. **Activation energy.** From the data plot, determine the slope of the linear plot ($= -E_a/R$) and calculate the activation energy for the reaction. You may need to seek the advice of your instructor for completing the calculations on the *Report Sheet*.

The Next Step

The rate law for any number of chemical reactions can be studied in the same manner—for example, see *Experiment 23*, Parts B, C, and F. Research the Internet for a kinetic study of interest (biochemical?) and design a systematic kinetic study of a chemical system.

Experiment **10** *Prelaboratory Assignment*

A Rate Law and Activation Energy

Date _____ Lab Sec. _____ Name _____ Desk No. _____

1. Three data plots are required for analyzing the data in this experiment, two plots from the kinetic trials outlined in Table 10.1 and one plot from Part E. From each data plot, a value is determined toward the completion of the analysis of the kinetic study for the reaction of I^- with H_2O_2. Complete the table in order to focus the analysis.

Source of Data	y-axis label	x-axis label	Data to be obtained from the data plot
Table 10.1, trials 1–4	_____	_____	_____
Table 10.1, trials 1, 5–7	_____	_____	_____
Part E	_____	_____	_____

2. **a.** In the collection of the rate data for the experiment, when do START TIME and STOP TIME occur for each kinetic trial in Table 10.1?

   b. What is the color of the solution at STOP TIME?

   c. What is the chemical reaction that accounts for the color of the solution at STOP TIME.

3. In the kinetic analysis of this experiment for the reaction of iodide ion with hydrogen peroxide, state the purpose for each of the following solutions (see Table 10.1):
   a. deionized water

   b. buffer solution (acetic acid, sodium acetate mixture)

4. Experimental Procedure, Part A, Table 10.1
   a. In Trial 1, what is the function of the sodium thiosulfate in studying the kinetics of the hydrogen peroxide–iodide reaction?

   b. Calculate the moles of $S_2O_3^{2-}$ that are consumed during the course of the reaction in Trial 1.

c. Calculate the moles of I_3^- that are produced during the course of the reaction. See equation 10.1.

d. Calculate the initial molar concentration of I^- (at time = 0), $[I^-]_0$ (not 0.3 M, but after mixing solutions A and B for a total volume of 10 mL).

e. Calculate the initial molar concentration of H_2O_2 (at time = 0), $[H_2O_2]_0$ (not 0.1 M, but after mixing solutions A and B for a total volume of 10 mL).

5. Experimental Procedure, Part C. The order of the reaction with respect to H_2O_2 is determined graphically in this experiment.
a. What are the labels for the x-axis and y-axis, respectively?

b. How is the value for the order of the reaction with respect to H_2O_2 determined from the graphical data?

6. Explain how the rate constant, k', is determined for the rate law in the experiment.

7. From the following data plot, calculate the activation energy, E_a, for the reaction.

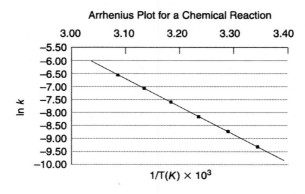

Arrhenius Plot for a Chemical Reaction

A Rate Law and Activation Energy

Date _____ Lab Sec. _____ Name _____ Desk No. _____

A. Determination of Reaction Times

Molar concentration of $Na_2S_2O_3$ _____; Volume of $Na_2S_2O_3$ (L) _____; Ambient temperature _____ °C

Molar concentration of KI _____; Molar concentration of H_2O_2 _____; Total volume of kinetic trials (mL) _____

Kinetic Trial	1*	2	3	4	5	6	7	8
1. Time for color change, Δt (sec)								

B. Calculations for Determining the Rate Law

	1*	2	3	4	5	6	7	8
1. Moles of $S_2O_3^{2-}$ consumed (mol)								
2. $\Delta(\text{mol } I_3^{-})$ produced								
3. $\dfrac{\Delta(\text{mol } I_3^{-})}{\Delta t}$								
4. $\log \dfrac{\Delta(\text{mol } I_3^{-})}{\Delta t}$								
5. Volume KI (mL)								
6. $[I^-]_0$ (mol/L)**								
7. $\log [I^-]_0$								
8. Volume H_2O_2 (mL)								
9. $[H_2O_2]_0$ (mol/L)**								
10. $\log [H_2O_2]_0$								

*Calculations for Kinetic Trial 1.

**Diluted initial molar concentration.

C. Determination of the Reaction Order, *p* and *q*, for Each Reactant

Instructor's approval of graphs:

1. $\log (\Delta \text{mol } I_3^-/\Delta t)$ versus $\log [I^-]_0$ _____

2. $\log (\Delta \text{mol } I_3^-/\Delta t)$ versus $\log [H_2O_2]_0$ _____

3. value of *p* from graph _____;   value of *q* from graph _____

Write the rate law for the reaction.

D. Determination of *k'*, the Specific Rate Constant for the Reaction

Kinetic Trial	1	2	3	4	5	6	7	8
1. Value of *k'*								
2. Average value of *k'*								
3. Standard deviation of *k'*				Appendix B				
4. Relative standard deviation of *k'* (*%RSD*)				Appendix B				

Class Data/Group	1	2	3	4	5	6
Average value of *k'*						

Calculate the average value and the standard deviation of the reaction rate constant for the class. See Appendix B.

Calculate the relative standard deviation of *k'* (*%RSD*).

E. Determination of Activation Energy

	Time for color change	Reaction rate	Calc. k'	ln k'	Temperature	$1/T(K)$
1. Trial 4	_____				_____	
2. Cold	_____				_____	
3. Warm	_____				_____	

4. Instructor's Approval of Data Plot _____

5. Value of $(-E_a/R)$ from ln k' versus $1/T$ graph _____

6. Activation Energy, E_a, from data plot. Show calculation. _____

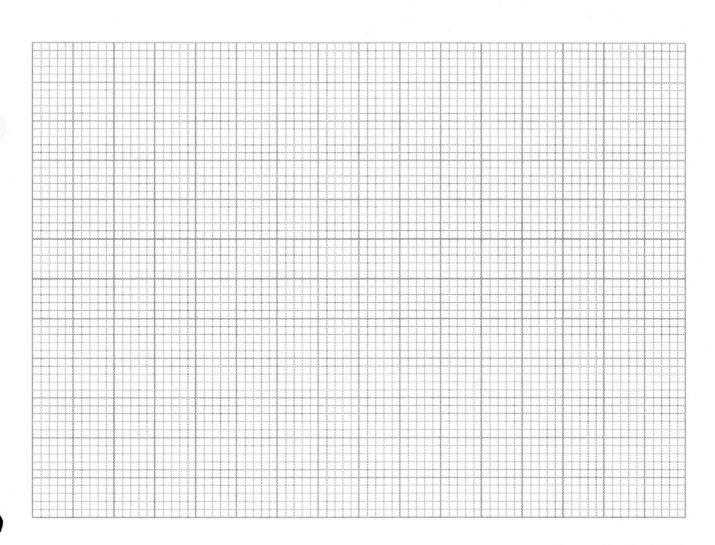

Laboratory Questions

Circle the questions that have been assigned.

1. Part A.4. Describe the chemistry that was occurring in the experiment between the time when solutions A and B were mixed and STOP TIME.

2. Part A.4. For kinetic trial 2, Alicia was distracted when the color change occurred but decided to record the time lapse read from her watch. Will this distraction cause an increase or decrease in the slope of the log (rate) versus log $[I^-]_o$? Explain.

3. Part A, Table 10.1.
   a. When doing the kinetic trials, Susan forgot to include the deionized water. Will this omission hasten or delay the formation of the blue color in the trials (exclusive of Trial 6)? Explain.
   b. When doing the kinetic trials, Oscar mistakenly omitted the sodium thiosulfate solution. How will this omission change the appearance of the resultant solution (from the mixing solutions A and B) from that of a correctly completed experiment? Explain your reasoning.
   c. When doing the kinetic trials, Peyton mistakenly omitted the starch solution from the kinetic trials. How will this omission change the appearance of the resultant solution (from the mixing solutions A and B) from that of a correctly completed experiment? Explain your reasoning.
   d. Of the three chemists above, which chemist will have the most accurate results? Explain.

4. Part C.2. Review the plotted data.
   a. What is the numerical value of the y-intercept?
   b. What is the kinetic interpretation of the value for the y-intercept?
   c. What does its value equal in equation 10.8?

5. State the effect that each of the following changes has on the reaction rate in this experiment—increase, decrease, or no effect. (Assume no volume change for any of the concentration changes.)
   a. An increase in the H_2O_2 concentration. Explain.
   b. An increase in the volume of water in solution A. Explain.
   c. An increase in the $Na_2S_2O_3$ concentration. Explain.
   d. The substitution of a 0.5% starch solution for one at 0.2%. Explain.

*6. If 0.2 M KI replaced the 0.3 M KI in this experiment, how would this affect the following—increase, decrease, or no effect?
   a. The rate of the reaction. Explain.
   b. The slopes of the graphs used to determine p and q. Explain.
   c. The value of the reaction rate constant. Explain.

7. Part E.2. The temperature of the warm water bath is recorded too high. How will this technique error affect the reported activation energy for the reaction—too high or too low? Explain.

8. Part E.4. Arnie's data plot has a greater negative slope than Bill's. Which student will record the higher activation energy for the reaction? Describe your reasoning.

Experiment 11

An Equilibrium Constant

The nearly colorless iron(III) ion (left) forms an intensely colored complex (right) in the presence of the thiocyanate ion.

OBJECTIVES

Spectrophotometer: a laboratory instrument that measures the amount of light transmitted through a sample

- To use a **spectrophotometer** to determine the equilibrium constant of a chemical system
- To use graphing techniques and data analysis to evaluate data
- To determine the equilibrium constant for a soluble equilibrium

TECHNIQUES

The following techniques are used in the Experimental Procedure:

INTRODUCTION

A spectrophotometric method of analysis involves the interaction of electromagnetic (EM) radiation with matter. The most common regions of the EM spectrum used for analyses are the ultraviolet, visible, and the infrared regions. We are most familiar with the visible region of the spectrum, in which wavelengths range from 400 to 700 nm.

The visible spectra of ions and molecules in solution arise from *electronic* transitions within their respective structures. The greater the concentration of the absorbing ions/molecules in solution, the greater is the absorption of the visible EM radiation (and the greater the transmittance of the *complementary* radiation). The degree of absorbed radiation (or the intensity of the transmitted radiation) is measured using an instrument called a **spectrophotometer**, which measures transmitted light intensities with a photosensitive detector at specific (but variable) visible wavelengths (Figure 11.1, page 166). The wavelength where the absorbing ions or molecules has a maximum absorption of visible radiation is determined and set on the spectrophotometer for the analysis.

The Introduction to Dry Lab 3 discusses in more detail the interaction of electromagnetic radiation with atoms, ions, and molecules in terms of energy states, excited states, wavelengths, and spectra.

The visible light path through the spectrophotometer from the light source through the sample to the photosensitive detector is shown in Figure 11.2, page 166.

Several factors control the amount of EM radiation (light energy) that a sample absorbs:

- Concentration of the absorbing substance
- Thickness of the sample containing the absorbing substance (determined by the width of the **cuvet**)
- Probability of light absorption by the absorbing substance (called the **molar absorptivity coefficient** or **extinction coefficient**)

Cuvet: a special piece of glassware to hold solutions for measurement in the spectrophotometer

Figure 11.1 Common laboratory visible spectrophotometer

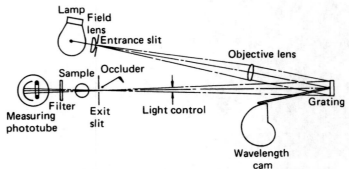

Figure 11.2 The light path through a visible spectrophotometer

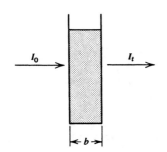

Figure 11.3 Incident light, I_0, and transmitted light, I_t, for a sample of thickness b

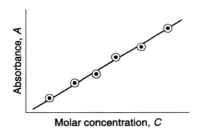

Figure 11.4 A data plot of absorbance versus concentration

The ratio of the intensity of the transmitted light, I_t, to that of the incident light, I_0 (Figure 11.3), is called the **transmittance**, T, of the EM radiation by the sample. This ratio, expressed as percent, is

$$\frac{I_t}{I_0} \times 100 = \%T \tag{11.1}$$

Most spectrophotometers have a $\%T$ (percent transmittance of light) scale. Because it is linear, the $\%T$ scale is easy to read and interpolate. However, chemists often perform calculations based on the amount of light *absorbed* by the sample rather than the amount of light transmitted because absorption is directly proportional to the concentration of the absorbing substance. The **absorbance**, A, of the substance is related to the intensity of the incident and transmitted light (and the percent transmittance) by the equations

$$A = \log \frac{I_0}{I_t} = \log \frac{1}{T} = \log \frac{100}{\%T} = a \cdot b \cdot c \tag{11.2}$$

The molar absorptivity coefficient, a, is a constant at any given wavelength for a particular absorbing substance, b is the thickness of the absorbing substance in centimeters, and c is the molar concentration of the absorbing substance.[1]

The absorbance value is directly proportional to the molar concentration of the absorbing substance *if* the same (or a matched) cuvet and a *set* wavelength are used for all measurements. A plot of absorbance versus concentration data is linear; a calculated slope and absorbance data can be used to determine the molar concentration of the same absorbing species in a solution of unknown concentration (Figure 11.4) from the linear relationship.

Measuring an Equilibrium Constant

The magnitude of an equilibrium constant, K_c, expresses the equilibrium position for a chemical system. For the reaction, $aA + bB \rightleftharpoons xX + yY$, the mass action expression, $\frac{[X]^x[Y]^y}{[A]^a[B]^b}$, equals the equilibrium constant, K_c, when a dynamic equilibrium has been established between reactants and products. The brackets in the mass action expression denote the equilibrium *molar concentration* of the respective substance.

The magnitude of the equilibrium constant indicates the principal species, products or reactants, that exist in the chemical system at equilibrium. For example, a large equilibrium constant indicates that the equilibrium lies to the right with a high concentration of products and correspondingly low concentration of reactants. The value of K_c is constant for a chemical system at a given temperature.

---

[1]Because the quantity log (I_0/I_t) is generally referred to as *absorbance*, equation 11.2 becomes $A = abc$. This equation is commonly referred to as **Beer's law.**

This experiment determines K_c for a chemical system in which all species are soluble. The chemical system involves the equilibrium between iron(III) ion, Fe^{3+}, thiocyanate ion, SCN^-, and thiocyanatoiron(III) ion, $FeNCS^{2+}$:

$$[Fe(H_2O)_6]^{3+}(aq) + SCN^-(aq) \rightleftharpoons [Fe(H_2O)_5NCS]^{2+}(aq) + H_2O(l) \quad (11.3)$$

The "free" thiocyanate ion is commonly written as SCN^-; however, its bond to the ferric ion is through the nitrogen atom, thus the formula of the complex is written $FeNCS^{2+}$.

Because the concentration of water is essentially constant in dilute aqueous solutions, we omit the waters of hydration and simplify the equation to read

$$Fe^{3+}(aq) + SCN^-(aq) \rightleftharpoons FeNCS^{2+}(aq) \quad (11.4)$$

The mass action expression for the equilibrium system, equal to the equilibrium constant, is

$$K_c = \frac{[FeNCS^{2+}]}{[Fe^{3+}][SCN^-]} \quad (11.5)$$

In Part A you will prepare a set of five **standard solutions** of the $FeNCS^{2+}$ ion. As $FeNCS^{2+}$ is a deep, blood-red complex, its absorption maximum occurs at about 447 nm. The absorbance at 447 nm for each solution is plotted versus the molar concentration of $FeNCS^{2+}$; this establishes a **calibration curve** from which the concentrations of $FeNCS^{2+}$ are determined for the chemical systems in Part B.

Standard solution: a solution with a very well known concentration of solute

Calibration curve: a plot of known data from which further interpretations can be made

In preparing the standard solutions of $FeNCS^{2+}$, the Fe^{3+} concentration is set to *far* exceed the SCN^- concentration. This huge excess of Fe^{3+} pushes the equilibrium (equation 11.4) *far* to the right, consuming nearly all of the SCN^- placed in the system. As a result, the $FeNCS^{2+}$ concentration at equilibrium approximates the original SCN^- concentration. In other words, we assume that the position of the equilibrium is driven so far to the right by the excess Fe^{3+} that all of the SCN^- is **complexed,** forming $FeNCS^{2+}$ (Figure 11.5).

Complexed: the formation of a bond between the Lewis base, SCN^-, and the Lewis acid, Fe^{3+}

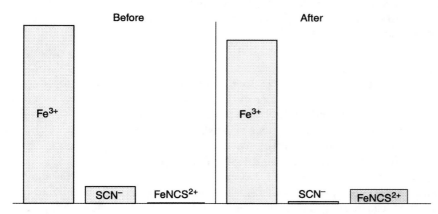

Figure 11.5 A large excess of Fe^{3+} consumes nearly all of the SCN^- to form $FeNCS^{2+}$. The amount of Fe^{3+} remains essentially unchanged in solution.

In Part B, the concentrations of the Fe^{3+} and SCN^- ions in the various test solutions are nearly the same, thus creating equilibrium systems in which there is an appreciable amount of each of the species after equilibrium is established (Figure 11.6).

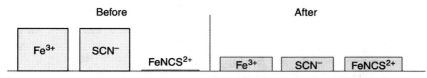

Figure 11.6 Amounts of Fe^{3+} and SCN^- are equally reduced in the formation of $FeNCS^{2+}$.

Measurements for K_c

In Part B, precise volumes of known molar concentrations of Fe^{3+} and SCN^- are mixed. The equilibrium molar concentration of $FeNCS^{2+}$ of the system is determined by measuring its absorbance and then using the calibration curve from Part A. Since the total volume of the mixed solution is measured precisely, the *initial* moles of Fe^{3+} and SCN^- and the *equilibrium* moles of $FeNCS^{2+}$ are easily calculated from known molar concentrations.

From equation 11.4, for every mole of $FeNCS^{2+}$ that exists at equilibrium, an equal number of moles of Fe^{3+} and SCN^- have reacted to reach equilibrium:

$$\text{mol FeNCS}^{2+}_{\text{equilibrium}} = \text{mol Fe}^{3+}_{\text{reacted}} = \text{mol SCN}^-_{\text{reacted}} \qquad (11.6)$$

Therefore, the moles of Fe^{3+} at equilibrium (unreacted) is

$$\text{mol Fe}^{3+}_{\text{equilibrium}} = \text{mol Fe}^{3+}_{\text{initial}} - \text{mol Fe}^{3+}_{\text{reacted}} \qquad (11.7)$$

Similarly, the moles of SCN^- at equilibrium (unreacted) is

$$\text{mol SCN}^-_{\text{equilibrium}} = \text{mol SCN}^-_{\text{initial}} - \text{mol SCN}^-_{\text{reacted}} \qquad (11.8)$$

Again, since the total volume of the reaction mixture is known precisely, the equilibrium molar concentrations of Fe^{3+} and SCN^- (their *equilibrium* concentrations) can be calculated. Knowing the measured equilibrium molar concentration of $FeNCS^{2+}$ from the calibration curve, substitution of the three equilibrium molar concentrations into the mass action expression provides the value of the equilibrium constant, K_c.

Calculations for K_c

The calculations for K_c are involved, but completion of the ***Prelaboratory Assignment*** should clarify most of the steps. The ***Report Sheet*** is also outlined in such detail as to assist with the calculations.

EXPERIMENTAL PROCEDURE

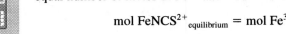

Procedure Overview: One set of solutions having known molar concentrations of $FeNCS^{2+}$ is prepared for a calibration curve, a plot of absorbance versus concentration. A second set of equilibrium solutions is prepared and mixed to determine the respective equilibrium molar concentrations of $FeNCS^{2+}$. By carefully measuring the initial amounts of reactants placed in the reaction systems and the absorbance, the mass action expression at equilibrium can be solved; this equals K_c.

A large number of pipets and 100-mL volumetric flasks are used in this experiment. Ask your instructor about working with a partner. A spectrophotometer is an expensive, delicate analytical instrument. Operate it with care, following the advice of your instructor, and it will give you good data.

A. A Set of Standard Solutions to Establish a Calibration Curve

The set of standard solutions is used to determine the absorbance of known molar concentrations of $FeNCS^{2+}$. A plot of the data, known as a **calibration curve**, is used to determine the equilibrium molar concentrations of $FeNCS^{2+}$ in Part B.

Once the standard solutions are prepared, proceed smoothly and methodically through Part A.4. Therefore, read through all of Part A before proceeding.

1. **Prepare a set of the standard solutions.** Prepare the solutions in Table 11.1. Pipet 0, 1, 2, 3, 4 and 5 mL of 0.001 *M* NaSCN into separate, labeled, and clean 25-mL volumetric flasks (or 200-mm test tubes). Pipet 10.0 mL of 0.2 *M* $Fe(NO_3)_3$ into each flask (or test tube) and *quantitatively* dilute to 25 mL (the mark on the volumetric flask) with 0.1 *M* HNO_3. Stir or agitate each solution thoroughly to ensure that equilibrium is established.

Table 11.1 Composition of the Set of Standard $FeNCS^{2+}$ Solutions for Preparing the Calibration Curve

Standard Solution	0.2 M $Fe(NO_3)_3$ (in 0.1 M HNO_3)	0.001 M NaSCN (in 0.1 M HNO_3)	0.1 M HNO_3
Blank	10.0 mL	0 mL	Dilute to 25 mL
1	10.0 mL	1 mL	Dilute to 25 mL
2	10.0 mL	2 mL	Dilute to 25 mL
3	10.0 mL	3 mL	Dilute to 25 mL
4	10.0 mL	4 mL	Dilute to 25 mL
5	10.0 mL	5 mL	Dilute to 25 mL

Record on the **Report Sheet** the *exact* molar concentrations of the $Fe(NO_3)_3$ and NaSCN reagent solutions.

2. **Prepare the blank solution.** After the spectrophotometer has been turned on for 10 minutes and the wavelength scale has been set at 447 nm, rinse a cuvet with several portions of the **blank solution.** Dry the outside of the cuvet with a clean Kimwipe, removing water and fingerprints.[2] Handle the lip of the cuvet thereafter. If a cuvet has two clear and two cloudy sides, be sure light passes through the clear sides and handle the cuvet on the cloudy sides.

3. **Calibrate the spectrophotometer.** Place the cuvet, three-fourths filled with the blank solution, into the sample compartment, align the mark on the cuvet with that on the sample holder, and close the cover. Set the meter on the spectrophotometer to read zero absorbance (or 100%T).[3] Remove the cuvet. Consult with your instructor for any further calibration procedures. Once the instrument is set, *do not* perform any additional adjustments for the remainder of the experiment. If you accidentally do, merely repeat the calibration procedure.

4. **Record the absorbance of the standard solutions.** Empty the cuvet and rinse it *thoroughly* with several small portions of solution 1.[4] Fill it approximately three-fourths full. Again, carefully dry the outside of the cuvet with a clean Kimwipe. Remember, handle only the lip of the cuvet. Place the cuvet into the sample compartment and align the cuvet and sample holder marks; read the absorbance (or percent transmittance if the spectrophotometer has a meter readout) and record. Repeat for solutions 2, 3, 4, and 5.

   Share the set of standard solutions with other chemists in the laboratory.

5. **Graph the data.** Plot absorbance, A (ordinate), versus $[FeNCS^{2+}]$ (abscissa) for the six solutions on linear graph paper or by using appropriate software. Draw the *best straight line* through the six points (see Figure 11.4) to establish the calibration curve. Ask your instructor to approve your graph.

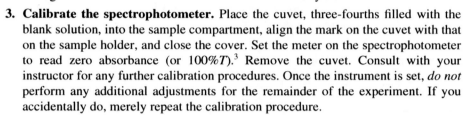

Blank 1 2 3 4 5
A set of labeled standard solutions.

Blank solution: a solution that contains all light-absorbing species except the one being investigated in the experiment

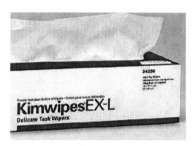

A box of lint-free tissue

Appendix C

---

1. **Prepare the test solutions.** In *clean* 150-mm test tubes (or 10-mL volumetric flasks)[5] prepare the test solutions in Table 11.2, page 376. Use pipets for the volumetric measurements. Be careful not to mix pipets to avoid contamination of the reagents prior to the preparation. Also note that the molar concentration of $Fe(NO_3)_3$

B. Absorbance for the Set of Test Solutions

---

[2]Water and fingerprints (or any foreign material) on the outside of the cuvet reduce the intensity of the light transmitted to the detector.

[3]For spectrophotometers with a meter readout (as opposed to digital), record the percent transmittance and then calculate the absorbance (equation 11.2). This procedure is more accurate because %T is a linear scale (whereas absorbance is logarithmic) and because it is easier to estimate the linear %T values more accurately and consistently.

[4]If possible, prepare six matched cuvets, one for each standard solution, and successively measure the absorbance of each, remembering that the first solution is the blank solution.

[5]If 10-mL volumetric flasks are used, use pipets to dispense the volumes of the NaSCN and $Fe(NO_3)_3$ solutions and then dilute to the mark with 0.1 M HNO_3.

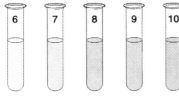

A set of labeled test solutions

Table 11.2 Composition of the Set of Equilibrium Test Solutions for the Determination of K_c

Test Solution	0.002 M Fe(NO$_3$)$_3$* (in 0.1 M HNO$_3$)	0.002 M NaSCN (in 0.1 M HNO$_3$)	0.1 M HNO$_3$
6	5 mL	1 mL	4 mL
7	5 mL	2 mL	3 mL
8	5 mL	3 mL	2 mL
9	5 mL	4 mL	1 mL
10	5 mL	5 mL	—

*If 0.002 M Fe(NO$_3$)$_3$ is not available, dilute 1.0 mL (measure with a 1.0-mL pipet) of the 0.2 M Fe(NO$_3$)$_3$ used in Part A with 0.1 M HNO$_3$ in a 100-mL volumetric flask and then share the remaining solution with other students.

for this set of solutions is 0.002 M, *not* the 0.2 M solution used in Part A and the molar concentration of NaSCN in 0.002 M, not 0.001 M.

Record the *exact* molar concentrations of the Fe(NO$_3$)$_3$ and NaSCN reagent solutions on the **Report Sheet**.

Once the test solutions are prepared, proceed smoothly and methodically (you need not hurry!) through Part B.3.

2. **Recalibrate the spectrophotometer.** Use the blank solution from Part A to check the calibration of the spectrophotometer. See Part A.3.

3. **Determine the absorbance of the test solutions.** Stir or agitate each test solution until equilibrium is reached (approximately 30 seconds). Rinse the cuvet thoroughly with several portions of the test solution and fill it three-fourths full. Clean and dry the outside of the cuvet. Be cautious in handling the cuvets. Record the absorbance of each test solution as was done in Part A.4.

Disposal: Dispose of all waste thiocyanatoiron(III) ion solutions from Parts A and B in the Waste Salts container.

CLEANUP: Rinse the volumetric flasks, the pipets, and the cuvets twice with tap water and twice with deionized water. Discard each rinse in the sink.

4. **Use data to determine equilibrium concentrations.** From the calibration curve prepared in Part A.5, use the recorded absorbance value for each test solution to determine the equilibrium molar concentration of FeNCS^{2+}.

C. Calculation of K_c

Appendix B

1. **Data analysis.** Complete the calculations as outlined on the **Report Sheet** and described in the Introduction. Complete an entire K_c calculation for Test Solution 6 before attempting the calculations for the remaining solutions.

The equilibrium constant will vary from solution to solution and from chemist to chemist in this experiment, depending on chemical technique and the accumulation and interpretation of the data. Consequently, it is beneficial to work through your own calculations with other colleagues and then pool your final, experimental K_c values to determine an accumulated probable value and a standard deviation and a relative standard deviation (%RSD) for K_c. The instructor may offer to assist in the calculations for K_c.

The Next Step

Spectrophotometry is a powerful tool for analyzing substances that have color such as aspirin (*Experiment 19*), transition metal ion complexes (*Experiments 34, 35, 36*), and anions (*Experiments 3 and 37*) to mention only a few. Research the spectrophotometric analysis of a specific substance and design a systematic study for its presence.

Experiment 11 *Prelaboratory Assignment*

An Equilibrium Constant

Date _____ Lab Sec. _____ Name _____ Desk No. _____

1. a. Why do chemists prefer to read and record the absorbance rather than the percent transmittance of light (electro-magnetic radiation) when analyzing a sample having a visible color?

b. Three parameters affect the absorbance of a sample. Which one is the focus of this experiment?

2. Experimental Procedure, Part A.1, Table 11.1. A 3.00-mL aliquot of 0.001 M NaSCN is diluted to 25.0 mL with 0.1 M HNO$_3$.

a. How many moles of SCN$^-$ are present?

b. If all of the SCN$^-$ is complexed with Fe^{3+} to form FeNCS^{2+}, what is the molar concentration of FeNCS^{2+}?

3. Experimental Procedure, Part A.1. For preparing a set of standard solutions of FeNCS^{2+}, the equilibrium molar concentration of FeNCS^{2+} is assumed to equal the initial molar concentration of the SCN$^-$ in the reaction mixture. Why is this assumption valid?

4. Experimental Procedure, Part A.3. The blank solution used to calibrate the spectrophotometer is 10.0 mL of 0.2 M Fe(NO$_3$)$_3$ diluted to 25.0 mL with 0.1 M HNO$_3$. Why is this solution preferred to simply using de-ionized water for the calibration?

5. Plot the following data as absorbance versus [M^{n+}] as a calibration curve:

Absorbance, A	Molar Concentration of M^{n+}
0.045	3.0×10^{-4} mol/L
0.097	6.2×10^{-4} mol/L
0.14	9.0×10^{-4} mol/L
0.35	2.2×10^{-3} mol/L
0.51	3.2×10^{-3} mol/L

A test solution showed a percent transmittance (%T) reading of 47.9%T. Interpret the calibration curve to determine the molar concentration of M^{n+} in the test solution.

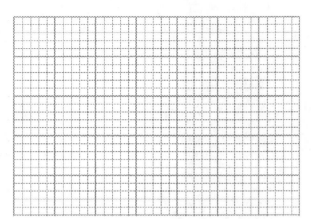

6. A reaction mixture of 4.00 mL of 0.00200 M SCN and 5.00 mL of 0.00200 M Fe^{3+} is diluted to 10.00 mL with 0.1 M HNO_3 to form the blood-red $FeNCS^{2+}$ complex. The equilibrium molar concentration of the $FeNCS^{2+}$ determined from a calibration curve, is 1.5×10^{-4} mol/L. Calculate, in sequence, each of the following quantities in the aqueous solution to determine the equilibrium constant for the reaction,

$$Fe^{3+}(aq) + SCN^-(aq) \rightleftharpoons FeNCS^{2+}(aq)$$

a. *moles* of $FeNCS^{2+}$ that form in reaching equilibrium   _____

b. moles of Fe^{3+} that react to form the $FeNCS^{2+}$ at equilibrium   _____

c. moles of SCN^- that react to form the $FeNCS^{2+}$ at equilibrium   _____

d. moles of Fe^{3+} initially placed in the reaction system   _____

e. moles of SCN^- initially placed in the reaction system   _____

f. moles of Fe^{3+} (*un*reacted) at equilibrium (equation 11.7)   _____

g. moles of SCN^- (*un*reacted) at equilibrium (equation 11.8)   _____

h. molar concentration of Fe^{3+} (*un*reacted) at equilibrium   _____

i. molar concentration of SCN^- (*un*reacted) at equilibrium   _____

j. molar concentration of $FeNCS^{2+}$ at equilibrium   _____ 1.5×10^{-4} mol/L _____

k. $K_c = \dfrac{[FeNCS^{2+}]}{[Fe^{3+}][SCN^-]}$ _____

7. When 90.0 mL of 0.10 M Fe^{3+} is added to 10.0 mL of an SCN^- solution, the equilibrium molar concentration of $FeNCS^{2+}$, as determined from a calibration curve, is 2.5×10^{-4} mol/L. Using the value of K_c from question 6, determine the equilibrium molar concentration of SCN^- in the system. *Hint:* What is the diluted molar concentration of Fe^{3+}?

An Equilibrium Constant

Date _____ Lab Sec. _____ Name _____ Desk No. _____

A. A Set of Standard Solutions to Establish a Standardization Curve

Molar concentration of $Fe(NO_3)_3$ _____; Molar concentration of NaSCN _____

Standard Solutions	Blank	1*	2	3	4	5
A.1. Volume of NaSCN (mL)						
A.2. Moles of SCN^- (mol)						
A.3. $[SCN^-]$ (25.0 mL)						
A.4. $[FeNCS^{2+}]$ (mol/L)						
A.5. Percent transmittance, %T (for meter readings only)						
A.6. Absorbance, A						

*Calculation for Standard Solution 1.

A.7. Plot data of A versus $[FeNCS^{2+}]$. Instructor's approval _____

B. Absorbance for the Set of Test Solutions

Molar concentration of $Fe(NO_3)_3$ _____ ; Molar concentration of NaSCN _____

Test Solutions	6	7	8	9	10
B.1. Volume of $Fe(NO_3)_3$ (*mL*)	___	___	___	___	___
B.2. Moles of Fe^{3+}, initial (*mol*)	*	___	___	___	___
B.3. Volume of NaSCN (*mL*)	___	___	___	___	___
B.4. Moles of SCN^-, initial (*mol*)	*	___	___	___	___
B.5. Percent transmittance, $\%T$ (for meter readings only)	___	___	___	___	___
B.6. Absorbance, A	___	___	___	___	___

*Calculation for Test Solution 6.

C. Calculation of K_c

	6	7	8	9	10
C.1. $[FeNCS^{2+}]$, equilibrium, from calibration curve (*mol/L*)	___	___	___	___	___
C.2. Moles $FeNCS^{2+}$ at equilibrium (10 mL) (*mol*)	___	___	___	___	___

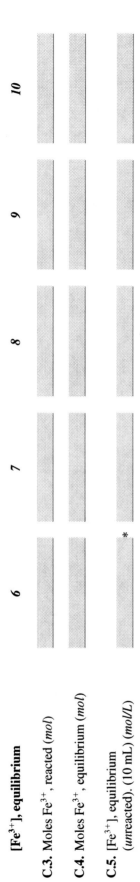

	6	7	8	9	10

[Fe³⁺], equilibrium

$[Fe^{3+}]$, equilibrium

C.3. Moles Fe^{3+}, reacted (*mol*)

C.4. Moles Fe^{3+}, equilibrium (*mol*)

C.5. $[Fe^{3+}]$, equilibrium (*unreacted*). (10 mL) (*mol/L*)   *

*Calculation for Test Solution 6. Express all $[Fe^{3+}]$ values with the correct number of significant figures.

[SCN⁻], equilibrium

$[SCN^-]$, equilibrium

C.6. Moles SCN^-, reacted (*mol*)

C.7. Moles SCN^-, equilibrium (*mol*)

C.8. $[SCN^-]$, equilibrium (*unreacted*). (10 mL) (*mol/L*)   *

*Calculation for Test Solution 6. Express all $[SCN^-]$ values with the correct number of significant figures.

C.9. $K_c = \dfrac{[FeNCS^{2+}]}{[Fe^{3+}][SCN^-]} = \dfrac{[C.1]}{[C.5][C.8]}$ *

*Calculation for Test Solution 6. Express all K_c values with the correct number of significant figures.

Experiment 11   **175**

C.10 Average K_c _____

C.11 Standard deviation of K_c _____ *Appendix B*

C.12 Relative standard deviation of K_c (%RSD) _____ *Appendix B*

Calculation for standard deviation.

Class Data/Group	1	2	3	4	5
Average K_c					

Calculate the standard deviation of K_c from class data.

Calculate the relative standard deviation of K_c (%RSD) from class data.

Laboratory Questions

Circle the questions that have been assigned.

1. Part A.2. All spectrophotometers are different. The spectrophotometer is to be set at 447 nm. What experiment could you do, what data would you collect, and how would you analyze the data to ensure that 447 nm is the best setting for measuring the absorbance of $FeNCS^{2+}$ in this experiment?

2. Part A.3. In a hurry to complete the experiment, Joseph failed to calibrate the spectrophotometer. As a result, all absorbance values for the standard solutions that are measured and recorded are too high. How will this affect the following for the Test Solutions in Parts B and C?
   a. Will the equilibrium concentrations of $FeNCS^{2+}$ be too high, too low, or unaffected? Explain.
   b. Will the equilibrium concentrations of Fe^{3+} be too high, too low, or unaffected? Explain.
   c. Will the calculated equilibrium constants be too high, too low, or unaffected? Explain.

3. Part A.5. One of the standard solutions had an abnormally low absorbance reading, causing a less positive slope for the data plot.
   a. Will the equilibrium concentrations of $FeNCS^{2+}$ in the Test Solutions (Part B) be too high or too low? Explain.
   b. Will the calculated K_c for the equilibrium be too high, too low, or unaffected by the erred data plot? Explain.

4. Part B.3. Fingerprint smudges are present on the cuvet containing the solution placed into the spectrophotometer for analysis.
   a. How does this technique error affect the absorbance reading for $FeNCS^{2+}$ in the analysis? Explain.
   b. Will the equilibrium concentration of $FeNCS^{2+}$ be recorded as being too high or too low? Explain.
   c. Will the equilibrium concentration of SCN^- be too high, too low, or unaffected by the technique error? Explain.
   d. Will the K_c for the equilibrium be too high, too low, or unaffected by the technique error? Explain.

5. Part B.3. For the preparation of Test Solution 8 (Table 11.2), the 2.0 mL of 0.1 M HNO_3 is omitted.
   a. Will this technique error cause the absorbance reading for $FeNCS^{2+}$ to be too high or too low? Explain.
   b. Will the K_c for the equilibrium be too high, too low, or unaffected by the technique error? Explain.

*6. The equation, $A = a \cdot b \cdot c$ (see **footnote 1**), becomes nonlinear at high concentrations of the absorbing substance. Suppose you prepare a solution with a very high absorbance that is suspect in *not* following the linear relationship. How might you still use the sample for your analysis rather than discarding the sample and the data?

Preface to Qualitative Analysis

A centrifuge compacts a precipitate by centrifugal force.

Some rocks have a reddish tint; others are nearly black. Table salt is white, but not all salts are white. A quick, yet simple, identification of the ions of a salt or in a salt mixture is often convenient. Gold prospectors were quick to identify the presence of gold or silver. It is the characteristic physical and chemical properties of an ion that will allow us in the next series of experiments to identify its presence in a sample. For example, the Ag^+ ion is identified as being present in a solution by its precipitation as the chloride $AgCl(s)$. Although other cations precipitate as the chloride, silver chloride is the only one that is soluble in an ammoniacal solution.[1]

Many ions have similar chemical properties, but each ion also has unique chemical properties. To characteristically identify a particular ion in a mixture, the interferences of ions with similar properties must be eliminated. The chemist must take advantage of the unique chemical properties of the ion in question to determine its presence in a mixture. A procedure that follows this pattern of analysis is called **qualitative analysis**.

With enough knowledge of the chemistry of the various ions, a unique separation and identification procedure for each ion can be developed. Some procedures are quick, one-step tests; others are more exhausting. The Experimental Procedure, however, must systematically eliminate all other ions that may interfere with the specific ion test.

Qualitative analysis: a systematic procedure by which the presence (or absence) of a substance (usually a cation or anion) can be determined

The separation and identification of the ions in a mixture require the application of many chemical principles, many of which we will cite as we proceed. An *understanding* of the chemistry of precipitate formation, ionic equilibrium, acids and bases, pH, oxidation and reduction reactions, and complex formation is necessary for their successful separation and identification. To help you understand these principles and test procedures, each experiment presents some pertinent chemical equations, but you are also asked to write equations for other reactions that occur in the separation and identification of the ions.

To complete the procedures for the separation and identification of ions, you will need to practice good laboratory techniques and also develop several new techniques. The most critical techniques in qualitative analysis are the maintenance of clean glassware and the prevention of contamination of the testing reagents.

---

[1] This was one test procedure that prospectors for silver used in the early prospecting days.

A. Measuring and Mixing Test Solutions

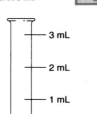

Figure D4.1 Use the 10-mL graduated cylinder or pipet to transfer 1 mL, 2 mL, and 3 mL of water to a small test tube. Mark the test tube at each mark.

Most of the testing for ions are performed in small (~3 mL) test tubes or centrifuge tubes that fit the centrifuges used in your laboratory. Reagents will be added with dropper bottles or dropping pipets (~15–20 drops/mL; you should do a preliminary check with your dropping pipet to determine the drops/mL). If the procedure dictates the addition of 1 mL, do *not* use a graduated cylinder to transfer the 1 mL; instead, use the dropping pipet or estimate the addition of 1 mL in the (~3-mL) test tube (Figure D4.1). Do *not* mix the different dropping pipets with the various test reagents you will be using and do *not* contaminate a reagent by inserting your pipet or dropping pipet into it. Instead, if the procedure calls for a larger volume, first dispense a small amount of reagent into one of your *small* beakers or test tubes.

When mixing solutions in a test tube, break up a precipitate with a stirring rod, agitate by tapping the side of the test tube, or stopper the test tube and invert, but *never* use your thumb (Figure D4.2)!

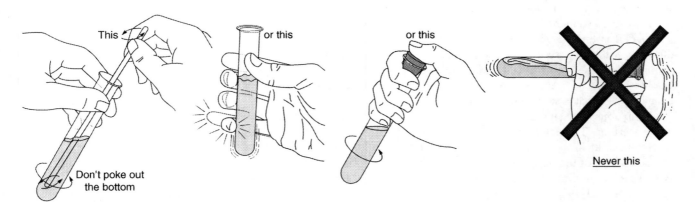

Figure D4.2 Technique for mixing solutions in a test tube

B. Testing for Complete Precipitation

Precipitating reagent: a solution containing an ion(s) that, when added to a second solution, causes a precipitate to form

Oftentimes it is advisable to test a supernatant to determine if complete precipitation of an ion has occurred. After the mixture has been centrifuged, add a drop of the **precipitating reagent** to the supernatant (Figure D4.3). If a precipitate forms, add several more drops, disperse the mixture with a stirring rod or by gentle agitation, and centrifuge. Repeat the test for complete precipitation.

C. Washing a Precipitate

A precipitate must often be washed to remove occluded impurities. Add deionized water or wash liquid to the precipitate, disperse the solid thoroughly with a stirring rod or by gentle agitation, centrifuge, and decant. Usually, the wash liquid can be discarded. Two washings are usually satisfactory. Failure to properly wash precipitates often leads to errors in the analysis (and arguments with your laboratory instructor!) because of the presence of occluded contaminating or interfering ions.

As you will be using the centrifuge frequently in the next several experiments, *be sure to read carefully Technique 11F in the **Laboratory Techniques** section of this manual.*

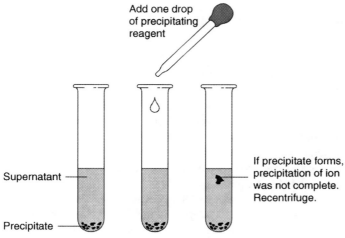

Add one drop
of precipitating
reagent

Supernatant

Precipitate

If precipitate forms,
precipitation of ion
was not complete.
Recentrifuge.

Figure D4.3 A test for the complete precipitation of an ion

Many procedures call for a solution to be heated. Heating a mixture either accelerates the rate of a chemical reaction or causes the formation of larger crystals of precipitate, allowing its separation to be more complete. *Never heat the small test tubes directly with a flame.* Heat one or several test tubes in a hot water bath; a 150-mL beaker containing 100 mL of deionized water is satisfactory. The test tube can be placed directly into the bath, supported against the wall of the beaker (*Technique 13B*). Read the Experimental Procedure before lab; if a hot water bath is needed, start heating the water at the beginning of the laboratory period and keep it warm with a hot plate or **cool flame.**

   A solution can be cooled by placing the test tube under cold running tap water or by submerging the test tube in a beaker of ice water.

D. Heating and Cooling Solutions

Cool flame: a nonluminous flame supplied with a reduced supply of fuel.

A flow diagram is often used to organize the sequence of test procedures for the separation and identification of the large number of ions in a mixture. A flow diagram uses several standard notations:

E. Constructing Flow Diagrams

* Brackets, [ ], indicate the use of a test reagent written in molecular form.
* A longer single horizontal line, _____, indicates a separation of a precipitate from a solution, most often with a centrifuge.
* A double horizontal line, ══, indicates the presence of soluble ions in the solution.
* Two short vertical lines, ‖, indicate the presence of a precipitate; these lines are drawn to the *left* of the single horizontal line.
* One short vertical line, |, indicates a supernatant and is drawn to the *right* of the single horizontal line.
* Two branching diagonal lines, ∧, indicate a separation of the existing solution into two portions.
* A rectangular box, □, placed around a compound or the result of a test confirms the presence of the ion.

   The flow diagram for the anions is presented in *Experiment 37*. Study it closely and become familiar with the symbols and notations as you read the Introduction and Experimental Procedure. Partially completed flow diagrams are presented in the ***Prelaboratory Assignments*** of *Experiments 38* and *39*.

F. How to Effectively Do "Qual"

The following suggestions are offered before and during the following "qual" experiments:

- Use good laboratory techniques during the analyses. Review the suggested techniques that appear as icons in the Experimental Procedure prior to beginning the analysis.
- *Always* read the Experimental Procedure in detail. Is extra equipment necessary? Is a hot water bath needed? Maintain a water bath during the laboratory period if one is needed. What cautions are to be taken?
- Understand the principles of the separation and identification of the ions. Is this an acid–base separation, redox reaction, or complex formation? Why is this reagent added at this time?
- Closely follow, simultaneously, the principles used in each test, the flow diagram, the Experimental Procedure, and the **Report Sheet** during the analysis.
- Mark with a magic marker 1-, 2-, and 3-mL intervals on the small test tube used for testing your sample to quickly estimate volumes (see Figure D4.1).

- Keep a number of *clean* dropping pipets, stirring rods, and small test tubes available; always rinse each test tube several times with deionized water immediately after use.[2]
- Estimate the drops/mL of one or more of your dropping pipets.
- Keep a wash bottle filled with deionized water available at all times.
- Maintain a file of confirmatory tests of the ions in the test tubes that result from the analysis on your *reference* solution; in that way, observations and comparisons of the *test* solution can be quick.

Caution: *In the next several experiments you will be handling a large number of chemicals (acids, bases, oxidizing and reducing agents, and, perhaps, even some toxic chemicals), some of which are more concentrated than others and must be handled with care and respect!*
Re-read the **Laboratory Safety** *section, pages 1–4, of this manual.*

Carefully handle all chemicals. **Read the label! Do not** *intentionally inhale the vapors of any chemical unless you are specifically told to do so.* **Avoid** *skin contact with any chemicals—wash the skin immediately in the laboratory sink, eye wash fountain, or safety shower.* **Clean up** *any spilled chemical—if you are uncertain of the proper cleanup procedure, flood with water, and consult your laboratory instructor.* **Be aware** *of the techniques and procedures of neighboring chemists—discuss potential hazards with them.*

Finally, **dispose of the waste chemicals** *in the appropriately labeled waste containers. Consult your laboratory instructor to ensure proper disposal.*

---

[2]Failure to maintain clean glassware during the analysis causes more spurious data and reported errors in interpretation than any other single factor in qualitative analysis.

Experiment 12

Qual: Common Anions

Calcium ion and carbonate ion combine to form a calcium carbonate precipitate, a preliminary test for the presence of carbonate ion in a solution.

- To observe and utilize some of the chemical and physical properties of anions
- To separate and identify the presence of a single anion in a solution containing a mixture of anions

TECHNIQUES

The following techniques are used in the Experimental Procedure:

INTRODUCTION

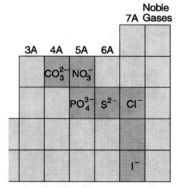

Common anions detected in this experiment

Flow diagram: a diagram that summarizes a procedure for following a rigid sequence of steps

Common anions in aqueous solution are either single atom anions (Cl^-, Br^-, I^-) or polyatomic anions usually containing oxygen (OH^-, SO_4^{2-}, CO_3^{2-}, PO_4^{3-}). In nature, the most common anions are chloride, silicate, carbonate, phosphate, sulfate, sulfide, nitrate, and aluminate and combinations thereof.

Specific anion tests are subject to interference from other anions and cations. Therefore, to characteristically identify an anion in a mixture, preliminary elimination of the interferences is necessary.[1]

Only six of the many known inorganic anions will be identified in this experiment: phosphate, PO_4^{3-}; carbonate, CO_3^{2-}; chloride, Cl^-; iodide, I^-; sulfide, S^{2-}; and nitrate, NO_3^-. The chemical properties of several of these anions have been seen in previous experiments in this manual (for example, see *Experiments 3, 11,* and *24*). Many anions can be detected directly in the sample solution by the addition of a single test reagent. However, some anion-detection procedures require a systematic removal of the interferences before the use of the test reagent. For example, a test for the presence of PO_4^{3-} requires the prior removal of AsO_4^{3-}; a test for CO_3^{2-} requires the prior removal of SO_3^{2-}.

The separation and identification of the anions are outlined in the **flow diagram** on page 182 (see *Dry Lab 4.E*). Follow the diagram as you read through the Introduction and follow the Experimental Procedure.

---

[1]For more information on anion qualitative analysis, go to www.chemlin.net/chemistry.

Flow Diagram for Anion "Qual" Scheme

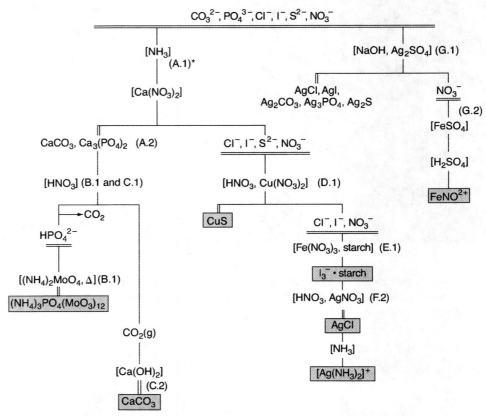

*Numbers in parentheses refer to parts of the Experimental Procedure

---

Phosphate Ion

The phosphate ion, PO_4^{3-}, is a strong Brønsted base (proton acceptor)

All phosphate salts are *insoluble* except those of the Group 1A cations and ammonium ion (Appendix G). The phosphate salt of calcium forms a *white precipitate* in a basic solution but subsequently dissolves in an acidic solution:

$$3\ Ca^{2+}(aq) + 2\ PO_4^{3-}(aq) \rightarrow Ca_3(PO_4)_2(s) \qquad (12.1)$$
$$\downarrow 2\ H^+(aq)$$
$$3\ Ca^{2+}(aq) + 2\ HPO_4^{2-}(aq)$$

Ammonium molybdate added to an acidified solution of the hydrogen phosphate ion precipitates *yellow* ammonium phosphomolybdate, confirming the presence of phosphate ion in the test solution.

The ☐ *is used to note the confirmation of the presence of an ion in the test solution*

$$HPO_4^{2-}(aq) + 12\ (NH_4)_2MoO_4(aq) + 23\ H^+(aq) \rightarrow$$
$$\boxed{(NH_4)_3PO_4(MoO_3)_{12}(s)} + 21\ NH_4^+(aq) + 12\ H_2O(l) \quad (12.2)$$

The rate of precipitate formation depends on the concentration of the phosphate ion in solution.

The reactions of the arsenate ion (AsO_4^{3-}) are identical to those of the phosphate ion and therefore would, if present, interfere with the test.

Carbonate Ion

All carbonate salts are *insoluble* except those of the Group 1A cations and ammonium ion (Appendix G). Acidification of a solution containing carbonate ion produces carbon dioxide gas (Figure 12.1).

$$CO_3^{2-}(aq) + 2\ H^+(aq) \rightarrow H_2O(l) + CO_2(g) \qquad (12.3)$$

When the evolved CO_2 (an acidic anhydride) comes into contact with a basic solution containing calcium ion, the carbonate ion re-forms and reacts with the calcium ion, forming a *white precipitate* of calcium carbonate:

$$CO_2(g) + 2\ OH^-(aq) \rightarrow CO_3^{2-}(aq) + H_2O(l) \tag{12.4}$$
$$\downarrow Ca^{2+}(aq)$$
$$\boxed{CaCO_3(s)} \tag{12.5}$$

The precipitate confirms the presence of carbonate ion in the test solution. The sulfite ion, SO_3^{2-}, if present, would interfere with the test; under similar conditions, it produces sulfur dioxide gas and insoluble calcium sulfite.

Figure 12.1 Acidifying a solution containing carbonate ion produces carbon dioxide gas.

Sulfide Ion

Most sulfide salts are insoluble, including CuS. When Cu^{2+} is added to a solution containing sulfide ion, a *black precipitate* of copper(II) sulfide, CuS, forms, confirming the presence of sulfide ion in the test solution:

$$Cu^{2+}(aq) + S^{2-}(aq) \rightarrow \boxed{CuS(s)} \tag{12.6}$$

Chloride and Iodide Ions

The salts of the chloride and iodide ions are soluble with the exception of the Ag^+, Pb^{2+}, and Hg_2^{2+} halides. A simple reaction with silver ion would cause a mixture of the silver halides to precipitate, and therefore no separation or identification could be made. Instead, differences in the ease of oxidation of the chloride and iodide ions are used for their identification (see *Experiment 11*, Part D). The iodide ion is most easily oxidized. A weak oxidizing agent oxidizes only the iodide ion. In this experiment, iron(III) ion oxidizes iodide ion to the yellow-brown triiodide complex, I_3^-:

$$2\ Fe^{3+}(aq) + 3\ I^-(aq) \rightarrow 2\ Fe^{2+}(aq) + I_3^-(aq) \tag{12.7}$$

The I_3^- then reacts with starch to form a *deep-blue complex*, $I_3^-\cdot$starch, confirming the presence of iodide ion in the sample:

$$I_3^-(aq) + starch(aq) \rightarrow I_3^-\cdot starch\ (aq,\ deep\ blue) \tag{12.8}$$

The chloride ion is then precipitated as a *white precipitate* of silver chloride.[2]

$$Cl^-(aq) + Ag^+(aq) \rightarrow \boxed{AgCl(s)} \tag{12.9}$$

To further confirm the presence of chloride ion in the test solution, aqueous ammonia is added to dissolve the silver chloride which again precipitates with the addition of nitric acid:

$$AgCl(s) + 2\ NH_3(aq) \rightleftharpoons [Ag(NH_3)_2]^+(aq) + Cl^-(aq) \tag{12.10}$$

$$[Ag(NH_3)_2]^+(aq) + Cl^-(aq) + 2\ H^+(aq) \rightarrow AgCl(s) + 2\ NH_4^+(aq) \tag{12.11}$$

Nitrate Ion

As all nitrate salts are soluble, no precipitate can be used for identification of the nitrate ion. The nitrate ion is identified by the brown ring test. The nitrate ion is reduced to nitric oxide by iron(II) ions in the presence of concentrated sulfuric acid:

$$NO_3^-(aq) + 3\ Fe^{2+}(aq) + 4\ H^+(aq) \xrightarrow{conc\ H_2SO_4}$$
$$3\ Fe^{3+}(aq) + NO(aq) + 2\ H_2O(l) \tag{12.12}$$

---

[2]A faint cloudiness with the addition of Ag^+ is inconclusive as the chloride ion is one of those *universal impurities* in aqueous solutions.

The nitric oxide, NO, combines with excess iron(II) ions, forming the *brown* $FeNO^{2+}$ ion at the interface of the aqueous layer and a concentrated sulfuric acid layer (where acidity is high) that underlies the aqueous layer:

$$Fe^{2+}(aq) + NO(aq) \rightarrow \boxed{FeNO^{2+}(aq)} \qquad (12.13)$$

$FeNO^{2+}$ is more stable at low temperatures. This test has many sources of interference: (1) Sulfuric acid oxidizes bromide and iodide ions to bromine and iodine, and (2) sulfites, sulfides, and other reducing agents interfere with the reduction of NO_3^- to NO. A preparatory step of adding sodium hydroxide and silver sulfate removes these interfering anions, leaving only the nitrate ion in solution.

EXPERIMENTAL PROCEDURE

Procedure Overview: Two solutions are tested with various reagents in this analysis: (1) a reference solution containing all six of the anions for this analysis and (2) a test solution containing any number of the anions. Separations and observations are made and recorded. Equations that describe the observations are also recorded. Comparative observations of the two solutions result in the identification of the anions in the test solution. All tests are qualitative; only identification of the anion(s) is required.

To simplify the analysis, take the following steps:

1. **Reference solution:** At each circled, superscript (e.g.,⓪), *stop* and record on the **Report Sheet**. After each anion is confirmed, *save* it in the test tube so that its appearance can be compared to that of your test solution.

2. **Test solution:** Simultaneously perform the same procedure on the test solution and make a comparative observation. Check ($\sqrt{}$) the findings on the **Report Sheet**. Do not discard any solutions (but keep all solutions labeled) until the experiment is complete. Record the test solution number on the **Report Sheet**.

The test solution may be a water sample from some location in the environment—for example, a lake, a stream, or a drinking water supply. Ask your instructor about this option.

Before proceeding, review the techniques outlined in *Dry Lab 4*, Parts A–D. The review of these procedures may expedite your analysis with less frustration.

Contamination by trace amounts of anions in test tubes and other glassware leads to unexplainable results in qualitative analysis. Thoroughly clean all glassware with soap and tap water; rinse twice with tap water and twice with deionized water before use (see *Dry Lab 4.F*).

Disposal: Dispose of all test solutions and precipitates in the appropriate waste container.

*Caution: A number of acids and bases are used in the analysis of these anions. Handle each of these solutions with care. Read the **Laboratory Safety** section for instructions in handling acids and bases.*

The expression "small test tube" that is mentioned throughout the Experimental Procedure refers to a 75-mm test tube (~3 mL volume) *or* a centrifuge tube of the size that fits into your laboratory centrifuge. Consult with your laboratory instructor.

A. Separation of Carbonate and Phosphate Anions

The Experimental Procedure is written for a single solution. If you are simultaneously identifying anions in *both* a reference solution *and* a test solution, adjust the procedure accordingly. If the test solution is a sample with an environmental origin, gravity filter 10–15 mL before beginning the Experimental Procedure.

Prepare the warm water bath for use in Part B.

1. **Precipitate the CO_3^{2-} and PO_4^{3-}.** Place ~1.5 mL of the reference solution in a small test tube (see *Dry Lab 4.A*). Test the solution with pH paper. If acidic, add drops of 3 *M* NH_3 until the solution is basic; then add 3–4 more drops; mix or stir the solution after each addition. Add 10–12 drops of 0.1 *M* $Ca(NO_3)_2$ until the precipitation of the anions is complete (see *Dry Lab 4.B*).[1]

2. **Separate the solution from precipitate.** Centrifuge the solution. Decant the supernatant[2] into a small test tube and save for Part D. Wash the precipitate *twice* with ~1 mL of deionized water (see *Dry Lab 4.C*). Discard the washings as directed by your instructor. Save the precipitate for Part B.

B. Test for Phosphate Ion

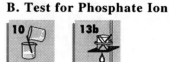

1. **Confirmatory test.** Dissolve the precipitate from Part A.2 with drops of 6 *M* HNO_3 (**Caution!**). Add ~1 mL of 0.5 *M* $(NH_4)_2MoO_4$. Shake and warm slightly in a warm water (~60°C) bath and let stand for 10–15 minutes (see *Dry Lab 4.D*). A *slow* formation of a *yellow precipitate* confirms the presence of the phosphate ion[3] in the solution.[3]

C. Test for Carbonate Ion

1. **Precipitate the CO_3^{2-}.** Repeat Part A. Centrifuge the mixture; save the precipitate but discard the supernatant or save for Part D. Dip a glass rod into a saturated $Ca(OH)_2$ solution.

2. **Confirmatory test.** Add 3–5 drops of 6 *M* HNO_3 to the precipitate and immediately insert the glass rod into the test tube (Figure 12.2). *Do not* let the glass rod touch the test tube wall or the solution. The evolution of the CO_2 gas causes the formation of a *milky solution* on the glass rod, confirming the presence of carbonate ion[4] in the solution.

D. Test for Sulfide Ion

1. **Confirmatory test.** To the supernatant from Part A.2 and/or C.1, add 2–4 drops of 6 *M* HNO_3 until the solution is acid to pH paper and then drops of 1 *M* $Cu(NO_3)_2$ until precipitation is complete. Be patient, allow ~2 minutes to form.[5] Centrifuge; save the supernatant for Part E. The *black precipitate* confirms the presence of sulfide ion in the solution.

E. Test for Iodide Ion

1. **Confirmatory test.** To ~1 mL of the supernatant from Part D.1 add ~5 drops of 0.2 *M* $Fe(NO_3)_3$. Agitate the solution. The formation of I_3^- is slow—allow 2–3 minutes. Add ~2 drops of 1 percent starch solution. The *deep-blue* I_3^-·starch complex confirms the presence of iodide ion in the sample.[6]

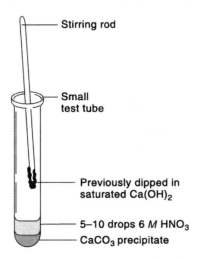

— Stirring rod

— Small test tube

— Previously dipped in saturated $Ca(OH)_2$

— 5–10 drops 6 *M* HNO_3
— $CaCO_3$ precipitate

Figure 12.2 Position a stirring rod dipped into a saturated $Ca(OH)_2$ solution just above the solid/HNO_3 mixture.

[3]A *white precipitate* may form if the solution is heated too long or if the solution is not acidic enough. The precipitate is MoO_3, *not* a pale form of the phosphomolybdate precipitate.

F. Test for Chloride Ion

1. Add 2–3 drops of 6 M HNO$_3$ to the solution from Part E.1.

2. **Confirmatory test.** Add drops of 0.01 M AgNO$_3$ to the aqueous solution (sample) and centrifuge. A *white precipitate* indicates the likely presence of Cl$^-$.[7] Discard the supernatant. The addition of several drops of 6 M NH$_3$ quickly dissolves the precipitate if Cl$^-$ is present.[8] Reacidification of the solution with 6 M HNO$_3$ re-forms the silver chloride precipitate.

G. Test for Nitrate Ion

1. **Precipitate the "other" anions.** Place ~1½ mL of the reference solution into a small test tube. Add drops of 3 M NaOH until the solution is basic to pH paper. Add drops of a saturated (0.04 M) Ag$_2$SO$_4$ solution until precipitation appears complete. Centrifuge and save the supernatant for Part G.2.[9] Test for complete precipitation in the supernatant (see *Dry Lab 4.B*) and, if necessary, centrifuge again.

2. **Confirmatory test.** Decant 0.5 mL (~10 drops) of the supernatant into a small test tube and acidify (to pH paper) with 3 M H$_2$SO$_4$. Add ~0.5 mL (see *Dry Lab 4.A*) of a saturated iron(II) sulfate, FeSO$_4$, solution and agitate. Cool the solution in an ice bath. Holding the test tube at a 45° angle (Figure 12.3), add, with a dropping pipet, *slowly and cautiously,* down its side, about 0.5 mL of *conc* H$_2$SO$_4$. (**Caution:** *Concentrated H$_2$SO$_4$ causes severe skin burns.*)[4] Do *not* draw *conc* H$_2$SO$_4$ into the bulb of the dropping pipet. Do *not* agitate the solution. The more dense *conc* H$_2$SO$_4$ underlies the aqueous layer. Use extreme care to avoid mixing the *conc* H$_2$SO$_4$ with the solution. Allow the mixture to stand for several minutes. A *brown ring* at the interface between the solution and the *conc* H$_2$SO$_4$ confirms the presence of the nitrate ion[10] in the test solution.

> *Disposal:* Dispose of the concentrated acid solution in the Waste Acids container.

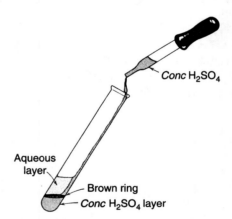

Figure 12.3 Test for the nitrate ion

---

[4]The *conc* H$_2$SO$_4$ has a greater density than water and therefore underlies the aqueous layer.

Date _____ Lab Sec. _____ Name _____ Desk No. _____

1. A review of the *Dry Lab 4* will make this experiment proceed more smoothly. Complete the following:
   a. The approximate volume of a standard 75-mm ("small") test tube is _____ mL.

   b. The clear solution above a precipitate is called the _____.

   c. A _____ is an instrument used to separate and compact a precipitate in a test tube.

   d. The number of drops of water equivalent to 1 mL is about _____.

2. The following references are made to *Dry Lab 4*, Preface to Qualitative Analysis, in this experiment. Identify what each reference provides for an effective separation and analysis.

Experimental Procedure	Dry Lab 4 Reference	Information Provided
Part A.1	Part A	
Part A.1	Part B	
Part A.2	Part C	
Part B.1	Part D	

3. **a.** Experimental Procedure, Part A.1. Describe the technique for mixing solutions in a "small" test tube.

   b. Experimental Procedure, Part A.2. Describe the technique for washing a precipitate.

4. Refer to *Dry Lab 4.E*. On a flow diagram, what is the meaning of
   a. a single horizontal line, —?

   b. a pair of short vertical lines, ‖?

   c. a pair of horizontal lines, ═?

   d. the brackets, [ ], around a reagent?

5. Three anions in this experiment are identified by the complexes they form. Which anions are so identified?

6. Four anions are confirmed present by the formation of a precipitate. Which anions are so confirmed? Write the formula and indicate the color of the precipitates.

7. Identify the reagent (and its concentration) that is used to confirm the presence of each of the following:

   a. CO_3^{2-}: _____

   b. S^{2-}: _____

   c. I^-: _____

8. Identify a single reagent used in this experiment that distinguishes between the carbonate and chloride ions in a solution, assuming no other anions are present. Write the balanced equation(s) that makes the distinction.

Qual: Common Anions

Date _____ Lab Sec. _____ Name _____ Desk No. _____

Procedure Number and Ion	Test Reagent or Technique	Evidence of Chemical Change	Chemical(s) Responsible for Observation	Equation(s) for Observed Reaction	Check (√) if Observed in Unknown
①	_____	_____	_____	_____	_____
②	_____	_____	_____	_____	_____
③ PO_4^{3-}	_____	_____	_____	_____	☐
④ CO_3^{2-}	_____	_____	_____	_____	☐
⑤ S^{2-}	_____	_____	_____	_____	☐
⑥ I^-	_____	_____	_____	_____	☐
⑦ Cl^-	_____	_____	_____	_____	☐
⑧	_____	_____	_____	_____	_____
⑨	_____	_____	_____	_____	_____
⑩ NO_3^-	_____	_____	_____	_____	☐

Anions present in unknown test solution no. _____: _____

Instructor's approval: _____

Laboratory Questions

Circle the questions that have been assigned.

1. Part A.1. The *test* solution is made basic and drops of 0.1 M $Ca(NO_3)_2$ are added but no precipitate forms. To what part of the Experimental Procedure do you proceed? Explain.

2. Part A.1. The *reference* solution is made acidic instead of basic. How would this change the composition of the precipitate and the test in Part C.1? Explain.

3. Part B. Identify the precipitate that dissolves when the HNO_3 is added. Write its formula.

4. Part C.2. The 6 M HNO_3 could not be found on the reagent shelf, so the 6 M HCl was used instead. Explain how (or if) the observation may be different.

5. Part D.1. 6 M HNO_3 could not be found on the reagent shelf. Instead 6 M HCl is added to the *test* solution.
   a. What effect does this have on the test for sulfide ion? Explain.
   b. What effect does this have on subsequent tests of the supernatant from Part D.1? Explain.

6. Part E.1. The starch solution was inadvertently omitted from the analysis. Assuming the iodide ion to be present, what would be observed after the addition of the ferric nitrate solution?

7. Part F.2. 6 M NH_3, a basic solution, cannot be found on the reagent shelf, but 6 M NaOH, also a base, is available. What would be observed if the 6 M NaOH is substituted for the 6 M NH_3 in testing the *reference* solution? Explain.

8. Part F.2. The *test* solution is known to contain only the iodide and chloride ions. Describe the appearance of the solution if drops of 0.01 M $AgNO_3$ had been added directly to the test solution and then centrifuged.

9. Part G.2. There is no other brown ring test commonly known in chemistry. What substance is producing the brown ring?

Experiment 13

Qual I. Na$^+$, K$^+$, NH$_4^+$, Mg^{2+}, Ca^{2+}, Cu^{2+}

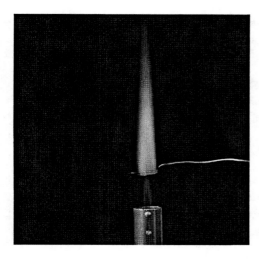

Flame tests provide a positive identification for many metal ions.

OBJECTIVES

- To observe and utilize the chemical and physical properties of Na$^+$, K$^+$, NH$_4^+$, Mg^{2+}, Ca^{2+}, and Cu^{2+}
- To separate and identify the presence of one or more of the cations, Na$^+$, K$^+$, NH$_4^+$, Mg^{2+}, Ca^{2+}, Cu^{2+} in an aqueous solution

TECHNIQUES

The following techniques are used in the Experimental Procedure:

INTRODUCTION

In identifying a particular cation in a mixture of cations, it would be ideal if we could detect each cation in the mixture by merely adding a specific reagent that would produce a characteristic color or precipitate; however, no such array of reagents has been developed. Instead, the cations must first be separated into groups having similar chemical properties. From there, the cations in each group respond to a specific reagent to produce the characteristic color or precipitate for identification. The qualitative analysis of a mixture of cations requires such a plan of investigation.[1]

The analysis of Qual I cations requires good laboratory technique for their separation and confirmation, as well as careful preparation and understanding of the procedure. If in following the prescribed steps for separation and identification, you only rely on a cookbook procedure, you should expect unexplainable results. Please read carefully the remainder of this Introduction and the Experimental Procedure, review your laboratory techniques, and complete the *Prelaboratory Assignment* before beginning the analysis; it will save you time and minimize frustration.

This experiment is the first of two in which a set of reagents and techniques are used to identify the presence of a particular cation among a larger selection of cations.[2] We will approach this study as an experimental chemist: we will conduct some tests, write down our observations, and then write balanced equations that agree with our data.

---

[1] For a more detailed grouping of cations for qualitative analysis, go to www.chemistry.about.com and search qualitative analysis.
[2] The ions Hg$_2^{2+}$, Pb^{2+}, Ag$^+$, and Bi^{3+} are not included in the cation analysis because of the disposal problems associated with their potential environmental effects.

As a way to understand the separation and identification of these six cations, read through the following chemistry of the Qual 1 cations, the Experimental Procedure and be sure to complete the flow diagram in *Prelaboratory Assignment* question 8 *before* beginning the experiment.

As an introduction to the chemistry of the cations in this experiment, keep in mind that most Na^+, K^+, and NH_4^+ salts are soluble. Thus, these ions can be separated from a large number of other cations.[3]

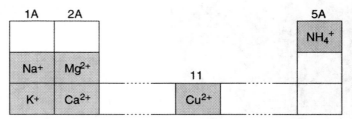

Cations of the Qual I group

Sodium and potassium ions form a very limited number of salts with low solubilities and only carefully controlled conditions provide confirmatory tests; however, both ions provide very sensitive, distinctive flame tests.

All ammonium salts are water soluble. The ammonium ion is a weak acid; its conjugate base is ammonia, which is a gas. When the pH of an aqueous solution of ammonium ion is increased, ammonia gas is evolved and is easily detected with red litmus.

The Mg^{2+}, Ca^{2+}, and Cu^{2+} ions are separated and identified by taking advantage of their chemical properties: Mg^{2+} and Ca^{2+} are confirmed present in a mixture by their HPO_4^{2-} and $C_2O_4^{2-}$ precipitates, respectively. The Cu^{2+} is reduced to copper metal and then subsequently oxidized to form its characteristic deep-blue color in the presence of ammonia.

Sodium Ion

A flame test to detect the sodium ion produces a characteristic fluffy *yellow flame*. The color is so intense that it masks the color produced by other ions and is comparatively persistent.[4]

Potassium Ion

A flame test is also used to detect the presence of potassium ion in a sample. The flame is viewed through cobalt blue glass. The glass absorbs the intense yellow color of sodium but transmits the *lavender* color of the potassium flame. The lavender flame is of short duration. A comparative test of a solution known to contain only potassium ion is often necessary for the determination.

Ammonium Ion

To test for ammonium ion, advantage is taken of the following equilibrium:

$$NH_3(aq) + H_2O(l) \rightleftharpoons NH_4^+(aq) + OH^-(aq) \qquad (13.1)$$

When hydroxide ion (a common ion in the equilibrium) is added to a solution containing ammonium ion, this equilibrium shifts *left*. Heating drives *ammonia gas* from the system; its presence is detected using moist litmus paper (its odor is also frequently detected).

The ☐ is used to note the confirmation of the presence of an ion in the test solution

$$\overset{\leftarrow}{\boxed{NH_3(g)}} + H_2O(l) \rightleftharpoons NH_4^+(aq) + OH^-(aq) \qquad (13.2)$$
$$\uparrow OH^-(aq)$$

---

[3]Review the solubility rules for salts in Appendix G or in your text.
[4]The sodium flame test is so sensitive that the sodium ion washed (with several drops of deionized water) from a fingerprint can be detected.

The copper(II) ion must be separated from the Mg^{2+} and Ca^{2+} to avoid any interference with their confirmatory tests. Copper(II) ion is readily reduced to copper metal by zinc metal:

$$Cu^{2+}(aq) + Zn(s) \rightarrow Cu(s) + Zn^{2+}(aq) \qquad (13.3)$$

The $Zn^{2+}(aq)$ does not interfere with the tests for Mg^{2+} and Ca^{2+}.

The copper metal is then oxidized back into an aqueous solution with nitric acid:

$$3\,Cu(s) + 8\,H^+(aq) + 2\,NO_3^-(aq) \rightarrow 3\,Cu^{2+}(aq) + 2\,NO(g) + 4\,H_2O(l) \quad (13.4)$$

The slow addition of aqueous NH_3 then complexes the Cu^{2+} as a soluble *deep-blue* $[Cu(NH_3)_4]^{2+}$ complex. This confirms the presence of Cu^{2+} in the test solution.

$$Cu^{2+}(aq) + 4\,NH_3(aq) \rightarrow \boxed{[Cu(NH_3)_4]^{2+}(aq)} \qquad (13.5)$$

A second confirmatory test for the presence of Cu^{2+} is the addition of potassium hexacyanoferrate(II), $K_4[Fe(CN)_6]$, which produces a *red-brown precipitate* of $Cu_2[Fe(CN)_6]$:

$$2\,[Cu(NH_3)_4]^{2+}(aq) + [Fe(CN)_6]^{4-}(aq) \rightarrow \boxed{Cu_2[Fe(CN)_6](s)} + 8\,NH_3(aq) \quad (13.6)$$

Copper Ion

Structure of $[Cu(NH_3)_4]^{2+}$

Structure of $[Fe(CN)_6]^{4-}$

The Cu^{2+} ion in solution (right) has a less intense color than does the deep-blue $[Cu(NH_3)_4]^{2+}$ complex.

Calcium Ion

A *white precipitate* of calcium oxalate forms in an ammoniacal solution, confirming the presence of calcium ion in the reference solution:

$$Ca^{2+}(aq) + C_2O_4^{2-}(aq) \rightarrow \boxed{CaC_2O_4(s)} \qquad (13.7)$$

The dissolution of calcium oxalate with hydrochloric acid, followed by a flame test, produces a *yellow-red flame* characteristic of the calcium ion.

Zinc oxalate, also a white insoluble salt, may interfere with the calcium oxalate confirmatory test, but the flame test confirms the calcium ion. Zinc ion does not produce a color for its flame test.

Magnesium Ion

The addition of monohydrogen phosphate ion, HPO_4^{2-}, to an ammoniacal solution containing magnesium ion causes, after heating, the formation of a *white precipitate*.

$$Mg^{2+}(aq) + HPO_4^{2-}(aq) + NH_3(aq) \xrightarrow{\Delta} \boxed{MgNH_4PO_4(s)} \qquad (13.8)$$

Magnesium ion does not produce a characteristic flame test.

EXPERIMENTAL PROCEDURE

Procedure Overview: Two solutions are tested with various reagents in this analysis: (1) a reference solution containing all six of the cations of Qual I and (2) a test solution containing any number of Qual I cations. Separations and observations are made and recorded. Equations that describe the observations are also recorded. Comparative observations of the two solutions result in the identification of the cations in the test solution. All tests are qualitative; only identification of the cation(s) is required.

To simplify the analysis, take the following steps:

1. **Reference solution:** At each circled superscript (e.g.,), *stop* and record data on the *Report Sheet*. After the presence of a cation is confirmed, *save* the characteristic appearance of the cation in the test tube so that it can be compared with observations made in the analysis of your test solution.

2. **Test solution:** Simultaneously perform the same procedure on the test solution and make a comparative observation. Check ($\sqrt{}$) the findings on the *Report Sheet*. Do not discard any solutions (but keep all solutions labeled) until the experiment is complete. Record the test solution number on the *Report Sheet*.

The test solution may be a water sample from some location in the environment—for example, a lake, a stream, or a drinking water supply. Ask your instructor about this option.

Before proceeding, review the techniques outlined in *Dry Lab 4*, Parts A–D. The review of these procedures may expedite your analysis with less frustration.

Contamination by trace amounts of metal ions in test tubes and other glassware leads to unexplainable results in qualitative analysis. Thoroughly clean all glassware with soap and tap water; rinse twice with tap water and twice with deionized water before use (see *Dry Lab 4.F*).

Caution: *A number of acids and bases are used in the analysis of these cations. Handle each of these solutions with care. Read the **Laboratory Safety** section for instructions in handling acids and bases.*

The expression "small test tube" that is mentioned throughout the Experimental Procedure refers to a 75-mm test tube (~3 mL volume) *or* a centrifuge tube of the size that fits into your laboratory centrifuge. Consult with your laboratory instructor.

The Experimental Procedure may begin with either Part A or Part D. Consult with your instructor.

A. Test for Sodium Ion

The Experimental Procedure is written for a single reference solution. If you are simultaneously identifying cations in *both* a reference solution *and* a test solution, adjust the procedure accordingly. If the test solution is a sample with an environmental origin, then gravity filter 10–15 mL before beginning the Experimental Procedure.

Prepare the hot water bath for use in Parts D, E, and F.

1. **Remove the interfering ions.** Place no more than 2 mL of the reference solution in an evaporating dish (Figure 13.1). Add a "pinch" or two of solid $(NH_4)_2C_2O_4$ (**Caution:** *avoid skin contact*), with stirring, until the solution is basic to pH paper; add a slight excess of the solid and then a pinch of solid $(NH_4)_2CO_3$. Heat the solution *slowly* in a fume hood (NH_3 fumes may be evolved) to a moist residue, *not* to dryness! Allow the evaporating dish to cool. Add up to 1 mL (see *Dry Lab 4.A*) of deionized water, stir, and decant into a small beaker.

2. **Confirmatory test.** The flame test for sodium ion is reliable but also requires some technique. Clean the flame test wire by dipping it in 6 *M* HCl (**Caution!**) and heating it in the hottest part of a Bunsen flame until the flame is colorless (five steps in Figure 13.2). Repeat as necessary. Dip the flame test wire into the solution in the beaker and place it in the flame (Figure 13.3). A *brilliant yellow* persistent flame indicates the presence of sodium.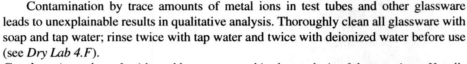 Conduct the sodium flame test on a 0.5 *M* NaCl solution for comparison.

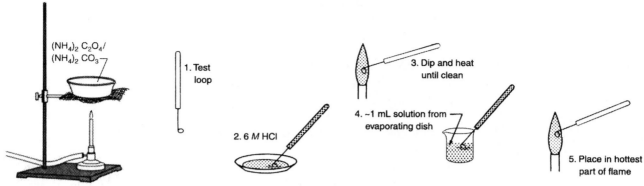

Figure 13.1 Slowly heat the test solution to a moist residue

Figure 13.2 Flame test procedure

Confirmatory Test. Repeat Part A.2. A *fleeting lavender* flame confirms the presence of potassium. If sodium *is* present, view the flame through cobalt blue glass. Several trials are necessary as the test is judgmental. Conduct the potassium flame test on a 0.5 *M* KCl solution for comparison.[2]

B. Test for Potassium Ion

1. **Prepare the sample.** Transfer 5 mL of the *original* reference solution to a 100-mL beaker, support it on a wire gauze, and heat until a moist residue forms (do not evaporate to dryness!). Moisten the residue with 1–2 mL of deionized water. Moisten a piece of red litmus paper with water.

2. **Confirmatory test.** Add 1–2 mL of 6 *M* NaOH to the reference solution, suspend the litmus *above* the solution (Figure 13.4), and very gently warm the mixture—*do not boil.* (**Caution:** *Be careful not to let the NaOH contact the litmus paper.*) A change in litmus from *red* to *blue* confirms ammonia.[3] The nose is also a good detector, but it is not always as sensitive as the litmus test.

C. Test for Ammonium Ion

Figure 13.3 Flame test for the presence of sodium ion

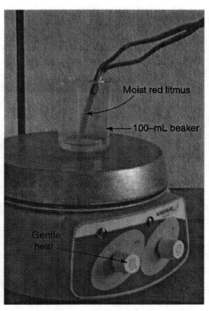

Figure 13.4 Absorbing NH₃ vapors on red litmus

D. Test for Copper Ion

1. **Reduction of copper(II) ion.** Begin with 5 mL of the *original* reference solution in a 150-mm test tube. Polish a 1-cm Zn strip and place it into the solution and let stand for 10–20 minutes.④ Decant the solution and save for Part E.1. Wash the solid (now copper metal and excess zinc metal) with *at least* three portions (see *Dry Lab 4.C*) of deionized water and discard the washings.

2. **Oxidation of copper metal.** Transfer the test tube containing the copper metal to a fume hood. Add drops of 6 M HNO_3 (**Caution:** 6 M HNO_3 *causes severe skin burns, and the evolved* NO *gas is toxic*) until the copper metal completely reacts.⑤ Be patient; some heating in a water bath may be necessary.

3. **Confirmatory test.** *Slowly* add drops of *conc* NH_3 (**Caution:** *Avoid inhalation or skin contact!*) to the solution from Part D.2. The *deep-blue* color confirms the presence of Cu^{2+} in the solution.⑥

4. **A second confirmatory test.** Acidify the solution from Part D.3 to pH paper with 6 M CH_3COOH (**Caution!**). Add 3 drops of 0.2 M $K_4[Fe(CN)_6]$. A *red-brown* precipitate reconfirms the presence of Cu^{2+} ion.⑦

E. Test for Calcium Ion

1. **Sample preparation.** The supernatant from Part D.1 contains Ca^{2+}, Mg^{2+}, and Zn^{2+} (from the reduction of Cu^{2+}). Add drops of 6 M NH_3 until the solution is just basic to pH paper. Add 2–3 drops of 1 M $K_2C_2O_4$ (see *Dry Lab 4.A*). A white precipitate⑧ confirms the presence of Ca^{2+} and/or Zn^{2+} as both CaC_2O_4 and ZnC_2O_4 have marginal solubility. If no precipitate forms immediately, warm the solution in a water bath (see *Dry Lab 4.D*), cool, and let stand. Centrifuge and save the supernatant for Part F.

2. **Confirmatory test.** Wet the precipitate to a moist paste with a drop of 6 M HCl and perform a flame test. A fleeting *yellow-red* flame is characteristic of calcium ion and confirms its presence.⑨

F. Test for Magnesium Ion

1. **Confirmatory test.** Add 1–2 drops of 6 M NH_3 to the supernatant from Part E.1. Add 2–3 drops of 1 M Na_2HPO_4, heat in a hot water ($\sim$90°C) bath, and allow to stand. The precipitate⑩ may be slow in forming; be patient. Observing the white precipitate confirms the presence of Mg^{2+} ion.

Disposal: Dispose of all test solutions and precipitates in the Waste Metal Salts container.

CLEANUP: Rinse each test tube twice with tap water. Discard each rinse in the Waste Metal Salts container. Thoroughly clean each test tube with soap and tap water; rinse twice with tap water and twice with deionized water.

Experiment 13 *Prelaboratory Assignment*

Qual I. Na^+, K^+, NH_4^+, Mg^{2+}, Ca^{2+}, Cu^{2+}

Date _____ Lab Sec. _____ Name _____ Desk No. _____

1. Identify the Qual I cation(s) that is (are) confirmed present in a reference solution by
   a. the formation of a precipitate:

   b. the color of a soluble complex ion:

   c. the characteristic color of a flame test:

   d. the evolution of a gas:

2. Identify the Qual I cation(s) that is (are) confirmed present in a test solution as a result of a Brønsted acid–base reaction.

3. The following references are made to *Dry Lab 4*, Preface to Qualitative Analysis, in this experiment. Identify what each reference provides for an effective separation and analysis.

Experimental Procedure	Dry Lab 4 Reference	Information Provided
Part D.1	Part C	
Part E.1	Part A	
Part E.1	Part D	

4. **a.** When operating a centrifuge, what is meant by the expression "balance the centrifuge"?

   b. How full should a test tube (or centrifuge tube) be when placed into a centrifuge?

5. Identify the reagent that separates
   a. NH_4^+ from Na^+. Explain the chemistry of the separation.

   b. Cu^{2+} from Ca^{2+}. Explain the chemistry of the separation.

6. Identify the reagent (and its concentration) that is used to confirm the presence of each of the following:

   a. NH_4^+ _____

   b. Cu^{2+} _____

   c. Ca^{2+} _____

7. Refer to *Dry Lab 4.E* to address the following questions.

   a. On a flow diagram, ═══════ , indicates _____.

   b. On a flow diagram, ☐_____☐ means _____.

   c. On a flow diagram, ‖ means _____.

8. Complete the following flow diagram for the Qual I cations. Refer to *Dry Lab 4.E* for a review of the symbolism on a flow diagram.

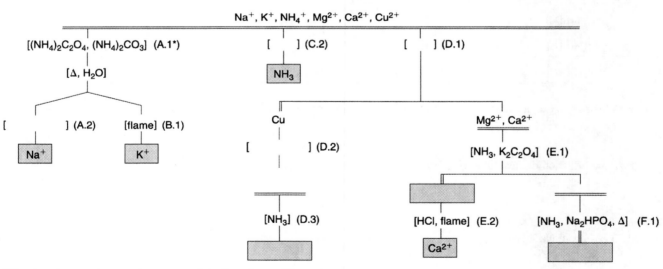

*Numbers in parentheses refer to parts of the Experimental Procedure.

Qual I. Na$^+$, K$^+$, NH$_4$$^+$, Mg^{2+}, Ca^{2+}, Cu^{2+}

Date _____ Lab Sec. _____ Name _____ Desk No. _____

Procedure Number and Ion	Test Reagent or Technique	Evidence of Chemical Change	Chemical(s) Responsible for Observation	Equation(s) for Observed Reaction	Check (√) if Observed in Unknown
① Na$^+$	flame	_____	_____	N/A	☐
② K$^+$	flame	_____	_____	N/A	☐
③ NH$_4$$^+$	_____	_____	_____	_____	☐
④ Cu^{2+}	_____	_____	_____	_____	_____
⑤	_____	_____	_____	_____	_____
⑥	_____	_____	_____	_____	☐
⑦	_____	_____	_____	_____	☐
⑧ Ca^{2+}	_____	_____	_____	_____	☐
⑨	flame	_____	_____	_____	☐
⑩ Mg^{2+}	_____	_____	_____	_____	☐

Cations present in unknown test solution no. _____ : _____

Instructor's approval: _____

Laboratory Questions

Circle the questions that have been assigned.

1. Explain why a positive flame test for sodium is *not* an absolute confirmation of sodium ion in a test sample.

2. Part A.1. The $(NH_4)_2C_2O_4$ addition is omitted in the procedure. How does this affect the appearance of the flame test in Part A.2?

3. Part B. Explain why it is good laboratory technique to conduct a comparative flame test for potassium using the 0.5 M KCl solution.

4. Part C.2. Only 6 M KOH was present on the reagent shelf—there was no 6 M NaOH. Explain what effect this substitution has on the test for the presence of the ammonium ion.

5. Part C.2. Instead of 6 M NaOH being added to the solution, 6 M HCl is added. How will this affect the test for the presence of ammonium ion in the solution? Explain.

6. Part D.1. What is the fate of Zn^{2+} in the experiment? Explain.

7. Part D.2. Instead of 6 M HNO_3 being added to the solution, 6 M HCl is added (both are strong acids). How will this affect the test for the presence of copper(II) ion in the solution? Explain.

8. Part D.3. Instead of *conc* NH_3 being added to the solution, 6 M NaOH is added (both are bases). How will this affect the test for the identification of copper(II) ion in the solution? Explain.

9. Part E.1. Instead of 6 M NH_3 being added to the solution, 6 M NaOH is added (both are bases) before the addition of the $K_2C_2O_4$. What would be the appearance of the solution? Explain.

Potentiometric Analyses

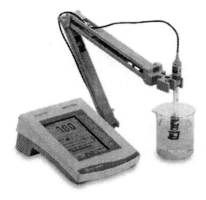

A modern pH meter with a combination electrode

- To operate a pH meter
- To graphically determine a stoichiometric point
- To determine the molar concentration of a weak acid solution
- To determine the molar mass of a solid weak acid
- To determine the pK_a of a weak acid

The following techniques are used in the Experimental Procedure:

A probe connected to an instrument that provides a direct reading of the concentration of a particular substance in an aqueous system is a convenient form of analysis. Such convenience is particularly advantageous when a large number of samples needs to be analyzed. The probe, or electrode, senses a difference in concentrations between the substance in solution and the substance in the probe itself. The concentration difference causes a voltage (or potential difference), which is recorded by an instrument called a **potentiometer.**

Such a potentiometer is a powerful, convenient instrument for determining the concentrations of various ions in solution. To list only a few, the molar concentrations of the cations H^+, Li^+, Na^+, K^+, Ag^+, Ca^{2+}, Cu^{2+}, Pb^{2+}; the anions F^-, Cl^-, Br^-, I^-, CN^-, SO_4^{2-}; and the gases O_2, CO_2, NH_3, SO_2, H_2S, NO_x can be measured directly using an electrode specifically designed for their measurement (a specific selective electrode).

The H^+ concentration of a solution is measured with a potentiometer called a **pH meter,** an instrument that measures a potential difference (or voltage) caused by a difference in the hydrogen concentration of the test solution relative to that of the 0.1 M HCl reference solution contained within the electrode. The electrode, called a *combination electrode*, is shown in Figure 14.1, page 202.

The measured voltage recorded by the potentiometer, E_{cell}, is a function of the pH of the solution at 25°C by the equation

$$E_{cell} = E' + 0.0592 \, pH \tag{14.1}$$

E' is a cell constant, an internal parameter that is characteristic of the pH meter and its electrode.

Potentiometer: an instrument that measures a potential difference— often called a voltmeter. See Experiment 32.

pH meter: an instrument that measures the pH of a solution

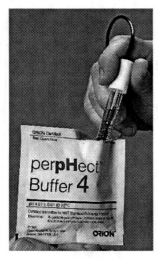

Buffer solutions are used to calibrate pH meters.

Buffer solution: a solution that maintains a relatively constant, reproducible pH

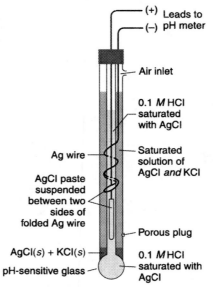

Figure 14.1 A combination electrode for measuring pH

Before any pH measurements are made, the pH meter is calibrated (that is, E' is set experimentally). The electrode is placed into a **buffer solution** of known pH (see margin photo), and the E_{cell}, the potential difference between the [H^+] of the glass electrode and the [H^+] of the buffer, is manually adjusted to read the pH of the buffer—this adjustment sets E'.

The readout of the pH meter is E_{cell}, expressed in volts, but since E_{cell} is directly proportional to pH (equation 14.1), the meter for the readout is expressed directly in pH units.

Indicators and pH of a Weak Acid Solution

The selection of an indicator for the titration of a strong acid with a strong base is relatively easy in that the color change at the stoichiometric point always occurs at a pH of 7 (at 25°C). Usually, phenolphthalein can be used because its color changes at a pH close to 7. However, when a weak acid is titrated with a strong base, the stoichiometric point is at a pH greater than 7, and a different indicator may need to be selected.[1] If the weak acid is an unknown acid, then the proper indicator cannot be selected because the pH at the stoichiometric point cannot be predetermined. The color change of a selected indicator may *not* occur at (or even near) the pH of the stoichiometric point for the titration. To better detect a stoichiometric point for the titration of an unknown weak acid, a pH meter is more reliable.

Molar Concentration of a Weak Acid Solution

Titrimetric analysis: a titration procedure that is chosen for an analysis

In Part A of this experiment, a **titrimetric analysis** is used to determine the molar concentration of a weak acid solution. A pH meter is used to detect the stoichiometric point of the titration. An acid–base indicator will *not* be used. A standardized sodium hydroxide solution is used as the titrant.[2]

The pH of a weak acid solution increases as the standardized NaOH solution is added. A plot of the pH of the weak acid solution as the strong base is being added, pH versus V_{NaOH}, is called the **titration curve** (Figure 14.2) for the reaction. The inflection

Titration curve: a data plot of pH versus volume of titrant

---

[1]The pH is greater than 7 at the stoichiometric point for the titration of a weak monoprotic acid because of the basicity of the conjugate base, A^-, of the weak acid, HA:

$$A^-(aq) + H_2O(l) \rightarrow HA(aq) + OH^-(aq)$$

[2]The procedure for preparing a standardized NaOH solution is described in *Experiment 9*.

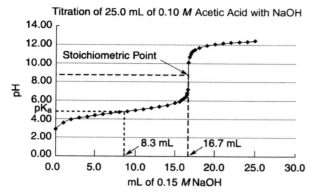

Titration of 25.0 mL of 0.10 *M* Acetic Acid with NaOH

Figure 14.2 Titration curve for 25.0 mL of 0.10 *M* CH_3COOH with 0.15 *M* NaOH

point in the sharp vertical portion of the plot (about midway on the vertical rise) is the **stoichiometric point.**

Stoichiometric point: also called the equivalence point

The moles of NaOH used for the analysis equals the volume of NaOH, dispensed from the buret, times its molar concentration:

$$\text{moles NaOH } (mol) = \text{volume } (L) \times \text{molar concentration } (mol/L) \quad (14.2)$$

For a **monoprotic acid,** HA, one mole of OH^-, neutralizes one mole of acid:

Monoprotic acid: a substance capable of donating a single proton, H^+

$$HA(aq) + OH^-(aq) \rightarrow H_2O(l) + A^-(aq) \quad (14.3)$$

The molar concentration of the acid is determined by dividing its number of moles in solution by its measured volume in liters:

$$\text{molar concentration HA } (mol/L) = \frac{\text{mol HA}}{\text{volume HA}(L)} \quad (14.4)$$

For a **diprotic acid,** H_2X, 2 mol of OH^- neutralizes 1 mol of acid:

Diprotic acid: a substance capable of donating two protons

$$H_2X(aq) + 2\,OH^-(aq) \rightarrow 2\,H_2O(l) + X^{2-}(aq) \quad (14.5)$$

Molar Mass of a Weak Acid

In Part B, the molar mass and the pK_a of an unknown *solid* weak acid are determined. The standardized NaOH solution is used to titrate a carefully measured mass of the *dissolved* acid to the stoichiometric point. A plot of pH versus V_{NaOH} is required to define the stoichiometric point.

The moles of acid is determined as described in equations 14.2 and 14.3.

The molar mass of the acid is calculated from the moles of the solid acid neutralized at the stoichiometric point and its measured mass:

$$\text{molar mass } (g/mol) = \frac{\text{mass of solid acid}(g)}{\text{moles of solid acid}} \quad (14.6)$$

---

pK_a of a Weak Acid

A weak acid, HA, in water undergoes only partial ionization:

$$HA(aq) + H_2O(l) \rightleftharpoons H_3O^+(aq) + A^-(aq) \quad (14.7)$$

At equilibrium conditions, the mass action expression for the weak acid system equals the equilibrium constant.

$$K_a = \frac{[H_3O^+][A^-]}{[HA]} \quad (14.8)$$

When one-half of the weak acid is neutralized by the NaOH titrant in a titration, mol HA = mol A^- and also [HA] = [A^-]. Since [HA] = [A^-] at this point in the titration, then $K_a = [H_3O^+]$. If one takes the negative logarithm of both sides of this equality, then $pK_a = pH$. As pH is recorded directly from the pH meter, the pK_a of the weak acid is readily obtained at the "halfway point" (halfway to the stoichiometric point) in the titration (Figure 14.2, page 203).

The stoichiometric point is again determined from the complete titration curve of pH versus V_{NaOH}. If the weak acid is diprotic and if both stoichiometric points are detected, then pK_{a1} and pK_{a2} can be determined.

EXPERIMENTAL
PROCEDURE

Procedure Overview: The pH meter is used in conjunction with a titration apparatus and a standardized sodium hydroxide solution to determine the molar concentration of a weak acid solution and the molar mass and pK_a of a solid, weak acid. Plots of pH versus volume of NaOH are used to determine the stoichiometric point of each titration.

The number of pH meters in the laboratory is limited. You may need to share one with a partner or with a larger group. Ask your instructor for details of the arrangement. Consult with your instructor for directions on the proper care and use of the pH meter. Also inquire about the calibration of the pH meter.

Because of time and equipment constraints, it may be impossible to do all parts of the experiment in one laboratory period. Time is required not only to collect and graph the data but also to interpret the data and complete the calculations. Discuss the expectations from the experiment with your instructor.

The pH versus V_{NaOH} curves to be plotted in Parts A.6 and B.3 can be established by using a pH probe that is connected directly to either a calculator or computer with the appropriate software. If this pH sensing/recording apparatus is available in the laboratory, consult with your instructor for its use and adaptation to the experiment. The probe merely replaces the pH electrode in Figure 14.3. However, volume readings from the buret will still need to be recorded.

A. Molar
Concentration of
a Weak Acid
Solution

Obtain about 90 mL of an acid solution with an unknown concentration from your instructor. Your instructor will advise you as to whether your acid is monoprotic or diprotic. Record the sample number on the **Report Sheet**. Clean three 250-mL beakers.

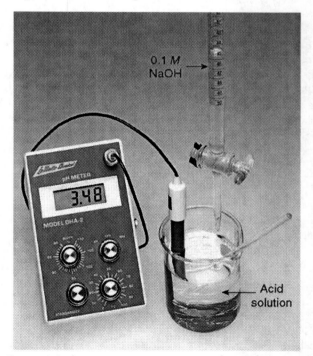

Figure 14.3 The setup for a potentiometric titration. Use a stirring rod or magnetic stirrer to stir the solution.

1. **Obtain a standardized NaOH solution.** A standardized (~0.1 M) NaOH solution was prepared in *Experiment 9*. If that solution was saved, it is to be used for this experiment. If the solution was not saved, you must either again prepare and standardize the solution (*Experiment 9*, Part A) or obtain about 200 mL of a standardized NaOH solution prepared by stockroom personnel. Record the *exact* molar concentration of the NaOH solution on the **Report Sheet**. Your instructor will advise you.

2. **Prepare the buret with the standardized NaOH solution.** Properly clean a buret; rinse twice with tap water, twice with deionized water, and finally with three 5-mL portions of the standardized 0.1 M NaOH. Drain each rinse through the tip of the buret. Fill the buret with the 0.1 M NaOH. After 10–15 seconds, properly read[3] and **record** the volume of solution, using all certain digits *plus* one uncertain digit.

Record the volume to the correct number of significant figures

3. **Prepare the weak acid solution for analysis.** Pipet 25 mL of the unknown weak acid solution into each of three *labeled* 250-mL beakers; add 50 mL of deionized water to each.

   Set up the titration apparatus as shown in Figure 14.3. Remove the electrode from the deionized water and touch-dry the electrode with lint-free paper (Kimwipes). Immerse the electrode about one-half inch deep into the solution of beaker 1. Swirl or stir the solution and read and record the initial pH.[4]

4. **Titrate the weak acid solution.** Add the NaOH titrant, initially in 1- to 2-mL increments, and swirl or stir the solution. After each addition, allow the pH meter to stabilize; read and record the pH and buret readings on a *self-designed* data sheet. Repeat the additions until the stoichiometric point is near,[5] then slow the addition. When the stoichiometric point is imminent, add the NaOH titrant drop-wise.[6] Use a minimum volume of deionized water from a wash bottle to rinse the wall of the beaker or to add half-drop volumes of NaOH. Dilution affects pH readings.

5. **Titrate beyond the stoichiometric point.** After reaching the stoichiometric point, first add drops of NaOH, then 1 mL, and finally 2- to 3-mL **aliquots** until at least 10 mL of NaOH solution have been added beyond the stoichiometric point. Read and record the pH and buret readings after each addition.

Aliquot: an undefined, generally small, volume of a solution

6. **Plot the data.** Use appropriate software, such as Excel, to plot the data for the titration curve, pH versus V_{NaOH}. Draw a smooth curve through the data points (do not connect the dots!). Properly label your graph and obtain your instructor's approval.

   From the plotted data, determine the volume of NaOH titrant added to reach the stoichiometric point.

Appendix C

7. **Repeat the analysis.** Repeat the titration of the samples of weak acid in beakers 2 and 3. Determine the average molar concentration of the acid.

Three samples of the solid weak acid are to be analyzed. Prepare three clean 250-mL beakers for this determination. Obtain an unknown solid acid from your instructor and record the sample number; your instructor will advise you as to whether your unknown acid is monoprotic or diprotic.

B. Molar Mass and the pK_a of a Solid Weak Acid

---

[3]Remember to read the bottom of the meniscus with the aid of a black mark drawn on a white card.
[4]A magnetic stirrer and magnetic stirring bar may be used to swirl the solution during the addition of the titrant. Ask your instructor.
[5]The stoichiometric point is near when larger changes in pH occur with smaller additions of the NaOH titrant.
[6]Suggestion: It may save time to quickly titrate a test sample to determine an approximate volume to reach the stoichiometric point.

Appendix C

Appendix B

1. **Prepare the unknown solid acid samples.** On a weighing paper or dish, measure a mass (± 0.001 g) (advised by your instructor) of a previously dried unknown solid acid. Complete the mass measurements for all three samples while operating the balance. Dissolve the acid with 75 mL of deionized water.[7]

2. **Fill the buret and titrate.** Refill the buret with the standardized NaOH solution and, after 10–15 seconds, read and record the initial volume and the initial pH. Refer to Parts A.4 and A.5. Titrate each sample to 10 mL beyond the stoichiometric point.

3. **Plot and interpret the data.** Use appropriate software, such as Excel, to plot the data for a titration curve, pH versus V_{NaOH}. From the plot, determine the volume of NaOH used to reach the stoichiometric point of the titration. Obtain your instructor's approval.

4. **Calculate the molar mass *and* the pK_a of the weak acid**

   a. Calculate the molar mass of the weak acid.

   b. Note the volume of NaOH titrant required to reach the stoichiometric point. Determine the pH (and therefore pK_a of the weak acid) at the point where one-half of the acid was neutralized.

5. **Repeat.** Similarly titrate the other unknown solid acid samples and handle the data accordingly.

Disposal: Dispose of all test solutions as directed by your instructor.

CLEANUP: Discard the sodium hydroxide solution remaining in the buret as directed by your instructor. Rinse the buret twice with tap water and twice with deionized water, discarding each rinse through the buret tip into the sink.

6. **Collect the data.** Obtain the pK_a for the same sample number from other student chemists in the laboratory. Calculate the standard deviation and the relative standard deviation (%RSD) for the pK_a measurement for the acid.

The Next Step

While most common for the determination of hydrogen ion concentrations (and pH), potentiometric titrations are also utilized for the determination of any ion's concentration where a specific ion electrode is available (see Introduction). Develop a plan or procedure for determining the concentration of an ion in solution potentiometrically, using a specific ion electrode.

For example, a chloride specific ion electrode would read pCl directly. What would be the *x*-axis label in the titration curve?

NOTES AND CALCULATIONS

---

[7]The solid acid may be relatively insoluble, but with the addition of the NaOH solution from the buret, it will gradually dissolve and react. The addition of 10 mL of ethanol may be necessary to dissolve the acid. Consult with your instructor.

Date _____ Lab Sec. _____ Name _____ Desk No. _____

1. **a.** For a weak acid (e.g., CH_3COOH) that is titrated with a strong base (e.g., NaOH), what species (ions/molecules) are present in the solution at the stoichiometric point?

   b. For a weak acid (e.g., CH_3COOH) that is titrated with a strong base (e.g., NaOH), what species (ions/molecules) are present in the solution at the halfway point in the titration toward the stoichiometric point?

2. A 21.54-mL volume of 0.130 *M* NaOH is required to reach the stoichiometric point for the titration of 25.00 mL of a 0.112 *M* HCl solution. Would the titration of 25.00 mL of a 0.112 *M* CH_3COOH solution require more, less, or the same volume of the 0.130 *M* NaOH solution? Explain.

3. Briefly explain how the pK_a for a weak acid is determined in this experiment.

4. A 23.74-mL volume of 0.0981 *M* NaOH was used to titrate 25.0 mL of a weak monoprotic acid solution to the stoichiometric point. Determine the molar concentration of the weak acid solution. Express your answer to the correct number of significant figures.

5. Data in the following table were obtained for the titration of a 0.297-g sample of a solid, monoprotic weak acid with a 0.150 M KOH solution. Plot (at right) pH (ordinate) versus V_{KOH} (abscissa).

V_{KOH} added (mL)	pH
0.00	1.96
2.00	2.22
4.00	2.46
7.00	2.77
10.00	3.06
12.00	3.29
14.00	3.60
16.00	4.26
17.00	11.08
18.00	11.67
20.00	12.05
25.00	12.40

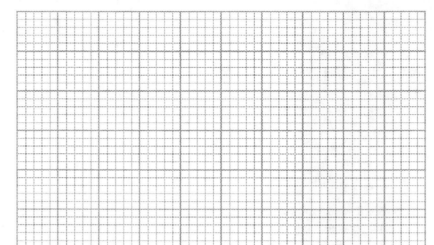

a. What volume of the KOH solution is required to reach the stoichiometric point?

b. What is the pH at the stoichiometric point?

c. What is the pK_a of the weak acid?

d. Calculate the number of moles of weak acid analyzed.

e. What is the molar mass of the solid weak acid, expressed to the correct number of significant figures?

Potentiometric Analyses

Date _____ Lab Sec. _____ Name _____ Desk No. _____

A. Molar Concentration of a Weak Acid Solution

Sample no. _____ Monoprotic or diprotic acid? _____

	Trial 1	Trial 2	Trial 3
1. Molar concentration of NaOH (*mol/L*)		_____	
2. Volume of weak acid (*mL*)	_____	_____	_____
3. Buret readng of NaOH, *initial* (*mL*)	_____	_____	_____
4. Buret reading NaOH at stoichiometric point, *final* (*mL*)	_____	_____	_____
5. Volume of NaOH dispensed (*mL*)			
6. Instructor's approval of pH vs. V_{NaOH} graph	_____	_____	_____
7. Moles of NaOH to stoichiometric point (*mol*)			
8. Moles of acid (*mol*)			
9. Molar concentration of acid (*mol/L*)			
10. Average molar concentration of acid (*mol/L*)			

B. Molar Mass and the pK_a of a Solid Weak Acid

Sample no. _____ Monoprotic or diprotic acid? _____ Suggested mass _____

	Trial 1	Trial 2	Trial 3
1. Mass of dry, solid acid (*g*)	_____	_____	_____
2. Molar concentration of NaOH (*mol/L*)		_____	
3. Buret readng of NaOH, *initial* (*mL*)	_____	_____	_____
4. Buret reading NaOH at stoichiometric point, *final* (*mL*)	_____	_____	_____
5. Volume of NaOH dispensed (*mL*)			
6. Instructor's approval of pH versus V_{NaOH} graph	_____	_____	_____
7. Moles of NaOH to stoichiometric point (*mol*)			
8. Moles of acid (*mol*)			
9. Molar mass of acid (*g/mol*)		*	
10. Average molar mass of acid (*g/mol*)			
11. Volume of NaOH halfway to stoichiometric point (*mL*)	_____	_____	_____
12. pK_{a1} of weak acid (from graph)	_____	_____	_____
13. Average pK_{a1}			

*Show calculations for Trial 1 on the next page.

*Calculations for Trial 1.

Class Data/Group	1	2	3	4	5	6
pK_a for Sample No. _____						

Standard deviation and the relative standard deviation (%RSD) for the pK_a of an acid from the class data. See Appendix B.

Laboratory Questions

Circle the questions that have been assigned.

1. The pH meter was not properly calibrated.
   a. How does this experimental error affect the precision of your data? Explain.
   b. How does this experimental error affect the accuracy of your data? Explain.

2. The pH meter was mistakenly calibrated to be 1.0 pH unit higher than the buffer.
   a. Part A. Will this miscalibration result in a reported molar concentration of the weak acid being too high, too low, or unaffected? Explain.
   b. Part B. Is the determined pK_a of the weak acid too high, too low, or unaffected by the miscalibration? Explain.

3. a. Part A.4. The pH reading is taken before the pH meter stabilizes. As a result, the pH reading may be too low. Explain.
   b. Part A.4. Explain why it is good technique to slow the addition of NaOH titrant near the stoichiometric point.
   c. Part A.5. While not absolutely necessary, why is it good technique to add NaOH titrant beyond the stoichiometric point?

4. Part B.1. The solid acid is dissolved in 100 mL of deionized water, followed by 10 mL of ethanol. How does this added volume affect the reported molar mass of the weak acid—too high, too low, or unaffected? Explain.

5. Part B.4. As a result of adding the NaOH titrant too rapidly and an unwillingness to allow the pH meter to equilibrate before reading its pH, the stoichiometric point is ill defined. As a result of this technique error,
   a. will the molar mass of the weak acid be reported as too high or too low? Explain.
   b. will the pK_a of the weak acid be reported as too high or too low? Explain.

6. Ideally, how many stoichiometric points would be observed on a pH titration curve for a diprotic acid? Sketch the appearance of its titration curve and explain.

Molar Solubility, Common-Ion Effect

Silver oxide forms a brown mudlike precipitate from a mixture of silver nitrate and sodium hydroxide solutions.

- To determine the molar solubility and the solubility constant of calcium hydroxide
- To study the effect of a common ion on the molar solubility of calcium hydroxide

The following techniques are used in the Experimental Procedure:

INTRODUCTION

Salts that have a very limited solubility in water are called **slightly soluble** (or "insoluble") **salts.** A saturated solution of a slightly soluble salt is a result of a dynamic equilibrium between the solid salt and its ions in solution; however, because the salt is only slightly soluble, the concentrations of the ions in solution are low. For example, in a saturated silver sulfate, Ag_2SO_4, solution, the **dynamic equilibrium** between solid Ag_2SO_4 and the Ag^+ and SO_4^{2-} ions in solution lies far to the *left* because of the low solubility of silver sulfate:

$$Ag_2SO_4(s) \rightleftharpoons 2\,Ag^+(aq) + SO_4^{2-}(aq) \qquad (15.1)$$

The mass action expression for this system is

$$[Ag^+]^2[SO_4^{2-}] \qquad (15.2)$$

As Ag_2SO_4 is a solid, its concentration is constant and therefore does not appear in the mass action expression. At equilibrium, the mass action expression equals K_{sp}, called the **solubility product** or, more simply, the equilibrium constant for this slightly soluble salt.

The **molar solubility** of Ag_2SO_4, determined experimentally, is 1.4×10^{-2} mol/L. This means that in 1.0 L of a saturated Ag_2SO_4 solution, only 1.4×10^{-2} mol of silver sulfate dissolves, forming 2.8×10^{-2} mol of Ag^+ and 1.4×10^{-2} mol of SO_4^{2-}. The solubility product of silver sulfate equals the product of the molar concentrations of the ions, each raised to the power of its coefficient in the balanced equation:

$$K_{sp} = [Ag^+]^2[SO_4^{2-}] = [2.8 \times 10^{-2}]^2[1.4 \times 10^{-2}] = 1.1 \times 10^{-5} \qquad (15.3)$$

What happens to the molar solubility of a salt when an ion, common to the salt, is added to the saturated solution? According to LeChâtelier's principle (*Experiment 16*),

Slightly soluble salt: a qualitative term that reflects the very low solubility of a salt

Dynamic equilibrium: the rate of the forward reaction equals the rate of the reverse reaction

Molar solubility: the number of moles of salt that dissolve per liter of (aqueous) solution

Figure 15.1 The addition of *conc* HCl to a saturated NaCl solution results in the formation of solid NaCl.

Figure 15.2 The solid $Ca(OH)_2$ in a saturated $Ca(OH)_2$ solution is slow to settle.

the equilibrium for the salt shifts to compensate for the added ions; that is, it shifts *left* to favor the formation of more of the solid salt. This effect, caused by the addition of an ion common to an existing equilibrium, is called the **common-ion effect.** As a result of the common-ion addition and the corresponding shift in the equilibrium, fewer moles of the salt dissolve in solution, lowering the molar solubility of the salt.

The equilibrium in equation 15.1 shows that both Ag^+ and SO_4^{2-} ions are present. Addition of Ag^+ and/or SO_4^{2-} (ions common to the equilibrium) will shift the equilibrium to the *left* (LeChâtelier's principle), resulting in the formation of additional $Ag_2SO_4(s)$, thereby decreasing the solubility of Ag_2SO_4.

While molar solubility is often associated with slightly soluble salts, soluble salts are also affected by the addition of a common-ion to the equilibrium. For example, consider the equilibrium for a saturated solution of sodium chloride:

$$NaCl(s) \rightleftharpoons Na^+(aq) + Cl^-(aq) \tag{15.4}$$

The addition of chloride ion, a common ion in the equilibrium, shifts the equilibrium left to cause the formation of solid sodium chloride (Figure 15.1).

Molar Solubility and Solubility Product

In Part A of this experiment, you will determine the molar solubility and the solubility product for calcium hydroxide, $Ca(OH)_2$. A saturated $Ca(OH)_2$ solution[1] (Figure 15.2) is prepared; after an equilibrium is established between the solid $Ca(OH)_2$ and the Ca^{2+} and OH^- ions in solution, the supernatant solution is analyzed. The hydroxide ion, OH^-, in the supernatant solution is titrated with a standardized HCl solution to determine its molar concentration.

According to the equation

$$Ca(OH)_2(s) \rightleftharpoons Ca^{2+}(aq) + 2\,OH^-(aq) \tag{15.5}$$

for each mole of $Ca(OH)_2$ that dissolves, 1 mol of Ca^{2+} and 2 mol of OH^- are present in solution. Thus, by determining the molar concentration of hydroxide ion, the $[Ca^{2+}]$, the K_{sp}, and the molar solubility of $Ca(OH)_2$ can be calculated.

$$[Ca^{2+}] = \tfrac{1}{2}[OH^-]$$
$$K_{sp} = [Ca^{2+}][OH^-]^2 = \tfrac{1}{2}[OH^-]^3 \tag{15.6}$$
$$\text{molar solubility of } Ca(OH)_2 = [Ca^{2+}] = \tfrac{1}{2}[OH^-]$$

---

[1]A saturated solution of calcium hydroxide is called **limewater.**

Likewise, the same procedure is used in Part B to determine the molar solubility of $Ca(OH)_2$ in the presence of added calcium ion, an ion common to the slightly soluble salt equilibrium.

Procedure Overview: The supernatant from a saturated calcium hydroxide solution is titrated with a standardized hydrochloric acid solution to the methyl orange endpoint. An analysis of the data results in the determination of the molar solubility and solubility product of calcium hydroxide. The procedure is repeated on the supernatant from a saturated calcium hydroxide solution containing added calcium ion.

EXPERIMENTAL PROCEDURE

Three analyses are to be completed. To hasten the analyses, prepare three *clean*, labeled 125- or 250-mL Erlenmeyer flasks. Obtain no more than 50 mL of standardized 0.05 *M* HCl for use in Part A.5.

A. Molar Solubility and Solubility Product of Calcium Hydroxide

Ask your laboratory instructor about the status of the saturated $Ca(OH)_2$ solution. If you are to prepare the solution, then omit Part A.3; if the stockroom personnel has prepared the solution, then omit Parts A.1 and A.2.

1. **Prepare the stock calcium hydroxide solution.** Prepare a saturated $Ca(OH)_2$ solution 1 week before the experiment by adding approximately 3 g of $Ca(OH)_2$ to 120 mL of boiled, deionized water in a 125-mL Erlenmeyer flask. Stir the solution and stopper the flask.

2. **Transfer the saturated calcium hydroxide solution.** Allow the solid $Ca(OH)_2$ to remain settled (from Part A.1). *Carefully* [do not disturb the finely divided $Ca(OH)_2$ solid] decant about 90 mL of the saturated $Ca(OH)_2$ solution into a second 125-mL flask. Proceed to Part A.4.

3. **Obtain a saturated calcium hydroxide solution (alternate).** Submit a clean, dry 150-mL beaker to your laboratory instructor (or stockroom) for the purpose of obtaining ~90 mL of supernatant from a saturated $Ca(OH)_2$ solution for analysis.

4. **Prepare a sample for analysis.** Rinse a 25-mL pipet at least twice with 1- to 2-mL portions of the saturated $Ca(OH)_2$ solution and discard. Pipet 25 mL of the saturated $Ca(OH)_2$ solution into a clean 125-mL flask and add 2 drops of methyl orange indicator.[2]

5. **Set up the titration apparatus.**

   a. Prepare a clean, 50-mL buret for titration. Rinse the clean buret and tip with three 5-mL portions of the standardized 0.05 *M* HCl solution and discard. Fill the buret with standardized 0.05 *M* HCl, remove the air bubbles in the buret tip, and, after 10–15 seconds, read and record the initial volume in the buret to the correct number of significant figures.

   b. Record the *actual* concentration of the 0.05 *M* HCl on the **Report Sheet**.

   c. Place a sheet of white paper beneath the receiving flask.

6. **Titrate.** Titrate the $Ca(OH)_2$ solution with the standardized HCl solution to the methyl orange endpoint, where the color changes from yellow to a faint red-orange. Remember the addition of HCl should stop within *one-half drop* of the endpoint. After 10–15 seconds of the persistent endpoint, read and record the final volume of standard HCl in the buret.

7. **Repeat.** Titrate two additional samples of the saturated $Ca(OH)_2$ solution until 1% reproducibility is achieved.

8. **Do the calculations.** Complete your calculations as outlined on the **Report Sheet**. The reported values for the K_{sp} of $Ca(OH)_2$ will vary from chemist to chemist.

[2]Methyl orange changes from red-orange to yellow in the pH range of from 3.2 to 4.4.

B. Molar Solubility of Calcium Hydroxide in the Presence of a Common Ion

Three analyses are to be completed. Clean and label three 125- or 250-mL Erlenmeyer flasks.

Again, as in Part A, ask your instructor about the procedure by which you are to obtain the saturated $Ca(OH)_2$ solution with the added $CaCl_2$ for analysis. If you are to prepare the solution, then complete Parts B.1 and A.2; if the stockroom personnel prepared the "spiked" saturated $Ca(OH)_2$ solution, then repeat Part A.3.

In either case, complete Part B.2 in its entirety for the analysis of the saturated $Ca(OH)_2$ solution with the added $CaCl_2$.

1. **Prepare the stock solution.** Mix ~3 g of $Ca(OH)_2$ and ~1 g of $CaCl_2 \cdot 2H_2O$ with 120 mL of boiled, deionized water in a 125-mL flask 1 week before the experiment. Stir and stopper the flask.

2. **Prepare a buret for analysis, prepare the sample, and titrate.** Repeat Parts A.4–A.8.

> *Disposal:* Discard all of the reaction mixtures as advised by your instructor.

CLEANUP: Discard the HCl solution in the buret as advised by your instructor. Rinse the buret twice with tap water and twice with deionized water.

The Next Step

(1) Design an experiment to determine the molar solubility of a salt without using a titration procedure. (2) How does the molar solubility of the hydroxide salts vary within a group and/or within a period of the periodic table? (3) Does the amount of $CaCl_2$ added to saturated $Ca(OH)_2$ solution produce a linear correlation to its molar solubility? Try additional sample preparations.

NOTES AND CALCULATIONS

Experiment 15 *Prelaboratory Assignment*

Molar Solubility, Common-Ion Effect

Date _____ Lab Sec. _____ Name _____ Desk No. _____

1. A saturated solution of lead(II) iodide, PbI_2 has an iodide concentration of 3.0×10^{-3} mol/L (see photo).
   a. What is the molar solubility of PbI_2.?

   b. Determine the solubility constant, K_{sp}, for lead(II) iodide.

Lead iodide precipitate.

   c. Does the molar solubility of lead(II) iodide increase, decrease, or remain unchanged with the addition of potassium iodide to the solution? Explain.

2. Experimental Procedure, Part A.4. What is the purpose of rinsing the pipet twice with aliquots of the saturated $Ca(OH)_2$ solution?

3. Experimental Procedure, Part A.4
   a. What is the indicator used to detect the endpoint in the titration for this experiment?

   b. What is the expected color change at the endpoint in this experiment?

4. Experimental Procedure, Part A.5. The directions are to read and record the initial volume of the buret to the correct number of significant figures. Explain what this means.

5. Experimental Procedure, Part A.6 versus Part B.2. Would you expect more or less standard 0.05 *M* HCl to be used to reach the methyl orange endpoint in Part B.2? Explain.

6. A saturated solution of magnesium hydroxide (commonly called *milk of magnesium*) is prepared and the excess solid magnesium hydroxide is allowed to settle. A 25.0-mL aliquot of the saturated solution is withdrawn and transferred to an Erlenmeyer flask, and two drops of methyl orange indicator are added. A 0.00053 *M* HCl solution (titrant) is dispensed from a buret into the solution (analyte). The solution turns from yellow to a very faint red-orange after the addition of 13.2 mL.
   a. How many moles of hydroxide ion are neutralized in the analysis?

   b. What is the molar concentration of the hydroxide ion in the saturated solution?

   c. What is the molar solubility of magnesium hydroxide? See equation 15.6.

   d. What is the solubility product, K_{sp}, for magnesium hydroxide? Express the K_{sp} with the correct number of significant figures.

*7. Phenolphthalein has a color change over the pH range of 8.2 to 10.0; methyl orange has a color change over the pH range of 3.2 to 4.4. Although the phenolphthalein indicator is commonly used for neutralization reactions, why instead is the methyl orange indicator recommended for this experiment?

Experiment 15 *Report Sheet*

Molar Solubility, Common-Ion Effect

Date _____ Lab Sec. _____ Name _____ Desk No. _____

A. Molar Solubility and Solubility Product of Calcium Hydroxide

	Trial 1	*Trial 2*	*Trial 3*
1. Volume of saturated $Ca(OH)_2$ solution (*mL*)	25.0	25.0	25.0
2. Concentration of standardized HCl solution (*mol/L*)			
3. Buret reading, *initial* (*mL*)			
4. Buret reading, *final* (*mL*)			
5. Volume of HCl added (*mL*)			
6. Moles of HCl added (*mol*)			
7. Moles of OH^- in saturated solution (*mol*)			
8. $[OH^-]$, equilibrium (*mol/L*)			
9. $[Ca^{2+}]$, equilibrium (*mol/L*)			
10. Molar solubility of $Ca(OH)_2$ (*mol/L*)	*		
11. Average molar solubility of $Ca(OH)_2$ (*mol/L*)			
12. K_{sp} of $Ca(OH)_2$	*		
13. Average K_{sp}			
14. Standard deviation of K_{sp}		*Appendix B*	
15. Relative standard deviation of K_{sp} (*%RSD*)		*Appendix B*	

*Calculations for Trial 1.

B. Molar Solubility of Calcium Hydroxide in the Presence of a Common Ion

	Trial 1	Trial 2	Trial 3
1. Volume of saturated Ca(OH)$_2$ with added CaCl$_2$ solution (mL)	25.0	25.0	25.0
2. Concentration of standardized HCl solution (mol/L)			
3. Buret reading, *initial* (mL)			
4. Buret reading, *final* (mL)			
5. Volume of HCl added (mL)			
6. Moles of HCl added (mol)			
7. Moles of OH$^-$ in saturated solution (mol)			
8. [OH$^-$], equilibrium (mol/L)			
9. Molar solubility of Ca(OH)$_2$ with added CaCl$_2$ (mol/L)			
10. Average molar solubility of Ca(OH)$_2$ with added CaCl$_2$ (mol/L)			

Account for the different molar solubilities in Part A.11 and Part B.10 (***Report Sheet***).

Laboratory Questions

Circle the questions that are to be answered.

1. Part A.2. Suppose some of the solid calcium hydroxide is inadvertently transferred along with the supernatant liquid for analysis.
   a. Will more, less, or the same amount of hydrochloric acid titrant be used for the analysis in Part A.6? Explain.
   b. Will this inadvertent transfer increase, decrease, or have no effect on the calculated solubility product for calcium hydroxide? Explain.
   c. Will this inadvertent transfer increase, decrease, or have no effect on the calculated molar solubility of calcium hydroxide? Explain.

2. Part A.6. Does adding boiled, deionized water to the titrating flask to wash the wall of the Erlenmeyer flask and the buret tip increase, decrease, or have no effect on the K_{sp} value of the Ca(OH)$_2$? Explain.

3. Part A.6. While titrating the saturated Ca(OH)$_2$ solution, Isabella was distracted, and the endpoint was surpassed—a dark red-orange. As a result of this technique error, will the reported molar solubility of Ca(OH)$_2$- be too high or too low? Explain.

*4. Part B.1. How will using tap water instead of boiled, deionized water affect the K_{sp} value of Ca(OH)$_2$—increase, decrease, or have no effect? Explain. *Hint:* How will the minerals in the water affect the solubility of Ca(OH)$_2$?

5. Part A.8. Jerry forgot to record the actual molar concentration of the standard HCl solution (which was actually 0.044 M). However, to complete the calculations quickly, the ~0.05 M concentration was used. Will the reported molar solubility of Ca(OH)$_2$ be too high or too low? Explain.

*6. The ethylenediaminetetraacetate ion, H$_2$Y^{2-}, forms a strong complex with the calcium ion. How does the addition of H$_2$Y^{2-} affect the molar solubility of Ca(OH)$_2$? Explain. See *Experiment 21* for the reaction of Ca^{2+} with H$_2$Y^{2-}.

Appendix A

Conversion Factors[1]

The magnitude of a measurement must be familiar to a chemist.

Length
1 meter (m) = 39.37 in. = 3.281 ft = distance light travels in 1/299,792,548th of a second
1 inch ($in.$) = 2.54 cm (exactly) = 0.0254 m
1 kilometer (km) = 0.6214 (statute) mile
1 angstrom (Å) = 1×10^{-10} m = 0.1 nm
1 micron or micrometer (μm) 1×10^{-6} m

Mass
1 gram (g) = 0.03527 oz = 15.43 grains
1 kilogram (kg) = 2.205 lb = 35.27 oz
1 metric ton = 1×10^6 g = 1.102 short ton
1 pound (lb) = 453.6 g = 7,000 grains
1 ounce (oz) = 28.35 g = 437.5 grains

Temperature
°F = 1.8°C + 32
K = °C + 273.15

Volume
1 liter (L) = 1 dm^3 = 1.057 fl qt = 1×10^3 mL = 1×10^3 cm^3 = 61.02 in.^{3} = 0.2642 gal
1 fluid quart ($fl\ qt$) = 946.4 mL = 0.250 gal = 0.00595 bbl (oil)
1 fluid ounce ($fl\ oz$) = 29.57 mL
1 cubic foot (ft^3) = 28.32 L = 0.02832 m^3

Pressure
1 atmosphere (atm) = 760 torr (exactly) = 760 mm Hg = 29.92 in. Hg = 14.696 lb/in.^{2} = 1.013 bar = 101.325 kPa
1 pascal (Pa) = 1 kg/(m • s^2) = 1 N/m^2
1 torr = 1 mm Hg = 133.3 N/m^2

Energy
1 joule (J) = 1 kg • m^2/s^2 = 0.2390 cal = 9.48×10^{-4} Btu 1 = 1×10^7 ergs
1 calorie (cal) = 4.184 J = 3.087 ft•lb
1 British thermal unit (Btu) = 252.0 cal = 1054 J = 3.93×10^{-4} hp • hr = 2.93×10^{-4} kW • hr
1 liter atmosphere ($L • atm$) = 24.2 cal = 101.3 J
1 electron volt (eV) = 1.602×10^{-19} J
1 kW • hr (kWh) = 3,412 Btu = 8.604×10^5 cal = 3.600×10^6 J = 1.341 hp•hr

Constants and Other Conversion Data
velocity of light (c) = 2.9979×10^8 m/s = 186,272 mi/s
gas constant (R) = 0.08206 L • atm/($mol • K$) = 8.314 J/($mol • K$) = 1.986 cal/($mol • K$) = 62.37 L • torr/($mol • K$)
Avogadro's number (N_o) = 6.0221×10^{23}/mol
Planck's constant (h) = 6.6261×10^{-34} J • s/photon
Faraday's constant ($\mathfrak{F}$) = 96,485 C/mol e^-

[1]For additional conversions, go to http://www.onlineconversion.com.

Appendix B

Treatment of Data

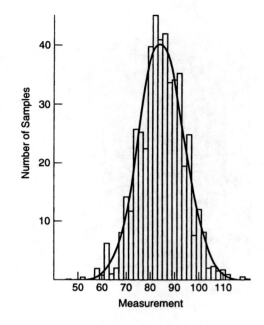

Bar graph and standard error curve for the multiple analysis of a sample.

Confidence in a scientific theory depends on the reliability of the experimental data on which the theory is based. For this reason, a scientist must be concerned about the quality of the data he or she collects. Of prime importance is the **accuracy** of the data—how closely the measured values lie to the true values.

To obtain accurate data, we must use instruments that are carefully calibrated for a properly designed experimental procedure. Miscalibrated equipment, such as a balance or buret, may result in reproducible but erred data. Flawed instruments or experimental procedures result in **systematic errors**—errors that can be detected and corrected. As a result of systematic errors, the data may have good **precision** but not necessarily have good **accuracy**. To have good accuracy of data, the systematic errors must be minimized.

Systematic errors: Determinate errors that arise from flawed equipment or experimental design

Precision: Data with small deviations from an average value have high precision

Accuracy: Data with small deviations from an accepted or accurate value have good accuracy

Random errors: Indeterminate errors that arise from the bias of a chemist in observing and recording measurements

Because scientists collect data, **random errors** may also occur in measurements. Random errors are a result of reading or interpreting the value from the measuring instrument. For example, reading the volume of a liquid in a graduated cylinder to the nearest milliliter depends on the best view of the bottom of the meniscus, the judgment of the bottom of the meniscus relative to the volume scale, and even the temperature of the liquid. A volume reading of 10.2 mL may be read as 10.1 or 10.3, depending on the chemist and the laboratory conditions. When the random errors are small, all measurements are close to one another, and we say the data are of *high precision*. When the random errors are large, the values cover a much broader range and the data are of *low precision*. Generally, data of high precision are also of high accuracy, especially if the measuring device is properly calibrated.

Remember that all measurements are to be expressed with the correct number of significant figures, the number being reflective of the measuring instrument.

Average (or Mean) Value, $\bar{x}$

Methods of analyzing experimental data, based on statistics, provide information on the degree of precision of the measured values. Applying the methods is simple, as you will see, but to understand their significance, examine briefly the **standard error curve** (Figure B.1a).

If we make a large number of measurements of a quantity, the values would fluctuate about the average value (also called the *mean value*). The **average, or mean, value** is obtained by dividing the sum of all the measured values by the total number of

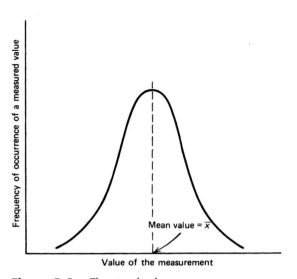

Figure B.1a The standard error curve

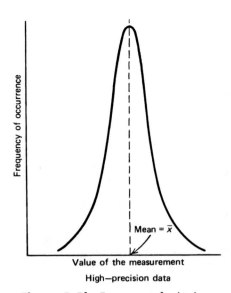

Figure B.1b Error curve for high-precision data

values. If x_1, x_2, x_3, and so on are measured values, and there are n of them, then the average value, $\bar{x}$, is computed as

$$\text{average (or mean) value, } \bar{x} = \frac{x_1 + x_2 + x_3 + \cdots + x_n}{n} \qquad \text{(B.1)}$$

Most values lie close to the average, but some lie farther away. If we plot the frequency with which a measured value occurs versus the value of the measurement, we obtain the curve in Figure B.1a. When the random errors are small (high-precision data, Figure B.1b), the curve is very narrow, and the peak is sharp. When the random errors are large (low-precision data, Figure B.1c), the data are more spread out, and the error curve is broader and less sharp.

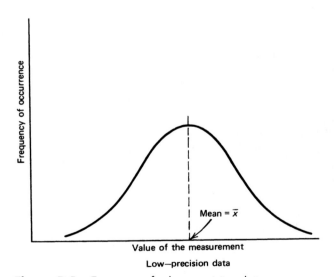

Figure B.1c Error curve for low-precision data

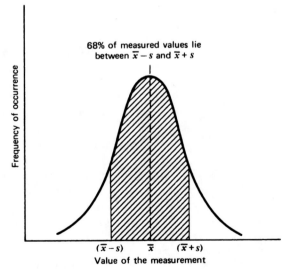

Figure B.2a Relationship of the standard deviation to the error curve

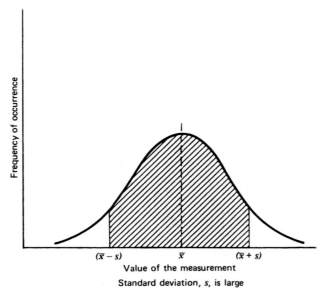

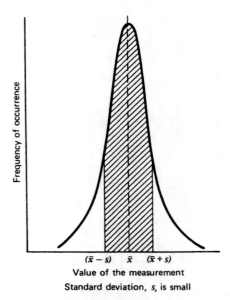

Figure B.2b Data set with a large standard deviation

Figure B.2c Data set with a small standard deviation

Standard Deviation, *s*

Statistics gives us methods for computing quantities that tell us about the width of the error curve for our data and, therefore, about the precision of the data, even when the amount of data is relatively small. One of the most important statistical measures of precision is the **standard deviation**, *s*. To calculate the standard deviation, we first compute the average value, $\bar{x}$. The next step is to compute the *deviation*, *d*, from the average value for *each* measurement—the difference between the average and each measured value:

$$\text{deviation, } d_i = \bar{x} - x_i \tag{B.2}$$

d_i is the deviation for the measured value, x_i. The standard deviation is obtained by squaring the deviations of all measurements, adding the squared values together, dividing this sum by $n - 1$ (where n is the number of measurements), and then taking the square root:

$$\text{standard deviation, } s = \sqrt{\frac{d_1^2 + d_2^2 + \cdots + d_n^2}{(n - 1)}} \tag{B.3}$$

The standard deviation means that if we make yet another measurement, the probability that its value will lie within $\pm s$ of the average value is 0.68. In other words, 68 percent of the measurements lie within $\pm s$ of the average value (i.e., within the range $\bar{x} - s$ to $\bar{x} + s$). On the error curve in Figure B.2a, page 221, this represents the measurements falling within the shaded area. If we obtain a large calculated *s* from a set of measured values, it means that the error curve for our data is broad and that the precision of the data is low (Figure B.2b); a small value of *s* for a set of data means that the error curve is narrow, and the precision of the data is high (see Figure B.2c). Thus, *s* is a statistical measure of the precision of the data.

For most scientific data, three results is the *absolute minimum* number for determining the standard deviation of the data. Chemists tend to require four or more results for a meaningful interpretation of the standard deviation value of the data.

Relative Standard Deviation

The ratio of the standard deviation to the average value of the data often gives a better appreciation for the precision of the data. The ratio, called the relative standard deviation (RSD), is either expressed in parts per thousand (ppt) or parts per hundred (pph or percent).

When expressed as a percentage, the RSD is referred to as %RSD or as the coefficient of variation (CV) of the data.

$$\text{RSD} = \frac{s}{\bar{x}} \times 1{,}000 \text{ ppt} \qquad (\text{B.4})$$

$$\%\text{RSD (or CV)} = \frac{s}{\bar{x}} \times 100\% \qquad (\text{B.5})$$

The RSD or CV expresses precision of the data—the smaller the RSD or CV, the greater the precision for the average value of the data.

As an example that illustrates how these statistical methods are applied, suppose that four analyses of an iron ore sample give the following data with four significant figures:

Trial	Mass of Iron per kg Ore Sample
1	39.74 g/kg
2	40.06 g/kg
3	39.06 g/kg
4	40.92 g/kg

$$\text{average (or mean) value, } \bar{x} = \frac{39.74 + 40.06 + 39.06 + 40.92}{4} = 39.94 \text{ g/kg}$$

To calculate the standard deviation and percent relative standard deviation (or coefficient of variation), compute the deviations and their squares. Let's set up a table.

Trial	Measured Values	$d_i = \bar{x} - x_i$	d_i^2
1	39.74 g	0.20	0.040
2	40.06 g	−0.12	0.014
3	39.06 g	0.88	0.77
4	40.92 g	−0.98	0.96
	$\bar{x} = 39.94$ g		Sum = 1.78

$$\text{standard deviation, } s = \sqrt{\frac{1.78}{4 - 1}} = 0.77$$

$$\%\text{RSD (or CV)} = \frac{0.77}{39.94} \times 100 = 1.93\%$$

The precision of our analysis is expressed in terms of a standard deviation; the amount of iron in the sample is reported as 39.94 ± 0.77 g Fe/kg of sample, meaning that 68 percent of subsequent analyses should be in the range of 39.94 ± 0.77 g Fe/kg of sample. The percent relative standard deviation, %RSD (or coefficient of variation, CV), of the precision of the data is 1.93 percent.

Relative Error

Scientists check the *accuracy* of their measurements by comparing their results with values that are well established and considered accepted values. Many reference books, such as the Chemical Rubber Company's (CRC) *Handbook of Chemistry and Physics*, are used to check a result against an accepted value. To report the relative error in *your* result, take the absolute value of the difference between your measured value and the accepted value and divide this difference by the accepted value. Taking x to be your measured value and y to be the accepted value,

$$\text{relative error} = \frac{|x - y|}{y} \qquad (\text{B.6})$$

Relative error may be expressed as percent or parts per thousand, multiplying the relative error by 100 or 1,000.

Appendix C

Graphing Data

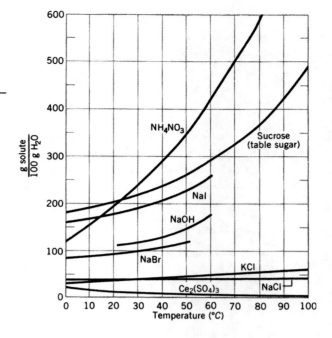

Plotted data show how the solubilities of salts vary with temperature.

A well-designed graph of experimental data is a very effective organization of the data for observing trends, discovering relationships, or predicting information. It is therefore worthwhile to learn how to effectively construct and present a graph and how to extract information from it.

Graph Construction

In general, a graph is constructed on a set of perpendicular axes (Figure C.1); the vertical axis (the y axis) is the **ordinate**, and the horizontal axis (the x axis) is the **abscissa**.

Constructing a graph involves the following five steps whether the graph is constructed manually or with the appropriate software such as Excel.

1. **Select the axes.** First choose which variable corresponds to the ordinate and which one corresponds to the abscissa. Usually, the dependent variable is plotted

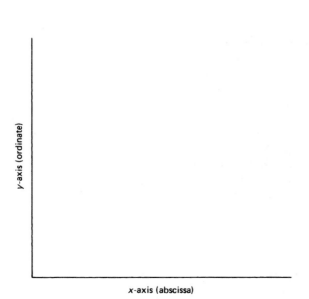

Figure C.1 A graph is usually constructed on a set of perpendicular axes.

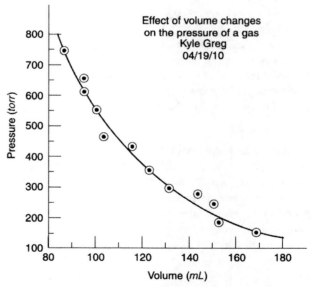

Figure C.2 An example of a properly drawn and labeled graph showing how the pressure of a gas depends on the volume of that gas

along the ordinate and values of the independent variable along the abscissa. For example, if we observe how the pressure of a gas responds to a change in volume, pressure is the dependent variable. We therefore assign pressure to the vertical axis and volume to the horizontal axis; we say we are plotting pressure versus volume. Be sure to label each axis by indicating the units that correspond to the variables being plotted (Figure C.2).

2. **Set the scales for the axes.** Construct the graph so that the data fill as much of the space of the graph paper as possible. Therefore, choose scales for the x- and y-axes that cover the range of the experimental data. For example, if the measured pressure range is 150 to 740 torr, choose a pressure scale that ranges from 100 to 800 torr. This covers the entire data range and allows us to mark the major divisions at intervals of 100 torr (Figure C.2). When choosing the scale, always choose values for the major divisions that make the smaller subdivisions easy to interpret. With major divisions at every 100 torr, minor divisions occur at every 50 torr. This makes plotting values such as 525 torr very simple.

   Construct the scale for the x-axis in the same manner. In Figure C.2, the volumes range from 170 mL at a pressure of 150 torr to 85 mL at a pressure of 750 torr. The scale on the x-axis ranges from 80 to 180 mL and is marked off in 20-mL intervals. Label each axis with the appropriate units.

   There are a few additional points to note about marking the scales of a graph:

   - The values plotted along the axes do not have to begin at zero at the origin; in fact, they seldom do.
   - The size of the minor subdivisions should permit estimation of all the significant figures used in obtaining the data (if pressure measurements are made to the nearest torr, then the pressure scale should be interpreted to read to the nearest torr).
   - If the graph is used for extrapolation, be sure that the range of scales covers the range of the extrapolation.

3. **Plot the data.** Place a dot for each data point at the appropriate place on the graph. Draw a small circle around the dot. *Ideally*, the size of the circle should approximate the estimated error in the measurement. For most software graphing programs, error bars can be added to the data points to better represent the precision of the data. If you plot two or more different data sets on the same graph, use different-shaped symbols (triangle, square, diamond, etc.) around the data points to distinguish one set of data from another.

4. **Draw a curve for the best fit.** Draw a *smooth* curve that best fits your data. This line does not have to pass through the centers of all the data points, or even through any of them, but it should pass as closely as possible to all of them. Most software has the option of adding a trendline to the plotted data. Generally, several options as to the type of trendline are offered—select the one that best fits your data.

   Note that the line in Figure C.2 is not drawn through the circles. It stops at the edge of the circle, passes undrawn through it, and then emerges from the other side.

5. **Title your graph.** Place a descriptive title in the upper portion of the graph, well away from the data points and the smooth curve. Include your name and date under the title.

Straight-Line Graphs

Often, the graphical relationship between measured quantities produces a straight line. This is the case, for example, when we plot pressure versus temperature for a fixed volume of gas. Such linear relationships are useful because the line corresponding to the best fit of the data points can be drawn with a straight edge and because quantitative (extrapolated) information about the relationship is easily obtained directly from the graph.

Algebraically, a straight line is described by the equation

$$y = mx + b \qquad \text{(C.1)}$$

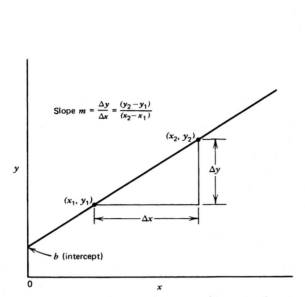

Figure C.3 The slope and intercept for a straight line, $y = mx + b$

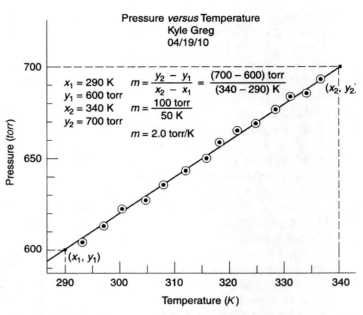

Figure C.4 Determination of the slope of a straight line drawn for a plot of pressure versus temperature for a gas

m is the slope of the straight line and b is the point of intersection of the line with the y-axis when $x = 0$ (Figure C.3). The slope of the line, which is usually of greatest interest, is determined from the relationship

$$m = \frac{y_2 - y_1}{x_2 - x_1} = \frac{\Delta y}{\Delta x} \qquad (C.2)$$

Figure C.4 illustrates the determination of the slope for a typical plot of pressure versus temperature. First plot the data and then draw the *best straight line*. Next, choose points *on the drawn line* corresponding to the easily readable values along the x-axis. Read corresponding y values along the y-axis, and then compute the slope.

Using appropriate software, if a straight line is the selected trendline, the equation for the straight line is generally given, from which the slope and y-intercept can be obtained. See Figure C.5.

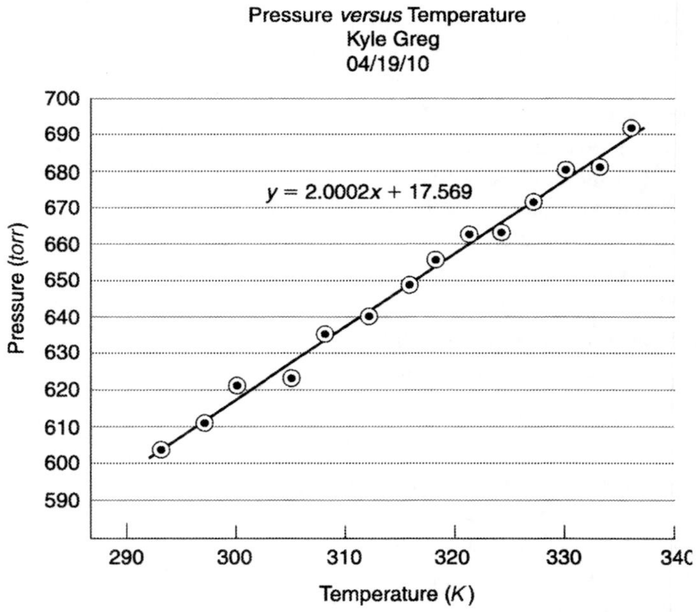

Pressure *versus* Temperature
Kyle Greg
04/19/10

$y = 2.0002x + 17.569$

Figure C.5 Using Microsoft Excel, the equation for the trendline provides the slope and y-intercept for the pressure versus temperature data.

Appendix D

Familiar Names of Common Chemicals

Sodium bicarbonate is commonly called baking soda or bicarbonate of soda.

Familiar Name	Chemical Name	Formula
alcohol	ethanol (ethyl alcohol)	C_2H_5OH
aqua regia	mixture of *conc* nitric and hydrochloric acids	$HNO_3 + 3$ HCl by volume
aspirin	acetylsalicylic acid	$CH_3COOC_6H_4COOH$
baking soda	sodium bicarbonate	$NaHCO_3$
banana oil	amyl acetate	$CH_3COOC_5H_{11}$
bauxite	hydrated aluminum oxide	$Al_2O_3 \cdot xH_2O$
bleaching powder	calcium chloride hypochlorite	$Ca(ClO)_2, Ca(ClO)Cl$
blue vitriol	copper(II) sulfate pentahydrate	$CuSO_4 \cdot 5H_2O$
borax (tincal)	sodium tetraborate decahydrate	$Na_2B_4O_7 \cdot 10H_2O$
brimstone	sulfur	S_8
calamine	zinc oxide	ZnO
calcite	calcium carbonate	$CaCO_3$
Calgon	polymer of sodium metaphosphate	$(NaPO_3)x$
calomel	mercury(I) chloride	Hg_2Cl_2
carborundum	silicon carbide	SiC
caustic soda	sodium hydroxide	$NaOH$
chalk	calcium carbonate	$CaCO_3$
Chile saltpeter	sodium nitrate	$NaNO_3$
copperas	iron(II) sulfate heptahydrate	$FeSO_4 \cdot 7H_2O$
cream of tartar	potassium hydrogen tartrate	$KHC_4H_4O_6$
DDT	dichlorodiphenyltrichloroethane	$(C_6H_4Cl)_2CHCCl_3$
dextrose	glucose	$C_6H_{12}O_6$
Epsom salt	magnesium sulfate heptahydrate	$MgSO_4 \cdot 7H_2O$
fool's gold	iron pyrite	FeS_2
Freon	dichlorodifluoromethane	CCl_2F_2
Glauber's salt	sodium sulfate decahydrate	$Na_2SO_4 \cdot 10H_2O$
glycerin	glycerol	$C_3H_5(OH)_3$
green vitriol	iron(II) sulfate heptahydrate	$FeSO_4 \cdot 7H_2O$
gypsum	calcium sulfate dihydrate	$CaSO_4 \cdot 2H_2O$
hypo	sodium thiosulfate pentahydrate	$Na_2S_2O_3 \cdot 5H_2O$
invert sugar	mixture of glucose and fructose	$C_6H_{12}O_6 + C_6H_{12}O_6$
laughing gas	nitrous oxide	N_2O
levulose	fructose	$C_6H_{12}O_6$
lye	sodium hydroxide	$NaOH$
magnesia	magnesium oxide	MgO
marble	calcium carbonate	$CaCO_3$
marsh gas	methane	CH_4
milk of lime (limewater)	calcium hydroxide	$Ca(OH)_2$
milk of magnesia	magnesium hydroxide	$Mg(OH)_2$
milk sugar	lactose	$C_{12}H_{22}O_{11}$
Mohr's salt	iron(II) ammonium sulfate hexahydrate	$Fe(NH_4)_2(SO_4)_2 \cdot 6H_2O$
moth balls	naphthalene	$C_{10}H_8$
muriatic acid	hydrochloric acid	$HCl(aq)$
oil of vitriol	sulfuric acid	$H_2SO_4(aq)$

Familiar Name	Chemical Name	Formula
oil of wintergreen	methyl salicylate	$C_6H_4(OH)COOCH_3$
oleum	fuming sulfuric acid	$H_2S_2O_7$
Paris green	double salt of copper(II) acetate and copper(II) arsenite	$Cu(CH_3CO_2)_2 \cdot Cu_3(AsO_3)_2$
plaster of Paris	calcium sulfate hemihydrate	$CaSO_4 \cdot \frac{1}{2}H_2O$
potash	potassium carbonate	K_2CO_3
quartz	silicon dioxide	SiO_2
quicklime	calcium oxide	CaO
Rochelle salt	potassium sodium tartrate	$KNaC_4H_4O_6$
rouge	iron(III) oxide	Fe_2O_3
sal ammoniac	ammonium chloride	NH_4Cl
salt (table salt)	sodium chloride	$NaCl$
saltpeter	potassium nitrate	KNO_3
silica	silicon dioxide	SiO_2
sugar (table sugar)	sucrose	$C_{12}H_{22}O_{11}$
Teflon	polymer of tetrafluoroethylene	$(C_2F_4)_x$
washing soda	sodium carbonate decahydrate	$Na_2CO_3 \cdot 10H_2O$
white lead	basic lead carbonate	$PbCO_3 \cdot Pb(OH)_2$
wood alcohol	methanol (methyl alcohol)	CH_3OH

For a listing of more common chemical names, go to www.chemistry.about.com and www.sciencecompany.com (patinas for metal artists).

Vapor Pressure of Water

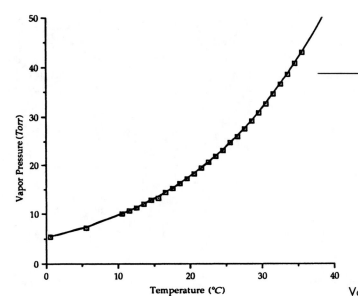

Vapor pressure of water as a function of temperature

Temperature (°C)	Pressure (*Torr*)
0	4.6
5	6.5
10	9.2
11	9.8
12	10.5
13	11.2
14	12.0
15	12.5
16	13.6
17	14.5
18	15.5
19	16.5
20	17.5
21	18.6
22	19.8
23	21.0
24	22.3
25	23.8
26	25.2
27	26.7
28	28.3
29	30.0
30	31.8
31	33.7
32	35.7
33	37.7
34	39.9
35	42.2
37*	47.1
—	—
100	760

*Body temperature

Appendix F

Concentrations of Acids and Bases

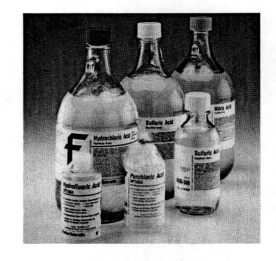

Concentrated laboratory acids and bases

Reagent	Approximate Molar Concentration	Approximate Mass Percent	Specific Gravity	mL to Dilute to 1 L for a 1.0 M Solution
Acetic acid	17.4 (*conc*)	99.5	1.05	57.5
Hydrochloric acid	11.6 (*conc*)	36	1.18	86.2
Nitric acid	16.0 (*conc*)	71	1.42	62.5
Phosphoric acid	18.1 (*conc*)	85	1.70	68.0
Sulfuric acid	18.0 (*conc*)	96	1.84	55.6
Ammonia (*aq*) (ammonium hydroxide)	14.8 (*conc*)	28%(NH_3)	0.90	67.6
Potassium hydroxide	13.5	50	1.52	74.1
Sodium hydroxide	19.1	50	1.53	52.4

Caution: *When diluting reagents, add the more concentrated reagent to the more dilute reagent (or solvent).* **Never** *add water to a concentrated acid!*

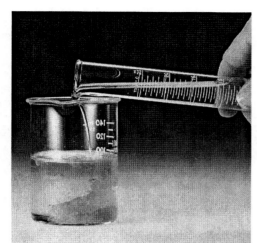

Water Solubility of Inorganic Salts

Many salts, such as cadmium sulfide, have very low solubilities.

Water-Soluble Salts

1. All salts of the chloride ion (Cl^-), bromide ion (Br^-), and iodide ion (I^-) are soluble *except* those of Ag^+, Hg_2^{2+}, Pb^{2+}, Cu^+, and Tl^+, BiI_3, and SnI_4 are insoluble. $PbCl_2$ is three to five times more soluble in hot water than in cold water.

2. All salts of the acetate ion ($CH_3CO_2^-$), nitrate ion (NO_3^-), chlorate ion (ClO_3^-), perchlorate ion (ClO_4^-), and permanganate ion (MnO_4^-) are soluble.

3. All common salts of the Group 1A cations and ammonium ion (NH_4^+) are soluble.

4. All common salts of the sulfate ion (SO_4^{2-}) are soluble *except* those of Ba^{2+}, Sr^{2+}, Pb^{2+}, and Hg^{2+}.

5. All Group 1A and 2A salts of the bicarbonate ion (HCO_3^-) are soluble.

6. *Most* salts of the fluorosilicate ion (SiF_6^{2-}), thiocyanate ion (SCN^-), and thiosulfate ion ($S_2O_3^{2-}$) are soluble. *Exceptions* are the Ba^{2+} and Group 1A fluorosilicates, the Ag^+, Hg_2^{2+}, and Pb^{2+} thiocyanates, and the Ag^+ and Pb^{2+} thiosulfates.

Water-Insoluble Salts

1. All common salts of the fluoride ion (F^-) are insoluble *except* those of Ag^+, NH_4^+, and Group 1A cations.

2. In general, all common salts of the carbonate ion (CO_3^{2-}), phosphate ion (PO_4^{3-}), borate ion (BO_3^{3-}), arsenate ion (AsO_4^{3-}), arsenite ion (AsO_3^{3-}), cyanide ion (CN^-), ferricyanide ion ($[Fe(CN)_6]^{3-}$), ferrocyanide ion ($[Fe(CN)_6]^{4-}$), oxalate ion ($C_2O_4^{2-}$), and the sulfite ion (SO_3^{2-}) are insoluble, *except* those of NH_4^+ and the Group 1A cations.

3. All common salts of the oxide ion (O^{2-}), and the hydroxide ion (OH^-) are insoluble *except* those of the Group 1A cations, Ba^{2+}, Sr^{2+}, and NH_4^+. $Ca(OH)_2$ is slightly soluble. Soluble oxides produce the corresponding hydroxides in water.

4. All common salts of the sulfide ion (S^{2-}) are insoluble *except* those of NH_4^+ and the cations that are isoelectronic with a noble gas (e.g., the Group 1A cations, the Group 2A cations, Al^{3+}, etc.).

5. Most common salts of the chromate ion (CrO_4^{2-}) are insoluble *except* those of NH_4^+, Ca^{2+}, Cu^{2+}, Mg^{2+}, and the Group 1A cations.

6. All common salts of the silicate ion (SiO_3^{2-}) are insoluble *except* those of the Group 1A cations.

Table G.1 Summary of the Solubility of Salts

Anion	Soluble Salts with These Cations	"Insoluble Salts" with These Cations
Acetate, $CH_3CO_2^-$	Most cations	None
Arsenate, AsO_4^{3-}	NH_4^+, Group 1A (except Li^+)	Most cations
Arsenite, AsO_3^{3-}	NH_4^+, Group 1A (except Li^+)	Most cations
Borate, BO_3^{3-}	NH_4^+, Group 1A (except Li^+)	Most cations
Bromide, Br^-	Most cations	Ag^+, Hg_2^{2+}, Pb^{2+}, Cu^+, Tl^+
Carbonate, CO_3^{2-}	NH_4^+, Group 1A (except Li^+)	Most cations
Chlorate, ClO_3^-	Most cations	None
Chloride, Cl^-	Most cations	Ag^+, Hg_2^{2+}, Pb^{2+}, Cu^+, Tl^+
Chromate, CrO_4^{2-}	NH_4^+, Ca^{2+}, Cu^{2+}, Mg^{2+}, Group 1A	Most cations
Cyanide, CN^-	NH_4^+, Group 1A (except Li^+)	Most cations
Ferricyanide, $[Fe(CN)_6]^{3-}$	NH_4^+, Group 1A (except Li^+)	Most cations
Ferrocyanide, $[Fe(CN)_6]^{4-}$	NH_4^+, Group 1A (except Li^+)	Most cations
Fluoride, F^-	Ag^+, NH_4^+, Group 1A	Most cations
Fluorosilicate, SiF_6^{2-}	Most cations	Ba^{2+}, Group 1A
Hydroxide, OH^-	NH_4^+, Sr^{2+}, Ba^{2+}, Group 1A	Most cations
Iodide, I^-	Most cations	Ag^+, Hg_2^{2+}, Pb^{2+}, Cu^+, Tl^+, Br^{3+}, Sn^{4+}
Nitrate, NO_3^-	Most cations	None
Nitrite, NO_2^-	Most cations	None
Oxalate, $C_2O_4^{2-}$	NH_4^+, Group 1A (except Li^+)	Most cations
Oxide, O^{2-}	NH_4^+, Sr^{2+}, Ba^{2+}, Group 1A	Most cations
Perchlorate, ClO_4^-	Most cations	None
Permanganate, MnO_4^-	Most cations	None
Phosphate, PO_4^{3-}	NH_4^+, Group 1A (except Li^+)	Most cations
Silicate, SiO_3^{2-}	Group 1A	Most cations
Sulfate, SO_4^{2-}	Most cations	Sr^{2+}, Ba^{2+}, Pb^{2+}, Hg^{2+}
Sulfide, S^{2-}	NH_4^+, Groups 1A and 2A	Most cations
Sulfite, SO_3^{2-}	NH_4^+, Group 1A (except Li^+)	Most cations
Thiocyanate, SCN^-	Most cations	Ag^+, Hg_2^{2+}, Pb^{2+}
Thiosulfate, $S_2O_3^{2-}$	Most cations	Ag^+, Pb^{2+}

Cations	Soluble Salts with These Anions	"Insoluble Salts" with These Anions
Ammonium, NH_4^+	Most anions	No common anions
Group 1A	Most anions	No common anions

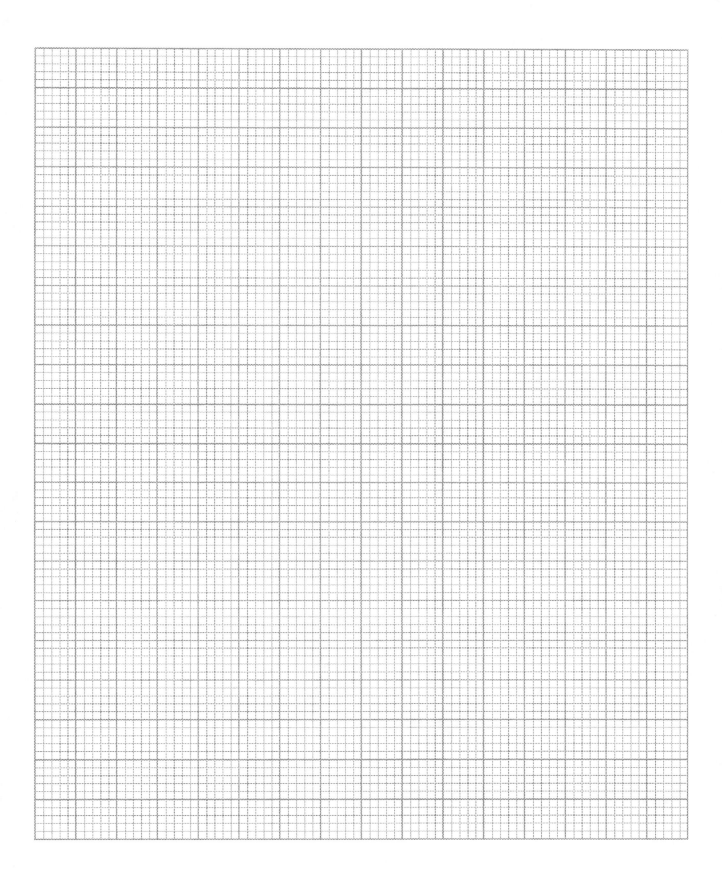

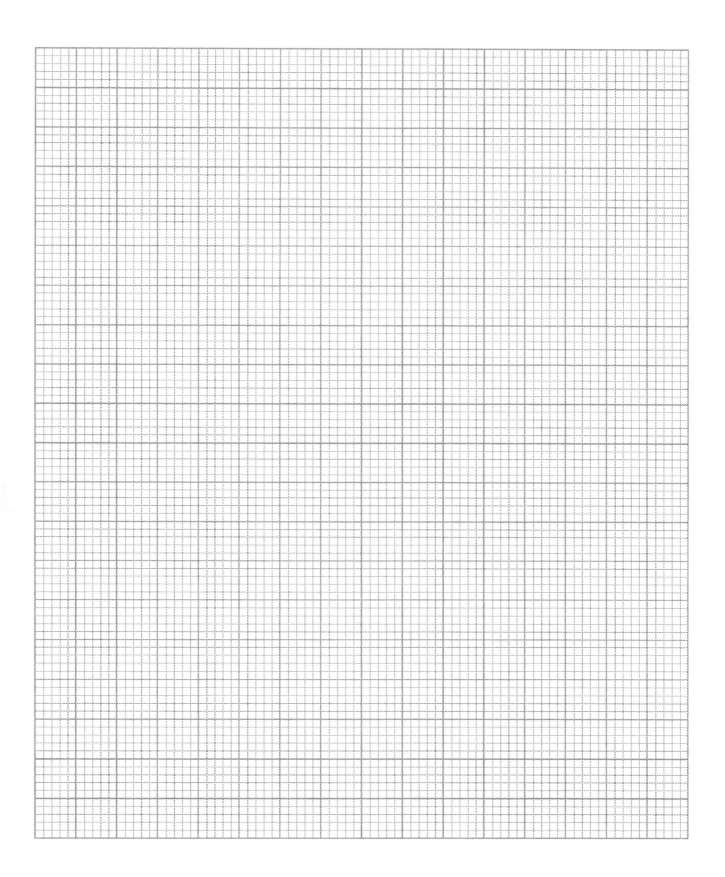

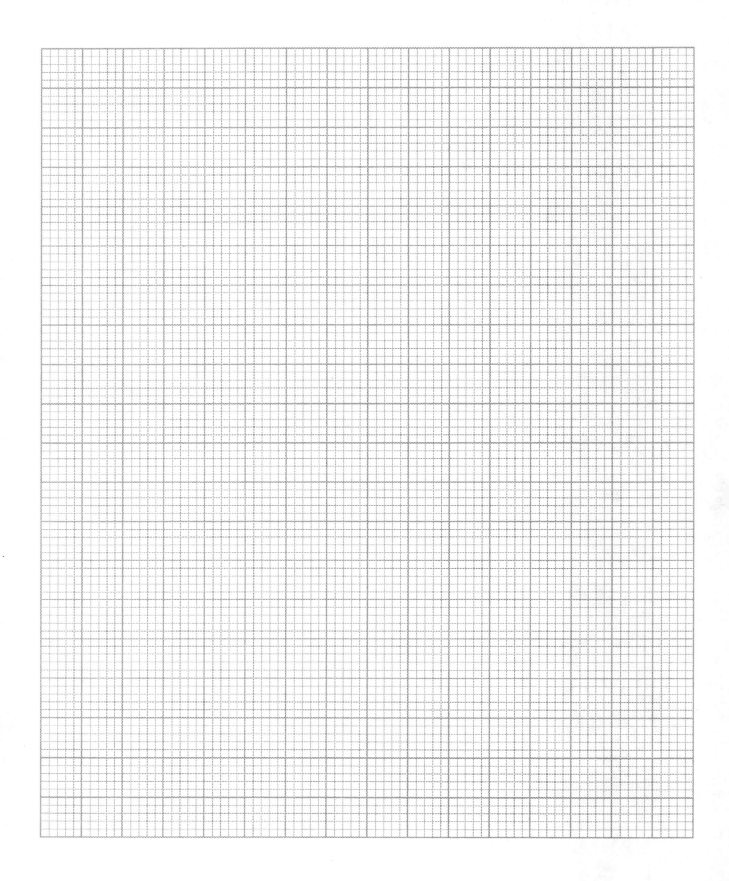